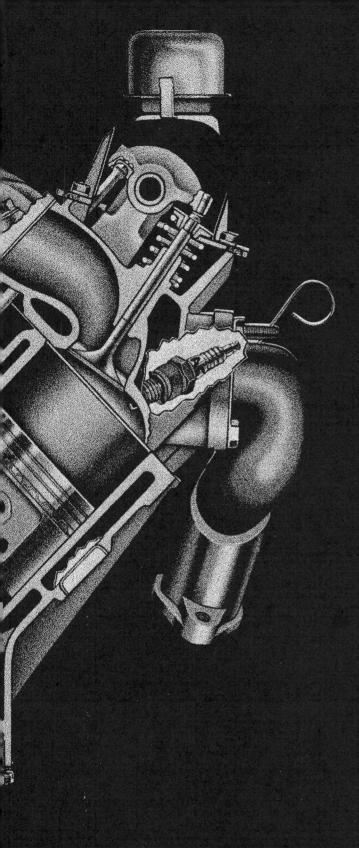

BASIC CAMS, VALVES & EXHAUST SYSTEMS

INTRODUCTION

Cams, valves and exhaust are so closely inter-related that they not only constitute a single engine system, they are the very *heart* of an engine. After all, they work together to regulate how much air gets into the engine (and how fast), and how much air gets out (and how fast). The internal combustion engine is, in essence, an air pump. It depends on air to function. If you don't take much stock in this simple fact, then ask the men at NASA why they used an electric motor and batteries to power the Lunar Roving Vehicle on the air-less moon! The flow of air through an engine dictates how fast it will run, how much power will be derived from it, and how efficiently (read gas mileage!) it operates. But because air is actually put to work by an engine 'way down inside where you can't see what's happening, many people take for granted that the fellows who design engines know what they're doing and, consequently, they don't get involved in such a "semi-secret" area. However, even though the air that flows into and out of an engine is virtually its lifeblood, it's really quite easy to improve on basic engine design to help that air flow faster and easier. You see, engineers must make compromises, and this is where the car-tinkerers come in.

This is what *Basic Cams, Valves and Exhaust Systems* is all about, as you'll learn when you leaf through this book. In the preceding editions we've given you an increasing number of special camshaft installation stories, mostly because our readers have asked for them. In this 3rd edition, we've expanded the number of Camming chapters even more by adding several of the newest engines in the latest small cars. This serves a dual purpose. First, power-producing cams are becoming increasingly available from aftermarket suppliers for our new family of cars to help regain horsepower that was lost through the necessary addition of "smog" hardware. Second, our new cars, even the smaller ones, are heavier now due to weighty energy absorbing bumpers, beefier body construction, and so forth. So with Detroit's power down and weight up, newer cars need whatever added power they can get. Improving air flow through the engine can do this, and cams, valves and the exhaust system are the items to work with.

Our goal in this revision, then, is to help you improve your engine, whether improvement to you means greater fuel economy, more power, or a happy combination of the two. Even if *you* don't want to dig into your engine, but simply want to learn about its inner workings, there's still sure to be something of interest in here for you, too.

Spence Murray

SPECIALTY PUBLICATIONS DIVISION

BASIC CAMS, VALVES AND EXHAUST SYSTEMS No.3

Revision edited by Jon Jay and the Technical Editors of Petersen Publishing Co. Copyright © 1974 by Petersen Publishing Co., 8490 Sunset Blvd., Los Angeles, CA 90069. Phone: (213) 657-5100. All rights reserved. No part of this book may be reproduced without written permission. Printed in U.S.A.

Spencer Murray/Editor
Robert I. Young/Art Director
Judy Shane/Managing Editor
Jay Storer/Feature Editor
Jon Jay/Technical Editor
Kalton C. Lahue/Contributing Editor

Library of Congress Catalog Card No. 70-902

ISBN 0-8227-0064-6

Hans Tanner/Editorial Director
Erwin M. Rosen/Executive Editor
George E. Shultz/Editorial Coordinator
Angie Ullrich/Secretary, Administrative
Holly Bjorseth/Secretary, Editorial

Automotive

Spencer Murray/Editor
Judy Shane/Managing Editor
Jay Storer/Feature Editor
Jon Jay/Technical Editor
Tom Senter/Associate Editor

General Subjects

Al Hall/Editor
Ronda Brown/Managing Editor
Richard L. Busenkell/Managing Editor
Harris R. Bierman/Associate Editor
Allen Bishop/Associate Editor
John T. Jo/Associate Editor
Terry Parsons/Associate Editor

Special Projects

Don Whitt/Editor
Steve Amos/Art Director
Ann C. Tidwell/Managing Editor
Jo Anne Peterson/Editorial Assistant

Directories

Merrill Ormes/Editor

ART SERVICES

Robert I. Young/Art Director
Steve Hirsch/Artist, Design
Pat Taketa/Artist, Design
Dick Fischer/Artist, Design
George Fukuda/Artist, Design
Celeste Swayne-Courtney/Artist, Design
Nancy Quinn/Artist, Design
Ellen Clark/Artist, Design
Kathy Philpott/Artist, Design

COVER

There is a no more fitting subject for the cover of a book about cams, valves and exhaust systems, than Chevy's 16-valve Cosworth Vega with its dual overhead cams. This unique cutaway was rendered especially for us by Shusei Nagaoka of Design Maru. Cover design by Pat Taketa.

PETERSEN PUBLISHING COMPANY

R. E. Petersen/Chairman of the Board
F. R. Waingrow/President
Robert E. Brown/Sr. V.P., Corporate Sales
Herb Metcalf/V.P., Circulation Director
Dick Day/V.P., Automotive Publications
Philip E. Trimbach/Controller-Treasurer
Robert Andersen/Director, Manufacturing
Al Isaacs/Director, Graphics
Bob D'Olivo/Director, Photography
Spencer Nilson/Director, Administrative Services

Larry Kent/Director, Corporate Merchandising
Ronald D. Salk/Director, Public Relations
William Porter/Director, Single Copy Sales
Jack Thompson/Director, Subscription Sales
Alan C. Hahn/Director, Market Development
Ralph D. Holt/Director, Editorial Research
Maria Cox/Manager, Data Processing Services
Robert Horton/Manager, Traffic
Harold L. Davis/Manager, Production
James J. Krenek/Manager, Purchasing

CONTENTS

Selecting a Cam

Understanding the why's and how's of camshaft design makes it easier to choose the cam that will do the most for your engine.

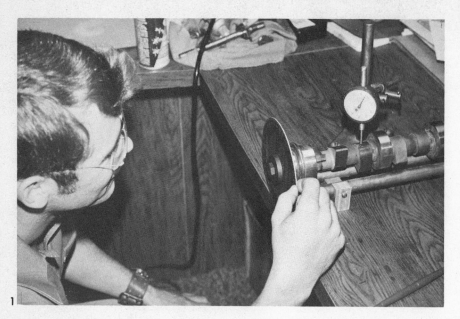

We don't know what modern cam designers are motivated by, but whatever it is that's pushing them, they are doing wonderful things with the camshaft. But don't forget that the cam and crank are married, so when we talk about one we have to include the other. The camshaft is either geared or connected by a chain to the crankshaft so that the exhaust and intake valves are opened and closed at the right time. (Because of the way the piston is hooked up to the crank, each time it does a stroke the crankshaft goes through half a turn. In the complete four-stroke cycle, the crankshaft will go through two complete revolutions. If it takes two revolutions to complete all the operations on one cylinder this amounts to 720° of crankshaft rotation.) During the completion of the four cycles, each valve—whether it's intake or exhaust—is opened only once. So what we need is a lobe on a camshaft that will open and close the exhaust valve and the intake valve once in every 720°. There are many ways that a designer could do this but the easiest way is to have one lobe on the camshaft for each valve. In order to time the cam lobe to the crankshaft, we run the camshaft slower so that every time the crankshaft does two revolutions the camshaft only does one, and as a result each valve opens once in each two crankshaft revolutions.

CAMSHAFT POSITION

The camshaft can be located just about any place on the engine, depending upon how the valves are situated. Once the designer has found the best camshaft position in relation to the cylinders, he has to provide bearing surfaces in the block or head casting.

Oil is usually pumped under pressure to each cam bearing and allowed to run out the sides of the bearing and back into the bottom of the engine. The lobes of the cam are lubricated by throw-off from the crank, and splash from other portions of the engine.

At this point the cam designer really gets down to the nitty-gritty. He not only has to know how often the engine fires, which is determined by the crankshaft, but he has to know where the valve lifters are positioned so that the lobe on the cam will be against the lifter ready to open the valve when the crankshaft is in the correct position.

A V-8 engine fires every 90°; therefore, it carries out everything else in the cycle every 90°, also. One intake valve opens every 90°; an exhaust valve somewhere opens every 90° and so on. If the cam designer knows the firing order of the engine and the exact location of the lifter bores, then all he has to do is make everything happen 90° apart in the right order and he will have a cam that works.

The timing of the cam is something else. That can be changed by changing the relationship between the camshaft and the crank, thus opening all the valves earlier or later. However, the degrees of rotation between the individual lobes on the cam must remain the same, being fixed by the way the crankshaft is designed.

LOBE SHAPE

After the hassle of lobe location has been solved, and the cam designer is once again friendly with the block and crank men, he turns to the problem of lobe shape. Valve lifters (tappets) sit right on top of the cam lobes and are in contact with the lobes at all times simply from the weight of the tappet. If the lobe of the cam is perfectly square and the bottom of the tappet is perfectly flat, then the tappet and the cam lobe are going to get along fine.

To take care of anything amiss between the lobe and the tappet, a flat tappet is really made with a spherical shape which is about .002-in. higher in the center than at the edges. The result is that even though the tappet or the cam should tip one direction or the other, it is impossible for the edge of the cam lobe to dig into the tappet.

The tappet is round and rests in a round bore, so it is free to turn if it wants to. In fact, it has to. When a tappet does not turn, it wears out much quicker because the cam always wipes across it at exactly the same spot. To make sure that the tappet is kept turning, cam lobes which appear to be square with the shaft, are really not. They are tapered from one side to the other as much as .002-in. over the width of the lobe. This taper causes the cam lobe to rub off-center on the tappet instead of exactly across the middle and makes the tappet revolve on its bore. On roller tappets this taper on the cam lobe is not necessary, so the lobes are made with the faces perfectly square with the shaft.

Problems of camshaft location, bearings, and timing are easy compared to the job that faces the designer when he starts to work on the actual shape of the lobe itself. The faster the engine turns, the harder it is to design a cam lobe that will do the job.

At one time cam lobes were all shaped with three curves and called a triple-curve or harmonic shape cam. One curve was duplicated on each ramp of the cam and the third curve went across the nose. Triple-curve cams worked fine in the days of flat-

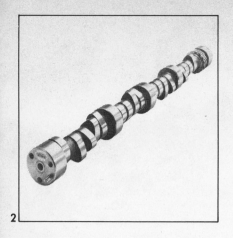

2

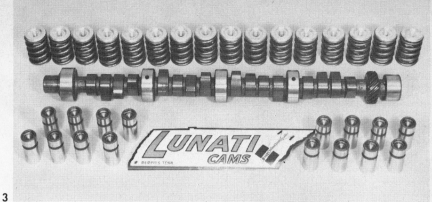

3

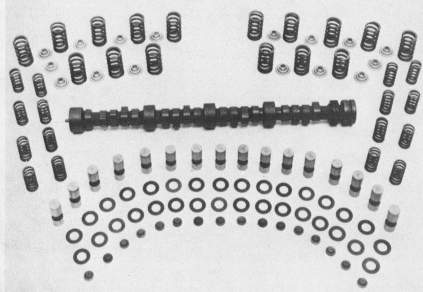

4

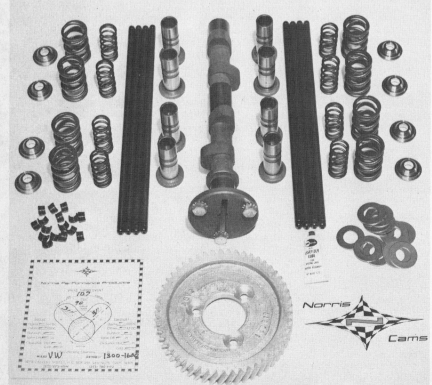

5

1. The starting point of any cam profile is the lift data. These machining figures may be arrived at by computer, calculator, or an empirical method. You can check lift data on centering blocks, using a dial indicator and a degree wheel.

2. The heart of an engine is the way it breathes. And the primary control of breathing comes from the cam. The choice of cams is a vital decision.

3. When you buy a cam, purchase the whole kit. It's a bit more expensive, but it will save you time, money, and performance in the long run.

4. Howard flat tappet cam kit for a 427-cu.-in. Chevy includes lifters, inner and outer valve springs, retainers and shims.

5. You can purchase a performance cam for VW's from almost any cam grinder. This kit from Norris contains everything you need to put some zip into your Bug.

heads when the only thing that the lobe had to lift was the valve lifter and the valve itself. When overheads came out, the cam lobe had a lot more work to do.

The designers came up with cam lobe shapes that are comprised of many curves joined together. These cam shapes are known as multi-sine wave or parabolic. Iskenderian was one of the first cam grinders to apply parabolic designs to reground racing camshafts. The multiple-curve cam has the advantage of starting out with a very slow curve to take up the clearance between the tappet and the valve stem. Once this clearance is taken up and everything is solid in the drivetrain, then another curve takes over and starts accelerating the lift so that the valve goes to full open as quickly as possible.

The time when the valve should open is determined by how fast the engine is running, the shape of the ports, the size of the valves, and so on. But because it takes time to open the valve, the designer has to make the cam lobe so that it actually starts to open the valve ahead of the time he actually wants it to open.

Selecting a Cam

Cams nowadays are designed with a clearance ramp which takes up the play if mechanical tappets are used, or just gets everything started in good shape if hydraulic tappets are used. From the clearance ramp, the lobe goes into a curve that will accelerate the opening rate of the valve up to a certain velocity. After the velocity is reached, then the speed of the valve's opening stays constant until it gets almost full open. Then another problem causes the cam designer to beat his head against the wall. If he maintains the full opening velocity of the lift, the valve lift and all the valve train will fly off the nose of the cam when it reaches the top of the lift, so the designer has to build in a curve right near the nose of the lobe that will decelerate the valve train and bring it down slowly to the full open position.

Some of the big advances in engine breathing in the last few years have come about not because of better cam designs but because the better valve springs and the lighter components in the valve train have allowed the cam designer to use the designs he's always wanted.

A cam designer has to use every trick he can think of to make things work. Sometimes the actual valve lift that a cam supplies is made higher than is necessary for engine breathing. It sounds silly but he does that because he wants to open the valve at a certain velocity up to a certain lift. When he gets to that lift, the only way he can keep the valve from flying off the lobe is to make the lobe a little bit higher.

Valve opening is another area where things get a little complicated. You might think that if you raised the valve a quarter-inch you would have a quarter-inch opening for the air to go through, but you don't because the valve seat is on an angle. The actual area of the valve opening is less than the lift. Valve seats and face angles are always measured from the horizontal. The result is, the greater the seat angle, the less actual valve opening for any given lift.

Now that we've seen some of the problems that the cam designer faces, let's see what happens when he puts the design down on paper and it goes through the processes to eventually end up as an actual cam.

CAM DESIGN MATHEMATICS

After the designer has the cam on paper he has to turn himself into a mathematician, because in order to make a model cam he must know exactly how far from the center of the cam the lobe is for each degree of

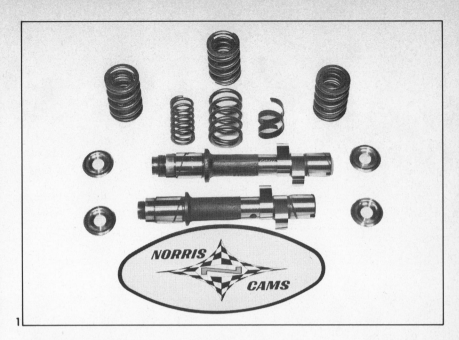

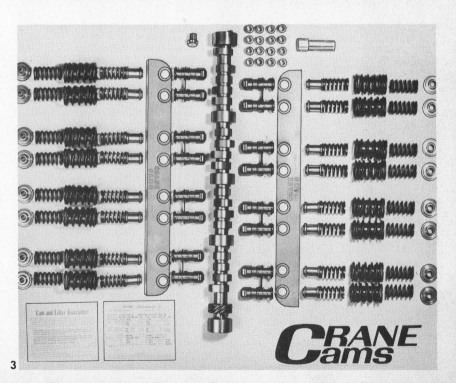

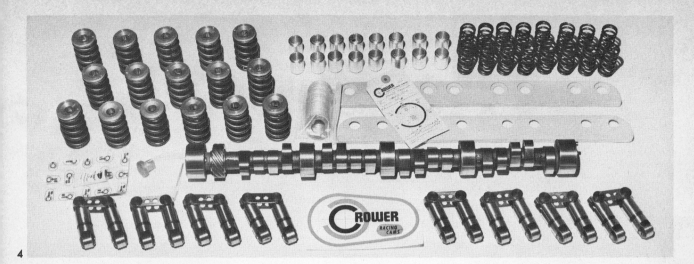

4

5

1. **Norris cam kit for 650cc Triumph cycle includes dual interference dampener springs and titanium retainers.**

2. **Engle kit for a 260-289 Ford contains everything you need to do the job right: cam, lifters, springs, retainers, hardened valve keepers, shims, and lube.**

3. **Crane roller tappet cams require a rev kit to keep the roller in constant contact with the cam. Poor performance and extensive damage will result if proper contact isn't kept at all times.**

4. **Crower offers a full line of roller tappet cams. Roller tappets are made with stock pushrod seat location. Tappets drop right in. No block modifications are required.**

5. **One of the original performance cam grinders, Clay Smith, offers cams for the VW owner who is seeking more go-power.**

rotation. This is where a high-speed electronic computer really comes in handy.

After the computer, or the man, finishes the mathematical calculations, we will know exactly how far from the center of the cam lobe the surface of the cam should be for each degree of rotation. At that point we move to a milling machine with a profiler and we make a model cam lobe. The milling machine operator begins with a hunk of metal, takes a cut off its surface, rotates the hunk 1°, moves the cutting tool to the new position as calculated by the computer, and then takes the second cut. And 360 cuts later, he has a model cam lobe.

Once we have the model cam lobe, we go to a special cam grinder and grind a master cam, using the model cam as a pattern.

Cam grinding is an art. There are so many cams on the market that it's bewildering trying to figure out which one you should use. Nobody can say definitely that one cam will be x-amount better than another one, but there are certain things that you can look for and certain mistakes that you can avoid.

A cam grinder can have the most beautiful theories in the world but if they don't prove out with horsepower gains, he might as well use his cam for a paperweight. Almost any cam will run in any car, providing there is a lobe for each valve. But how well it runs is something else. The cam must be matched to the engine, particularly considering the kind of equipment the engine is using.

Consulting with a cam grinder is like consulting with a doctor or lawyer. You have to trust him and you have to tell him everything if he's going to do you any good.

Cams can be made of cast iron, cast steel or turned from a solid block of steel on a lathe. The cast iron is tough but brittle; drop one on a concrete floor and that's the end of your camshaft. Most cams, nowadays

are cast steel which is a little more flexible, can be straightened if it gets bent, but is still reasonably priced. The cam that is turned out of a solid billet is the ultimate because the machinist can select a block of the finest steel. But this cam really costs a bundle because of all of the time required to cut it on a lathe.

If you are putting fantastic loads on a camshaft with tremendous spring pressures and extremely high rpm, then you may need the best cam you can get. The thing to do is check out the cam you have now. If it is OK, then there is no point in paying good money for a cam that is exactly like the one you have.

A much better buy for the money is a "cheater" cam with stock lift and timing but a quicker opening. The initial movement of the valve when it starts to open will occur at the same number of degrees as the stock cam, but from that point on this cheater will open the valve more quickly. The quicker we get the valve open (therefore, the longer it stays open), the more air and fuel mixture we can get into the cylinder. Holding the intake valve open longer at high rpm or maybe allowing more overlap between it and the exhaust valve will give better cylinder filling, which gives more horsepower in most cases.

VALVE LIFT

Valve lift is one of the big factors in engine breathing. The higher you lift it, the more opening you'll get and the more air/fuel mixture will be allowed to enter. But you want to stay away from the trap of figuring that the more valve lift you have, the better your engine will run. Excessive lift won't necessarily hurt anything but you may be paying for an extreme high lift cam when you don't need it. If the valve lift is such that the valve will flow more air than the port will flow, or perhaps more air than the carburetor will flow, then the

Selecting a Cam

extra lift over the capacity of the parts that are upstream is wasted.

The value of the camshaft is not in how the valve lift will measure but in how good the engine runs with it. It would be better if cam grinders didn't tell you anything about the cam that they furnished but just sold it to you and let you run it. Engine builders would be a lot happier if attention was given only to results, and specifications left to the cam grinder.

We need duration in valve opening because the gasoline and air mixture is slow to move. We have to open the valve before we want to and close it later than we would like. Duration is only correct at one rpm or over a small rpm range. If we open the intake valve at top dead center on the intake stroke, the piston will be quite a ways down in the cylinder before the column of air in the manifold gets moving enough to come through the valve opening. If we had an extremely low rpm engine, it would be possible and maybe even desirable to open the valve at exactly top dead center. The faster the engine turns, the earlier the intake valve has to be opened in order to fill the cylinder.

All we are doing with cam design is trying to get the cylinders as full as possible. The more gas and air mixture we get into the cylinder, the more horsepower we'll get out of it. If you get an engine that will run well with a lot of duration at high rpm, and then you try to run it at slow speed, the column of air is not moving as fast in the manifold so the piston will actually push air back into the intake manifold when the intake valve opens. That is one of the reasons that a racing engine does not run smoothly at low speed.

OVERLAP

When the piston comes up on the exhaust stroke and pushes the spent gases out through the exhaust valve, it really doesn't clear the chamber of all exhaust gas. The intake valve opens and allows the incoming mixture to enter the combustion chamber where it mixes with the exhaust gas and is diluted, which doesn't help us a bit in the power department.

You remember from our discussion of duration that by opening the intake valve before the piston gets to top dead center, we allow the column of air in the manifold to build up its speed so that it can fill the chamber. By experiments the engineers have found out that if they leave the exhaust valve open after the piston passes top dead center and starts back down, the exhaust gas will continue to flow out of the cylinder. What

we have here is an overlap period in which both exhaust and intake valves are open. The exhaust gas is flowing out, the intake mixture is flowing in and the result is that we get all of the exhaust gases purged from the combustion chamber and get a more complete filling of the cylinder with intake mixture.

1. Now here's a trick cam. Crower cam turns on roller bearing journals. For the serious racer only.

2. Pictured here is a typical timing card, attached to every new cam when you buy it.

Overlap really works at the rpm range where it was designed to work. That's another place where you have to confide in your cam grinder and tell him what rpm your engine is going to turn.

If you don't know such things, then you're not giving the cam grinder enough information for him to give you the right cam. With a fairly popular car you can tell your cam grinder your gear ratio and tire size and he will know what rpm range your engine will best operate in.

Some cam grinders furnish the same cam with a blown engine that

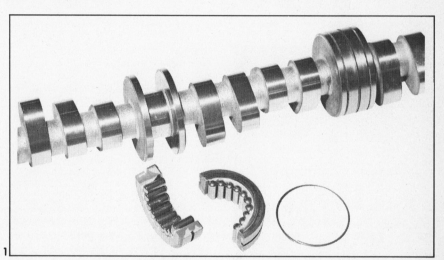

1

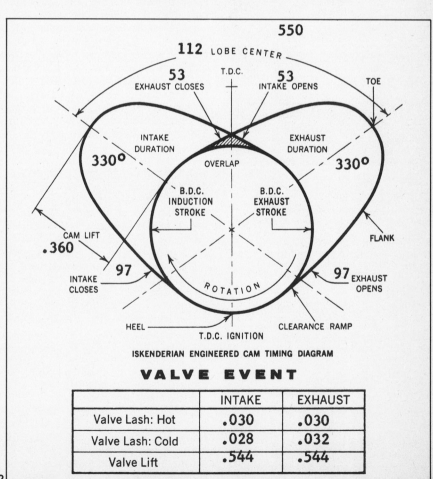

ISKENDERIAN ENGINEERED CAM TIMING DIAGRAM

VALVE EVENT

	INTAKE	EXHAUST
Valve Lash: Hot	.030	.030
Valve Lash: Cold	.028	.032
Valve Lift	.544	.544

2

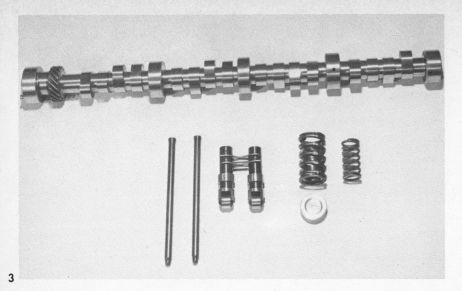

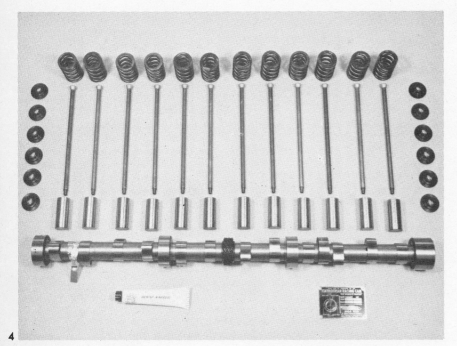

3. Isky's roller tappet cam takes high-revving pressures of super-stiff valve springs. This one is going into a MoPar small-block.

4. Another Isky cam. This one is for a MoPar. Set includes everything needed for the strip or street including alloy iron lifters, chrome moly pushrods and silicon chrome valve springs.

5. Crower's new "Gas Stretcher" is their answer to the gas shortage. Cam design changes valve timing and closes intakes sooner on compression stroke. The result is more low-end torque and less fuel loss during valve overlap; 20% mileage increases have been claimed. Isky's new Mile-A-Mor answers the same needs.

they do with an un-blown setup. It would seem that the blown engine with the positive pressure forcing the intake mixture into the cylinder would not need as much overlap, but the opposite is true. Engle, who supplies cams for some of the most famous engine builders in the country—such as Dan Gurney and Keith Black—has special cams for engines with super-chargers.

DESIGNING FOR SPEED

Whether you get a roller tappet, flat tappet, or hydraulic cam will be determined pretty much by how fast you want to turn your engine. Maybe we should say it's determined by how fast you *have* to turn your engine, because sometimes that's the only way you can get enough speed to win the race. A stock cam will turn about 5000, maybe 5500 rpm, before the lifters pump up. Using a racing hydraulic cam with special lifters you would probably get another 1000 rpm. To go as high as 7000 rpm you should use a flat tappet cam, although many flat tappet cams will go considerably faster than that.

Once you get into the extremely high ranges, say 8000 rpm or over, the roller tappet cam is the only way to go. At such high rpm, tremendous spring pressures are necessary to keep the valve gear in contact with the cam lobe at all times. Whenever the valve gear does not stay in contact with the cam lobe we call it valve float, but you could just as easily call it lifter float, pushrod float, or rocker arm float.

With the popularity of the hydraulic lifter cam increasing, everybody talks about lifter pump-up. Lifter pump-up *does* occur but not for the reasons that most people think it does. What happens is that valve float occurs, and the lifter, because it is designed to take up any clearance in the system, will automatically fill the extra space.

If you are real sharp, you can take an ordinary stock lifter (if you are lucky enough to have an engine with adjustable rocker arms) and adjust the lifter so it is operating at the top of its range. Then when the valves float and the lifter tries to pump up to fill the spaces, it runs out of travel and you have what amounts to an anti-pump-up lifter. If you don't have adjustable rockers, pump-up can be eliminated by using the special lifters or installing adjustable rocker arms or pushrods.

A successful engine builder, car owner or driver does not throw something together and go racing. He does a lot of thinking about what's needed to produce results. The cam grinder does a lot of thinking and figuring too. When you ask him to select a cam for you, tell him the whole story . . . if he knows what you are trying to accomplish, he can give you a cam that will really work as you think it should. 🏆

Camshaft Drives

Need more power and more reliability?
Install a special cam drive on your engine and get both.

1. Pete Jackson, of Jackson Gear Drives located in Glendale Calif., displays his unique "dual idler" gear drive set on the front of a 427-in. Chevrolet block. Units are also available for 327 Chevys, 426 Chryslers and 289-in. Ford engines.

For the sake of keeping the costs down and turning out a product that is relatively quiet, practically every engine designed and manufactured in the U.S. comes equipped with a chain-driven camshaft sprocket. For plain, everyday, going-to-the-market use, these chains suffice, but even under these normal conditions, they do tend to wear out. The first sign of wear is revealed when the slack encountered through loosened pins and stretched links turns up in a retarded camshaft. If the rest of the engine is in pretty healthy shape, a few good blips on the throttle will cause the chain to break. When this happens, open valves in some chambers tend to kiss the pistons, since the crank doesn't know it is no longer connected to the camshaft via that synchronizing chain.

It's bad enough when the chain stretches and/or breaks on a stock engine, but let this same thing occur on an expensive high-performance engine, and watch the cost go up. You can not only lose races, and money, from a "tired" engine, but you can lose the entire engine if the chain quits on you.

ROLLER CHAIN VERSUS LINK CHAIN

There's a number of ways out of this predicament, with costs varying from a few bucks to a couple "hun." It all depends on how much reliability you want, to what purpose the cam drive will be put, and how much you can afford. Cloyes (in Cleveland, Ohio), for example, offers three distinct types of gear sets to choose from. The Cloyes Speed Set consists of a true roller chain designed for double-tooth sprockets, a balanced, Tufftrided, magnafluxed cam sprocket, and a Tufftrided crank sprocket. The crank sprockets also feature three keyways for precision timing: one keyway for standard timing, one for 4° advance, and one for 4° retard. Their roller chain reportedly will operate at higher rpm's than stock link-type chains, give an increase in horsepower, last longer due to a reduction in friction, and will stretch less, to as little as ¾ of a degree. Cloyes also manufactures matched gear sets for 6-cyl. Ford and Chevrolet engines. These twin gear sets require a camshaft that rotates in the opposite direction of a normal cam. This is due to the natural change in gear rotation.

Iskenderian Racing Cams (Gardena, Calif.) also manufacture a set of twin gears for Chevy engines. These gears are specifically recommended for sprint and super-modified racing, where there is increased torsional vibration of the crankshaft caused by running the engine for prolonged periods in the critical 5500-rpm range. Isky heavy-duty gears provide extra protection for the engine under this condition. Their cam gear is high-strength ductile iron, and the crank gear is 4140 steel. Both are induction hardened and nitrided for minimum wear. These gears also require a reverse ground camshaft due to the forced change in rotating direction at the cam.

DUAL IDLER GEARS

Because the 2-gear drive sets require a reverse grind cam, don't think that all gear sets are in the same bag, because they aren't. Most camshaft gear drive sets feature a cam gear, crank gear and one idler gear (the idler allows use of a normal rotation camshaft). However, one firm that manufactures gear drives utilizes dual idler gears rather than one. All of these units do away with troublesome timing chains.

Some of the firms manufacturing gear drive sets are: Milodon Engineering (Van Nuys, Calif.); Summers Brothers (Ontario, Calif.); Donovan Engineering (Torrance, Calif.); Ramchargers (Taylor, Mich.); and Pete Jackson Gear Drives (Glendale, Calif.; also the manufacturer of fuel injection systems.) With the exception of Jackson drives, all of these units feature a single idler gear. Jackson drives are of the dual idler type, completely new to engine building.

While all of these different drive units perform in the same manner, each is installed in a slightly different fashion. Many must be set up in a specific way to provide proper backlash between the idler and cam gear, and the idler and crank gear. On some installations, the two dowel pins in the front of the block must be replaced with others when this last is set. Some models are designed so that the stock timing gear cover can be utilized; others are designed so you can use your stock water pump. In a few units, the idler gear is supported by the aluminum gear housing; in others, it is attached to the new block plate that comes in the kit. For these and many other reasons, we have featured three step-by-step articles in this particular chapter, dealing with the installation steps involved in setting up typical gear drives. Every unit comes from the manufacturer with complete instructions, but there's nothing like a thousand photos to speak for ten thousand words.

What's great to know is that there's a grand variety of camshaft gear drives available, and you can get 'em in a wide spectrum of prices, too. So, without belaboring the point any further, we'll cease this idle chatter and leave room for the graphics.

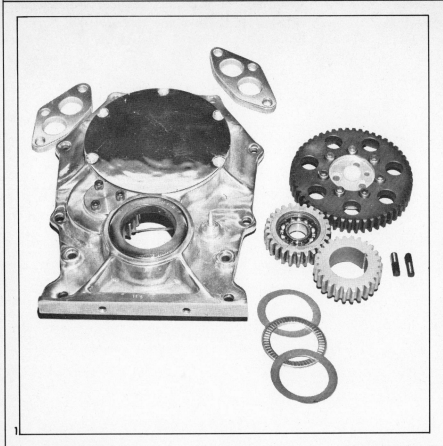

1. Milodon Engineering, Van Nuys, Calif., also offers a complete line of gear drives for popular makes of engines. This unit is for super stock use on a late Hemi Chrysler; stock water pump goes over drive cover.

2. Same gear drive assembly by Milodon is also adaptable to supercharged engines by use of a 4- or 6-in. pump extension to clear the blower belt. Another cover plate allows installation of pump drive where engine is injected.

3. Milodon's small-block Chevy (283-350 in.) precision gear drive is displayed here. Like all other units, the gears in this set are made of super-hard chrome moly and are heat treated. This unit is for street use where water pump is required.

4. This is the same Milodon Chevy unit, for small blocks, fitted with either a 4- or 6-in. pump extension for clearing the blower belt.

5. For unblown Chevys, the front removable plate is changed to this unit allowing use of a pump drive. No machine work is required to install Milodon drives, though two dowel pins in block must be replaced to accurately locate the cover.

Camshaft Drives

1. First step in installing a Milodon gear drive on a small-block Chevy is to replace the stock crank drive gear with the new Milodon chrome moly gear.

2. A super bite with a pair of vise grips will remove the stock dowel pins in face of block. New, larger Milodon pin is lying at left.

3. Forward thrust is controlled by a ball bearing in front plate of blown and unblown versions by nylon button in super stock models, while rear thrust is controlled by a needle bearing package. These needle thrust bearings are shown being installed on cam face here.

4. Special cam hub is positioned on face of cam. Note that nose has been broached for use of hex drive for fuel pump or any other accessory.

5. Socket head screws are next inserted in hub and tightened, securing hub to camshaft.

6. Now you can install Milodon's cam gear on the hub. Any bolt location is okay, then run the seven socket head screws down tight.

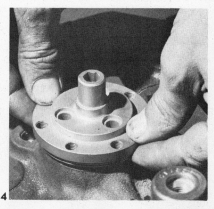

7

8

9

10

11

7. Now the aluminum front cover, which contains the idler gear, is slipped over the other gears. Start all the cover hold-down bolts. Slip a piece of newsprint between both the crank and idler and cam and idler gears. Apply pressure to the idler side of the timing cover to hold tight gear clearance, then tighten the 10 cover bolts.

8. After tightening the cover bolts, remove center cover plate and rotate gears to remove newsprint and check for smooth operation of the gears.

9. At this point, run a 19/64ths drill through the hardened drill bushings located at each side of the timing cover down into the old dowel pin holes. These bushings will remain in the cover.

10. Next, ream the holes with a .312-in. reamer. Now the Milodon front cover comes off.

11. Drive the larger end of the 5/16-in. dowel pins into the reamed holes in block. They will locate the new cover.

Camshaft Drives

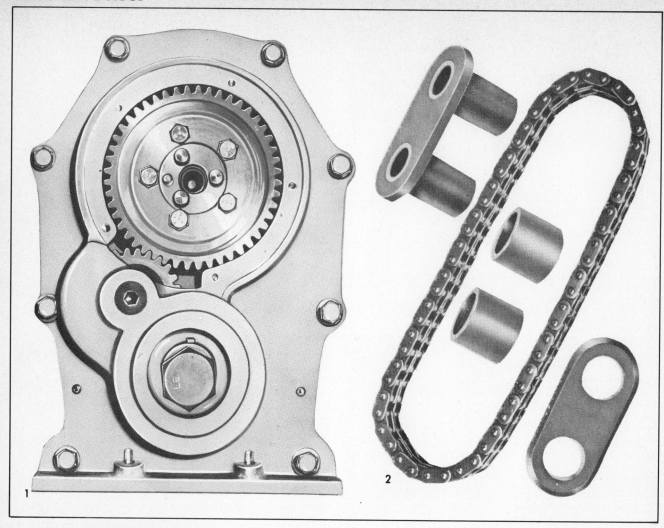

1. The Ramchargers, Taylor, Mich., renowned for their funny cars, diggers and race engines, manufactures gear drives for Chrysler "B" engines and 426-in. Hemis. They are available for super stock use where a stock water pump is retained, injected engines and supercharged engines where a pump extension is required.

2. Cloyes Gear & Products, Inc., Cleveland, Ohio, produces a true roller chain for their cam and crank gears. Solid bushings roll on the pins.

3. Cloyes crank sprockets are also Tufftrided for long wearing ability. Each sprocket is also cut with three keyways for precision timing. Distinctive marks allow for 4° advance or retard in cam timing.

4. A twin gear set is available from Cloyes, too. Designed for 6-cylinder Chevys and Fords, the cam gear for Chevys is in aluminum only, while steel or aluminum may be had for Fords.

5. The Cloyes double-row-tooth cam sprocket is Tufftrided, magnafluxed and dynamically balanced in addition to being precision matched with its crank sprocket and chain.

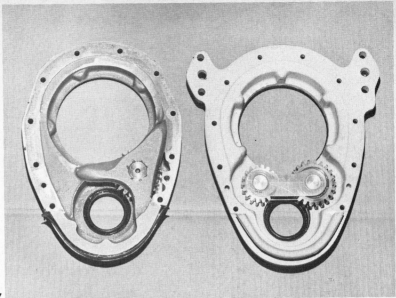

6. Here is a complete Cloyes "Speed Set" chain drive assembly. Large rollers in chain reduce friction, improve performance.

7. This rear view of two Chevy timing covers shows the basic difference between the single-idler gear drive and Jackson's dual-idler gear drive. At left is a Donovan cover with the idler installed in the cover. Jackson's cover merely shrouds the twin gears, which ride free between other two gears.

8. Typical of many modern V-8 cam drive assemblies is this set for a 427-in. Ford engine. The aluminum cam gear features nylon-coated teeth.

9. This is one of Jackson's gear drive kits for competition use. It contains cam and crank gears, dual idler gears, front cover, thrust washers, injector pump drive kit and offset buttons for altering cam timing. It's priced less than most other units, and there is no machine work required to install this kit. Likewise, you don't have to worry about gear lash. Jackson's drive is as easy to install as any stock timing chain set.

Camshaft Drives

1. Whether the engine is in a boat or car, the Jackson gear drive is simple to install. Pull the timing cover, cam gear and chain, then pull the crank gear.

2. Install Jackson's new super-hard crankshaft gear. The left idler gear is slightly larger than the right and is installed to the left when you're facing the engine. Note that the setup features two timing marks, one that will align with each gear.

3. The large thrust washer set goes behind the camshaft gear, controlling rearward thrust.

4. After slipping the thrust washer package on the face of the cam, place the cam gear on. If the engine was rotated previously so that the dowel pin is at 3 o'clock position and crank keyway 45° to the right of vertical, timing marks will line right up.

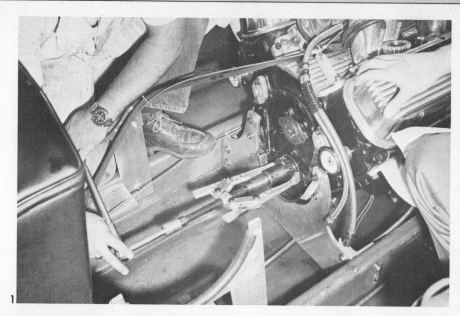

5. Depending upon how much advance or retard you want, install the proper offset button.

6. After temporarily removing the three socket head screws that retain the cam gear, slip the injector pump drive hub (or flat washer, if it's for street use) over the gear and replace hold-down screws.

7. This view is strictly for illustration purposes, to show where the timing marks are.

8. Once the four gears are all in place, Jackson's front cover can be installed. If you are going to run on the street, the stock timing cover will fit. In this instance, the engine is injected and the Jackson aluminum cover is going to be used along with a front-drive fuel pump. The short drive extension (arrow) being installed will drive the fuel pump.

9. Whereas with some gear drives, the entire cam gear is rotated to advance or retard the cam, Jackson uses a standard offset bushing. Cover does not have to come off when changing bushings, only center cap. Power idler gear (left one of dual idlers as seen from front) runs with zero clearance for full tooth contact. The other idler gear runs very loose. As crank gets closer to cam gear due to line bore jobs, clearance is reduced. There is enough clearance "built-in" to allow three line bore jobs if your block will last that long.

Camshaft Drives

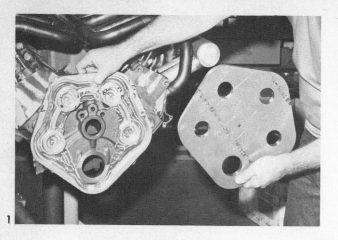

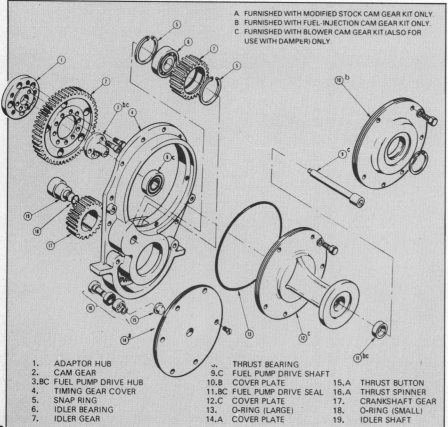

1. When developing a small-block Chevy engine for Indy recently, cam grinder Bruce Crower worked up an ingenious accessory drive. Shown here are the housing and aluminum cover plate.

2. This Crower Z-gear drive set consists of a heat-treated chrome-moly crank gear and a reinforced ductile iron cam gear. These are popular with circle trackers and boatmen. Set requires a reverse-ground cam. Crower highly recommends his special bar stock steel billet cam which is ground in the correct phase to operate properly. A reverse distributor gear is supplied with this camshaft.

3. The Crower Chrysler Hemi gear drive setup functions the same as other 3-gear units. It features a needle bearing thrust package that takes up rearward thrust.

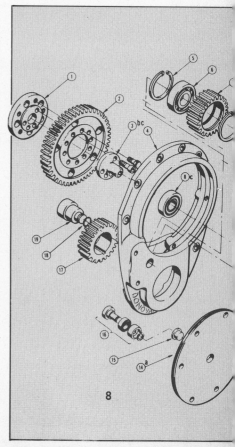

A. FURNISHED WITH MODIFIED STOCK CAM GEAR KIT ONLY.
B. FURNISHED WITH FUEL-INJECTION CAM GEAR KIT ONLY.
C. FURNISHED WITH BLOWER CAM GEAR KIT (ALSO FOR USE WITH DAMPER) ONLY.

1.	ADAPTOR HUB	8.	THRUST BEARING		
2.	CAM GEAR	9.C	FUEL PUMP DRIVE SHAFT		
3.BC	FUEL PUMP DRIVE HUB	10.B	COVER PLATE	15.A	THRUST BUTTON
4.	TIMING GEAR COVER	11.BC	FUEL PUMP DRIVE SEAL	16.A	THRUST SPINNER
5.	SNAP RING	12.C	COVER PLATE	17.	CRANKSHAFT GEAR
6.	IDLER BEARING	13.	O-RING (LARGE)	18.	O-RING (SMALL)
7.	IDLER GEAR	14.A	COVER PLATE	19.	IDLER SHAFT

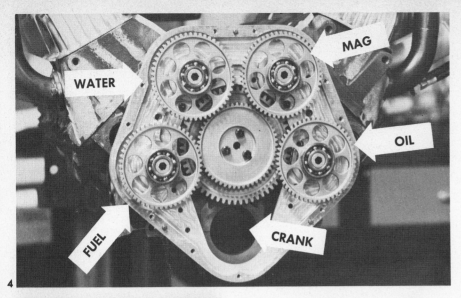

WATER — MAG — OIL — FUEL — CRANK

4

5

6

4. Note the larger rear gear, which is driven off the crank. The straight-cut teeth afford strength, holes reduce weight. Accessories plug into the four gear hubs via hex shafts.

5. Iskenderian Racing Cams, Gardena, Calif., was one of the first cam grinders to offer a 2-gear drive kit for small-block Chevys.

6. Crower Cams & Equipment Co., Chula Vista, Calif., also offers a 3-gear-drive kit for small-block (shown here) and big-block Chevys and Chrysler Hemis. The chrome moly gears are all heat-treated, hardened, with idler gear ball bearing mounted.

7. Donovan Engineering, in Torrance, Calif., produces a number of gear drive assemblies for Chrysler and Chevy engines. This unit is for the 427-in. Chevy engine, with the cover plates designed for stock use, injected engines and blown engines. Gears are all hardened and of aircraft quality steel.

8. This exploded view is of a Donovan 283 Chevy cam drive kit. All gears are machined from solid bar stock for added strength and durability.

9. The Donovan cam drive kit for 426 Chrysler Hemis is similar to the Chevys, relative to gears and front drives. The camshaft can be removed and changed without disturbing the timing gear housing. The vernier cam gear allows precision cam timing as well as advancing or retarding the camshaft.

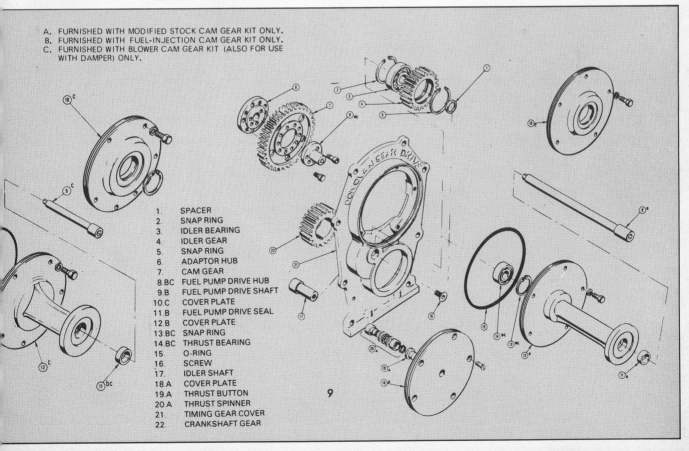

A. FURNISHED WITH MODIFIED STOCK CAM GEAR KIT ONLY.
B. FURNISHED WITH FUEL-INJECTION CAM GEAR KIT ONLY.
C. FURNISHED WITH BLOWER CAM GEAR KIT (ALSO FOR USE WITH DAMPER) ONLY.

1. SPACER
2. SNAP RING
3. IDLER BEARING
4. IDLER GEAR
5. SNAP RING
6. ADAPTOR HUB
7. CAM GEAR
8.BC FUEL PUMP DRIVE HUB
9.B FUEL PUMP DRIVE SHAFT
10.C COVER PLATE
11.B FUEL PUMP DRIVE SEAL
12.B COVER PLATE
13.BC SNAP RING
14.BC THRUST BEARING
15. O-RING
16. SCREW
17. IDLER SHAFT
18.A COVER PLATE
19.A THRUST BUTTON
20.A THRUST SPINNER
21. TIMING GEAR COVER
22. CRANKSHAFT GEAR

9

Camshaft Drives

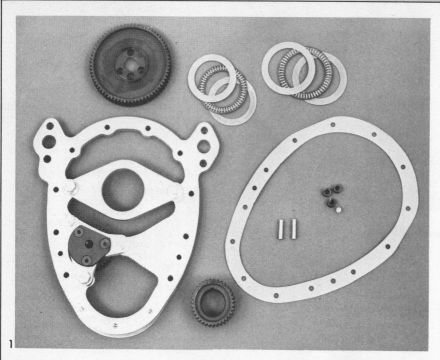

1. This 3-gear kit is designed by the Summers Brothers, Ontario, Calif., for use on any small-block Chevy. It fits under a stock timing cover and water pump. Idler gear mount is held in place by three Allen screws. This is a new modification for the older style on this page uses a nut to hold mount. There had been some problems with nut working loose; hence, reason for the new design.

2. First step to installing a Summers Brothers small-block Chevy gear drive is to replace the two dowel pins with theirs.

3. Place the furnished gasket on block and remove oil seal lip from inside of timing chain cover plate. Thrust washer package goes behind the new cam gear, with needle bearings greased.

4. Pen points out the timing bushing, installed from rear of gear, that allows 0°, 2° or 4° timing changes. These are in crankshaft degrees.

5. The crankshaft gear can now be installed on shaft.

6

7

8

9

6. At this juncture, the front thrust bearing package is set in place on top of cam gear. Races (washers) fit on each side of the bearing.

7. The three cam gear mounting screws can be tightened down now.

8. A small steel rule is used to align the timing marks on both gears prior to installing the main adapter plate on block.

9. Main adapter plate that supports the idler gear and cam thrust plate is installed.

10. Thrust plate over cam gear is shimmed. Brass shims go between steel washers and thrust plate to provide .002-.007-in. movement.

10

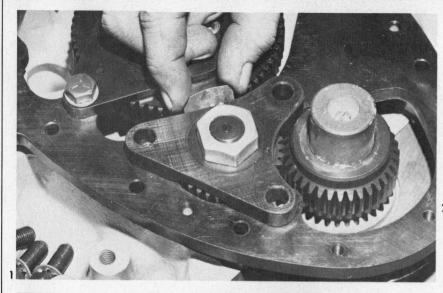

1. Brass shim stock, .003-.004-in. thick, is placed between both idler gear and cam and crank gears.

2. Idler gear bracket is pressed toward other gears, squeezing shims. With third hand, install and tighten idler gear mount.

3. With idler mount tightened, shim can be removed. This will provide backlash equal to two times the shim thickness.

4. Because the Summers adapter includes three more timing cover screws, a transfer screw is installed, one at a time, in the three lower holes, the cover dropped in place and rapped with a hammer. Then the cover can be drilled accurately.

5. This is the completed small-block Chevy gear drive by Summers Brothers, ready for the timing cover to be installed.

6. This is the rear side of the small-block adapter plate, showing the new oil seal that Summers installs. The seal on your stock cover, or other aluminum cover, must be removed.

7. This gear drive kit for the 426-in. Chrysler Hemi is by Summers Brothers. Adjustable idler gear, in addition to enabling gear backlash to be set, allows for changes in center-to-center spacing brought about by line-boring the block. Gear drives also provide precise ignition timing by doing away with timing chain stretch.

8. Summers also have a gear drive for 354-to 392-in. Chryslers. This unit allows the stock pressed steel timing cover to be retained and allows use of stock fuel pump drives. However, Summers tells us that demand for these drives is so low that once their stock is sold, there will be no more for the 354 and 392.

9. Summers Brothers direct gear drive for the big-block Chevys, 396, 427 and 454, are of the same high quality as the others. No machining is necessary on the block, but adapter plate must be attached to front main cap.

5

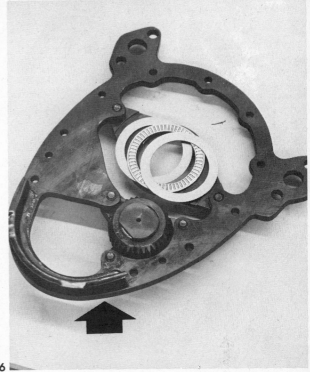

6

7

8

9

Camming a Chevy Vega

Before buying that cam, read on and see what's required for installation.

The Vega engine seems about as weird to us as the Volkswagen did when it first came out. Unfortunately, the history of oddly designed engines in the U.S. is dismal, but presently their future never looked brighter. As annual import sales approached the $2 million mark, Detroit decided none-too-soon to enter the mini-car field thus producing a need for small, lightweight powerplants. Pinto inherited its engines from Ford of Europe and Chrysler's Colt comes from Japan, but Chevrolet started from scratch with an ohc 4 of their own.

The engine, die cast in aluminum, is a 140 cu. in. (2300 cc) inline four with the camshaft mounted over a cast iron cylinder head. Until now, most aluminum blocks have been produced with iron cylinder liners, but the Vega block uses a different technique. Chevy casts the block at its Massena, N.Y., aluminum foundry from aluminum alloy brought in hot from nearby Alcoa and Reynolds. The alloy, which Chevy calls 390, contains 17% silicon and when cast, the hard silicon distributes itself throughout the aluminum to produce a more durable product—the same process used on Chevy's Cam-Am big blocks. The rough engines are then sent to the Tonawanda, N.Y., engine plant where the bores undergo an electrochemical etching process that removes just the outer .0001-in. of aluminum bore surface. This exposes the hard silicon that lies beneath the aluminum. As a result, iron cylinder liners, common in other aluminum blocks, are not necessary; however, the skirts of the aluminum pistons are too soft to survive against the hard silicon cylinder walls. Since iron is compatible with silicon, the skirts are plated with zincate, copper and then iron, followed by a coating of tin to prevent pre-shipment rusting. The iron rings, two compression and one oil, are chrome plated to reduce friction and increase durability.

VEGA'S VALVETRAIN

Due to its ohc design, the Vega valvetrain is much more efficient and higher revving than a similar engine having pushrods. There are no pushrods, no rocker arms, followers (as on Pinto), studs or shaft to slow down valve action but rather a cam making direct contact with tappets.

As the crankshaft turns, so does the cam for they are connected at the front by a neoprene (fiberglass reinforced) rubber belt. The camshaft has eight lobes (one for each valve) and each lobe is situated directly above a cylindrical tappet. Through one cam rotation, (equal to two crankshaft revolutions), the pointed side (the nose) of each lobe makes direct contact with its respective tappet. Each tappet is in contact with a valve stem and as the tappet is pushed downward by the lobe, the valve also descends and opens.

As viewed from the top, the Vega tappet resembles a conventional American lifter; however, its diameter is about twice that of most. Turn it over and its conventionality ends because, unlike others, it is not closed at either end but rather open at the bottom and hollow within. This results in some pretty noisy lifters but nevertheless, it's really a clever idea. By making the tappet large and hollow, the valve stem with attaching spring can fit inside.

The end of each valve stem rides against the flat side of the valve lash adjusting screw located in the ceiling of each tappet. This adjusting screw has got to be the neatest thing since sliced pumpernickel. The screw is slightly wedge-shaped, threaded on all sides but one and fits into a hole in the upper side of the tappet. Of course, the hole into which it fits is also threaded but has a downward slope. That is, the hole goes all the way through the tappet at an angle so that one side is a bit higher than the other. As a result, if the tappet is out of the engine and the screw is removed, then it must be replaced in the hole closest to the top of the tappet so that it will slant in exactly the right direction.

Using an Allen wrench, the lash is adjusted by turning the screw in or out. However, only one side of the screw is flat and since the valve stem must contact that side, adjustments can only be made in full turns. Each full turn of the screw changes the adjustment .003-in.—clockwise to de-

crease the clearance and counter-clockwise to increase it. Clearance measurement is made by inserting the proper feeler gauge between the base circle of the lobe (area opposite the nose) and the top of the tappet.

Turning the screw clockwise decreases this clearance because as you turn in on the screw, the screw gets wider (see applicable picture) and pushes down on the valve stem. The valve resists movement because of its spring pressure but the tappet doesn't and, as a result, the tappet moves upward closer to the cam lobe and clearance is decreased. Turn the magic screw counterclockwise and just the opposite occurs. A pencil, like the screw, is wedge-shaped. Place a book on a table and insert just the pointed end of a pencil beneath it. Slowly push the pencil in further and watch the book rise. The table can be compared to the valve stem for it offers more resistance to movement than the book which, like the tappet, moves upward.

Chevy claims that valve adjustment will be necessary only once every 25,000 miles. The total range of adjustment of the tappet screw is .030-in., but a normally adjusted screw has probably used up at least half of that already. When doing a valve job, the clearance may decrease to the point where you have to almost take the screw clear out of the tappet in order to get the clearance right. If this happens, a few thousandths of an inch should be ground off the end of the valve stem in a valve machine so that the adjusting screw will work at about the middle of its range.

You may be surprised to learn that this odd tappet adjustment with the tapered screw is not new. It has been out for several years, first appearing in 1967 in the Vauxhall Victor which is produced in England by a division of GM. The Vauxhall Victor did not use the same Vega engine, however. The Victor was a slant-4 with the distributor in the front. About the only similarity between the two engines that we can see is the tappet adjustment and the rubber belt that drives the cam.

CAM REMOVAL

The home mechanic will not find the Vega easy to work on, especially in the valve gear area. To remove the cam, Chevy dealers have an expensive tool that bolts onto the head and depresses the lifters so the cam will come out. After four years of Vegas, we figured that cheaper tools would be easy to find, but after calling numerous shops, it seems that this is still the only one available. The tool is manufactured by the Kent-Moore Corp. in Jackson, Mich., and can be purchased from IECO, a Vega specialist, located at 1431 Broadway in Santa Monica, Calif. The cost is approximately $90. For a tool that's going to be used only once, that's a lot of cash, and Sonny Balcaen agrees. If you plan on installing a performance cam, there are a few reputable companies selling them, including IECO. Sonny, IECO's boss, will loan you the tool free for two weeks if you purchase the cam from them. That's a great way to save $90 and get a quality (ground by Crower) cam too. However, IECO doesn't sell stock cams, so for the guy who merely wants to replace a bad cam with original equipment, Sonny's good deal doesn't help. It's unfortunate, but without the special tool, it would be impossible to get the cam out of the head, as long as the head is on the engine. With the head removed, you might be able to do the job without the tool if you are desperate. Try this. Remove the head and depress the lifters one at a time and hold them in that position by putting a spacer under each valve head. This will keep the lifters out of the way for cam removal. The choice is yours. You can either pull the head and try it this way or you can lay out a lot of bread for a one-time tool or maybe

go halvsies with a Vega-owning friend. But remember, if you install a new cam, it's best to do a valve job at the same time and that requires head removal. So, before you invest in the tool, try the alternate method.

But first, a word to the wise: when buying a replacement head gasket, make sure that it's made of stainless steel. The '71 and '72 Vegas came from the factory with steel gaskets which quickly rusted out and allowed water to enter the cylinder. The silicon cylinder does have one drawback—it scuffs easily, and water in the cylinder is enough to do it. As a result, Chevy dealers see a lot of '71 and '72 Vegas for engine replacement due to blown head gaskets. So many, in fact, that the 12,000 mile engine warranty on those models has been extended to 24,000 miles parts and labor and 36,000 miles parts to cover all those engines ruined as a direct result of the faulty gaskets. The stainless steel replacement, introduced in mid-'72, has apparently solved this problem. However, there may be a few of the old type still floating around so be sure to check the gasket composition before buying a replacement gasket.

PERFORMANCE CAMS

Performance grinds for Vega are few in number because the present engine in stock condition, greatly restricts horsepower increase with only a cam change. Unlike most conventional 8's, to get any appreciable improvement in Vega performance from just a cam, other modifications must be made. Iskenderian, a respected

name in camshafts, was contacted on this matter and their spokesman recounted experiments that they ran with the Vega engine using an assortment of test grinds. Due primarily to restrictive head and exhaust design, a camshaft didn't do much for horsepower gain. Speed equipment is expensive enough already and Isky has too good a reputation to lose by selling an expensive cam that does very little. If Isky sold heads and other Vega speed equipment, they could justifiably make and sell a whole load of Vega cams, but Isky is in the cam business and not heads. IECO, on the other hand, specializes in a complete line of Vega go-parts, and they believe in treating the engine as a system with its individual components working together for a desired end. Their No. 1 cam, when combined with a tune-up kit, low-restriction muffler and exhaust extractor does get desirable results, but the cam alone is not recommended. For details, send a buck to IECO for their Vega catalogue. Priminion Enterprises of 1860 E. 3rd St. in Tempe, Ariz., also specializes in Vega equipment including a couple of cams ground by Crower. They'll sell you a modified head with cam installed, but unfortunately, they don't have a rental deal like IECO. Other manufacturers to consider are: Howards Cams in Los Angeles, Calif., Sig Erson of Long Beach, Calif., Crower Cams & Equipment Co. in Chula Vista, Calif. and Crane Cams, Inc., of Hallandale, Fla.

Now that we have gone through some of the basics, let's take a look at how to extract a cam from the Vega 4-cylinder . . .

HOW-TO: Vega Camshaft Exchange

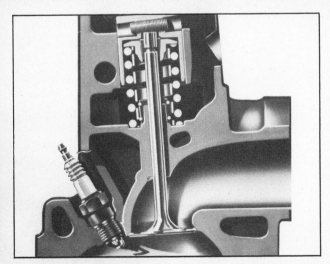

1. Vega's valvetrain uses large, hollow tappet. Valve stem and spring fit inside tappet and stem rides on adjusting screw. When tappet is pushed down, valve opens.

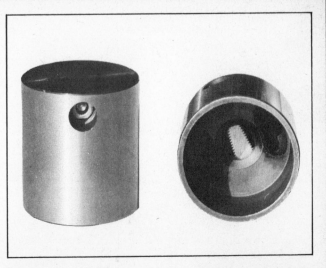

2. No, this isn't a lawnmower piston but rather a Vega valve tappet. Unlike conventional tappets, it's open at one end—a clever design.

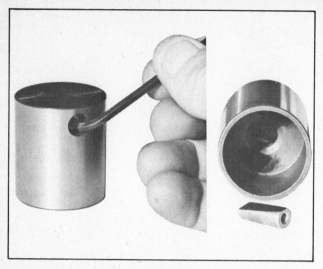

3. Valves are adjusted by turning the lash adjusting screw. Valve stem must ride on flat unthreaded portion making adjustments possible only in full turns.

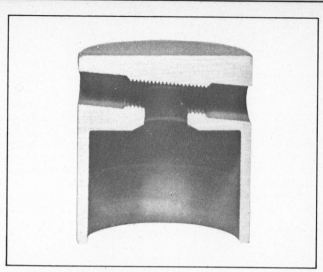

4. Wedge-shaped screw enters at top of sloping hole and, as screw is turned inward, wider part of wedge pushes against stem and raises tappet to reduce lash.

5. Drain the cooling system, remove hood, radiator and anything else in the way. Some mechanics prefer to remove the head instead. We copped out with an engine stand.

6. If you choose to remove head, don't pry; remove bolts and loosen by turning ignition key. When installing, coat bolts with anti-seize, torque in sequence to 60 ft. lbs.

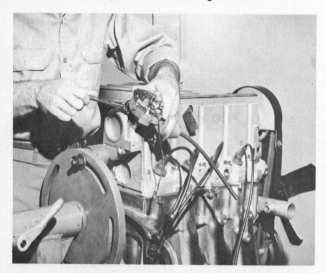

7. Remove distributor cap and then distributor. Distributor must be removed because it's driven by a gear on the back end of the cam.

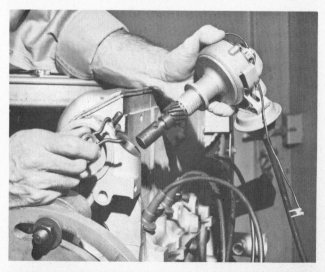

8. Note the large metal piece at the bottom of the shaft. Oil pressure creates a force on it which pushes up on the shaft and eliminates play in the gears.

9. The air cleaner is one piece with the element sealed in. When the element gets dirty, you throw the whole thing away. Seems like a real waste of good metal.

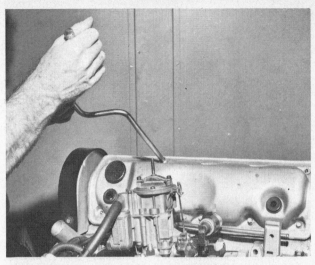

10. Remove cover screws and disconnect front engine mounts. Jack up engine and lower onto 1½-in. wood blocks. This provides room for cam to clear the body.

11. Cam cover has double-wall construction for reducing valve noise. Hollow, solid tappets are a great design, but they do get a bit noisy.

12. The fan must be removed before the belt cover will come off. Hold fan blade and, with the other hand, use a short wrench to loosen bolts but spare your knuckles.

13. Long spacer block on back of fan is necessary to keep blades a safe distance from alternator and closer to radiator for improved cooling.

14. Remove the belt cover. Although engine can run without it, cover isn't merely decorative; its purpose is to keep out grease, fingers and shirtsleeves.

HOW-TO: Vega Camshaft Exchange

15. Exposing the valve gear for inspection is amazingly easy on overhead cam engines. Just a couple of covers, and everything is out in the open.

16. Loosen the cam bolt before removing the belt. The belt functions as a cloth wrench by holding the sprocket in position, and that makes the job a lot easier.

17. Removing the belt is a bit harder than it may look because the water pump has to be moved. Just loosening the bolts is not enough; they have to be removed.

18. We had to move the water pump out of its hole and over to one side in order to get enough play in the belt to remove it. It's best to replace pump gasket now.

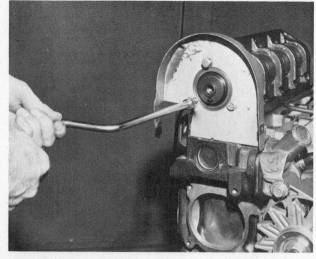

19. If you took our advice and loosened the bolt before the belt, the sprocket will come off easily. With the sprocket off, you can remove the upper cover.

20. To make room for the special tappet-depressing tool, you will have to remove a few of the items from the area between the carburetor and the head.

21. You're going to have to remove some brackets too but first, hold the tool up to the head to determine which ones. To avoid later confusion, tag them before removing.

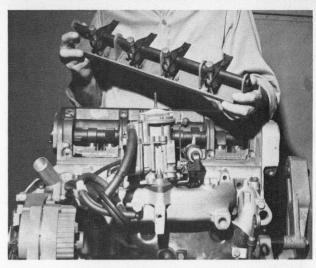

22. This is the gadget you have to have in order to remove the cam on a Vega. It was designed especially for this particular engine and won't fit anything else.

23. Back off all the screws on the tool and then place it between the carburetor and the cylinder head. The carburetor is not in the way, so don't remove it.

24. Line the tool up with the lower row of cam cover bolt holes. The tool is attached here and the cam cover bolts are sufficient to hold it.

25. Tighten down on all the cap screws and then run down the slotted-head screws until they are just snug against the head. Do not overtighten them.

26. As shown, the tool is now in position and ready to depress and hold the tappets to permit cam removal. But don't do anything just yet.

HOW-TO: Vega Camshaft Exchange

27. A vital step is the positioning of the crankshaft so the pistons are not at top dead center. Putting the timing marks 90° from each other (arrows) will do it.

28. With the pistons down in the bores, you can tighten the tool and depress the tappets without fear of pushing the valve heads into the pistons.

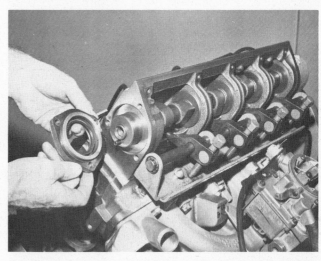

29. As you can see, the tool works very easily. The tappets on the left have been depressed while those on the right have not yet been tightened down.

30. Remove the seal retainer (also called the cam thrust plate) from the cam. Inspect the seal and gasket and replace if any damage is found.

31. When the tappets are all depressed, you can slide the cam right out. To avoid scratching the bearings, with the sharp lobes, remove the cam carefully.

32. Since most of you will be doing this step in the car, you'll now discover why we advised raising the engine and removing the radiator.

33. The tool does a great job by depressing just the edges and still allowing clearance for cam removal. At this time, remove tool and lift out tappets.

34. Inspect the cam bearings and if they look scratched or slightly scored, rent a cam bearing driver and carefully push them out of the head.

35. After the first bearing is out, place the guide in the bearing hole to keep the driver straight. Check for any casting flash and file off before using any force.

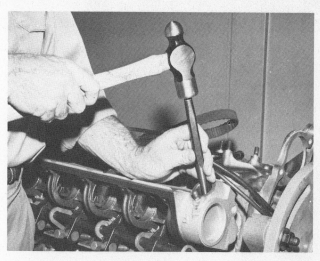

36. Push the rear bearing into the cavity at end of head and, using a punch, collapse the bearing to permit removal. Removing the rear plug will not help.

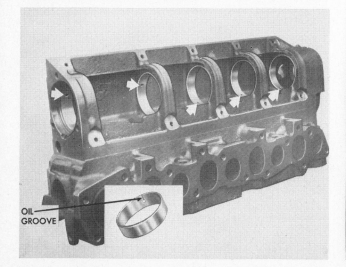

37. When installing new cam bearings, make sure that holes in three rear bearings align with those in head. Front two holes must be at 11 o'clock with groove in front.

38. Coat bearings, cam lobes and tappet tops with STP and carefully insert cam. Put the gasket and seal retainer loosely on front of head.

HOW-TO: Vega Camshaft Exchange

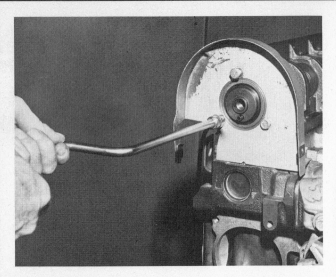

39. Align retainer with bolt holes, and position the upper belt cover over it. The same three cap screws hold both the retainer and cover in place.

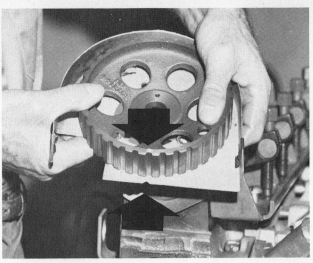

40. The camshaft timing marks are notches (arrows) in the upper cover and the camshaft sprocket. They must be aligned when the belt is put on.

41. Ignition timing marks (arrow) are also used for cam timing. After aligning them, check them after putting on belt; otherwise, timing will be off if they move.

42. Put on the cam sprocket, align the marks and snug down on the bolt. Do the final tightening after the belt has been installed.

43. With the belt in position, a belt tensioner adapter tool (available from Kent-Moore) will help you set belt tension. However, many mechanics use a pry bar instead.

44. Setting belt tension is much easier if you have two more hands. The torque wrench and tool push against the pump while you tighten the pump bolts.

45. Fifteen ft. lbs. are used to push the water pump against the belt before you tighten pump to block. If you use pry bar, pry until belt is tight, then tighten bolts.

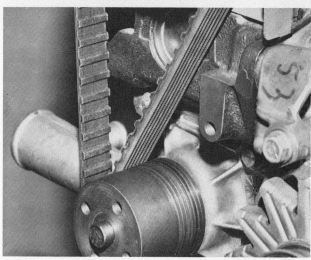

46. Make sure that you have the belt grooves in the right grooves on the hub. Misaligning them by one or two notches will wear out belt.

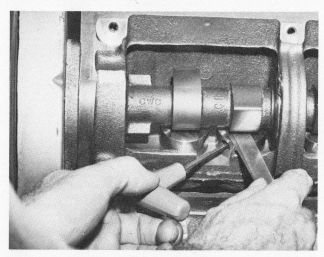

47. Adjust valves according to procedure in "Adjusting Valves" chapter in manual. Clean up cam cover, install new gasket and tighten down cover.

48. Install distributor with vacuum advance facing front and set points. Rotate distributor until car starts and, using a light, set the timing to specs.

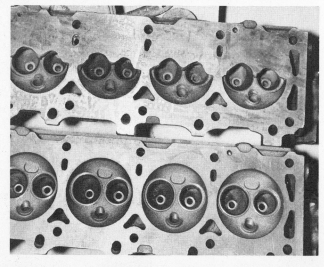

49. Priminion Enterprises will sell you a cam already installed in their trick head. Metal is welded to top of combustion chamber for more compression and power.

50. IECO engine develops 175 dyno hp with headers, dual Webers, special head and cam and deep sump pan. Engine has potential for more.

Camming a Small-Block Chevy

Ever since the first '55 rolled off the assembly line, the Chevy small-block has been this country's most popular engine. Its introduction revolutionized hot rodding. For years, the Olds backed by a La-Salle box was the hot setup. However, lines quickly formed for Chevy's 265. Everywhere shade-tree limbs groaned from the weight of Rocket 88's swinging from chains—hung by the block until dead and the first of many to die at the hand of Chevrolet. The 265, complete with powerpack heads and dual exhaust, weighed in at 550 lbs., some 150 lbs. lighter than the Olds. Available over the counter with dual 4 bbls. and solid

lifters, the engine produced 225 hp, and overnight the horses grew. In '57, came the 283—a compression jump from 9.25:1 to 10:5 and Rochester fuel injection. At the time, it was incredible—1 hp for each cubic inch. 1958 brought the 4-speed and 290 hp. 1961 was the last year for Corvette's 283 and its most outstanding year for power—11.0:1 compression and f.i. developed 315 hp. Displacement took a big jump in '62 with the first 327, another winner from Chevy. At that point, the heavy Olds was nearly forgotten, merely a rusting memory in a basement corner. The greatest hp rating for the 327 and the largest rating for a Chevy small-block

came in '65 when a Corvette could be ordered with fuel injection and 375 showroom horsepower. The famous Z28 made its limited debut in '67 powered by a beautiful new engine, the 302 and greatly underrated at 290 hp. Its last year was '69. Also small but very tame was the 307, produced as an economy 8 for the '68 Nova and Chevelle. The 350, introduced on the '67 Camaro, replaced the 327 in '70 supplemented by a new small-block, the 400.

They're everywhere—millions of Chevy small-blocks, and there's sure to be thousands of guys out there wanting to install a new cam but needing some direction to do so. We

HOW-TO: Chevy Camshaft Exchange

1. Remove the No. 1 plug, before removing distributor. Turn engine until compression is felt at plug hole and then turn fan until timing mark (arrow) aligns with "O."

2. Remove distributor cap and mark position of rotor pointer in relation to distributor body (arrow). This guarantees that it will be returned to the same spot.

3. Removing the distributor in this way ensures that ignition timing will not be disturbed. To prevent any shocking experiences, remove the battery ground cable.

4. Drain radiator, loosen hose clamps and, if the hoses are good, pry them off and save for reuse. Remove mounting bolts and carefully lift out radiator.

ran this story last year too, and we'll probably continue to do it as long as the demand exists.

Cam installation is the same for all of Chevy's small V-8's if the engine is out of the car. However, with the engine installed, the story changes a little. Due to a difference in body styles, accessory locations (does it have air conditioning?) and emissions equipment (smog pump?), getting to the timing chain cover is going to vary a bit from car to car. Unfortunately, we don't have the space to include all of the variations. From the chain cover back, it's all the same. Making notes as you go, remove or move everything blocking cam removal using our instructions as a guide and, once you've reached the timing cover, follow our instructions exactly. The car undergoing the swap is a '55 Chevy running a 283 and the cam

and kit is a Howard #295 street unit. However, with the present gas situation, we would probably choose a mileage cam from Racer Brown.

Before climbing into those old clothes, there are a few things that must be stressed. Distributor removal must be performed according to a prescribed procedure; if not, you can expect one heck of a time getting that engine started. To prevent the engine from starting, disconnect the coil wire and then remove No. 1 spark plug. While holding your thumb over the open plug hole, have someone crank the engine until you feel the compression on your thumb. This indicates that the piston is on its compression stroke. Turn off the key and with your hands, turn the fan until the slash on the harmonic balancer aligns with the "O" mark on the timing tab. This indicates that No. 1 pis-

ton is at top dead center (TDC). Remove the distributor cap and mark its position so that it will point in the same direction when distributor is to be reinstalled.

If you replace the timing chain, you'll probably receive new cam and crank gears. The crank gear is a tight fit and removal requires a puller and installation may require an oven. Using a wood block and a hammer, try pounding the new gear on the shaft. If that doesn't work, heat the gear in the oven (250°) and shrink the crankshaft nose with ice and pound some more. It should go on. The same applies to the harmonic balancer. If it won't go on, lightly sand the crank nose with crocus cloth (don't overdo it) and try again. If unsuccessful, heat the balancer. Now that we've "told you so," put on those old clothes and get started.

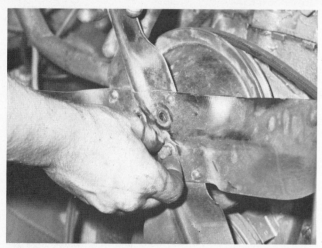

5. With the radiator out, you've got some working room, so climb in there and remove the fan, pulley and fan belt. Keep everything together to ensure proper installation.

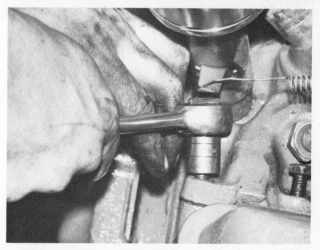

6. Remove the manifold bolts. Due to limited accessibility, some bolts are a little hard to get to so a socket wrench and a box wrench will be necessary.

7. Now you can pull the valve covers from the engine, along with any smog equipment that might be attached. Scrape old gaskets from covers.

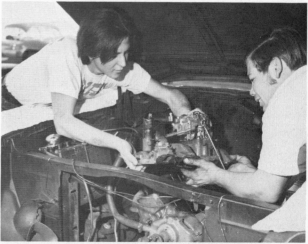

8. Disconnect throttle linkage and remove the manifold. Gaskets are usually sealed with Permatex No. 2 so it may take some gentle prying to loosen.

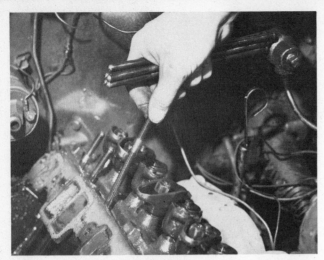

9. If you plan on reusing the pushrods, find yourself some masking tape and label each as to location before removing. Original rods must be returned to same rockers.

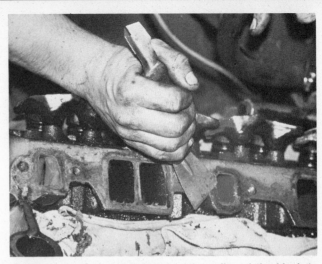

10. Clean shop rags are placed in the valley of the block to prevent gasket scrapings from contaminating the engine. Tissue is jammed into the ports.

11. Manifold facings of heads should be cleaned with solvent. Don't forget to remove tissue from ports. Using a pair of needle-nose pliers, remove the lifters.

12. Loosen the clamp and remove the heater hose from water pump. Remove the four pump bolts and note which ones go where. Remove the water pump from the block.

13. Wedge a bar into gear puller to prevent pulley from moving and, using an adjustable wrench, remove pulley and harmonic balancer from crankshaft.

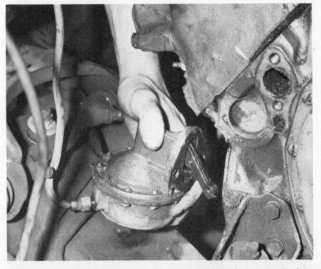

14. The fuel pump is actuated by a pushrod that extends into the block and rides on the cam. In order to free cam, pump and pushrod must be removed.

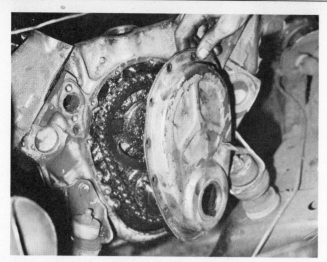

15. Lower part of timing chain cover is held by oil pan so loosen the front pan bolts and then remove the cover bolts. Pry off cover and clean gasket surfaces.

16. Remove the cam gear and timing chain. Chains stretch with age causing timing fluctuations, and after 50,000 miles, it's advisable to install a new one.

17. Now you're ready to remove the cam but easy does it. Lobes are sharp and it's pretty easy to damage the cam bearings. Support the cam as you go.

18. This is the Howard cam and kit that went into the Chevy. Kit is complete with pushrods, double springs, retainers, solid lifters and a tube of moly lube.

19. Wash the cam with solvent to remove any oil, dust or grease. Coat the journals and cam lobes with moly lube or STP to ensure initial lubrication.

20. Once cam is lubricated, insert into block but do so very slowly and gently to avoid damaging the journal bearings. Once again, support cam as you insert.

HOW-TO: Chevy Camshaft Exchange

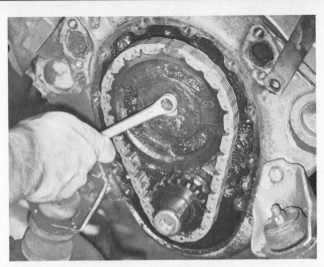

21. Install gear and chain and align timing marks (arrows) so that mark on cam gear is at a 6 o'clock position and mark on crank gear at 12. Cam pin must be at 3.

22. Don't force gear onto cam. Place gear over locating dowel and draw it into place with bolts. Using a hammer to seat gear might dislodge welsh plug at end of cam.

23. Using a small screwdriver, remove the old oil seal from the timing chain cover. Clean off gasket surfaces before installing cover to block.

24. Working from the front, tap in a new oil seal. Seal should be lightly oiled and installed so open end is toward the inside of the cover.

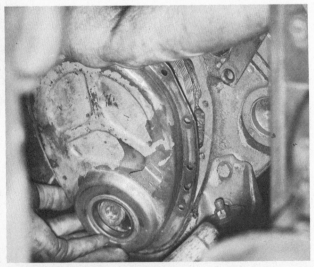

25. Coat timing chain with engine oil and stick a new cover gasket to block using some non-hardening sealer. Install timing chain cover.

26. New cam should be accompanied by new lifters. Wash lifters with solvent and lube the bases with moly lube or STP to ensure lubrication when engine is first started.

27. Once the lifters are in their bores, slide in the pushrods. If the originals are being reused, make sure they are returned to the same rocker arms.

28. This would be a good time to get some head work done. Here the guides are being cut for new seals and the spring seats are being cut for larger springs.

29. The two guides at left are cut for seals and large dual springs. Next guide is stock, one at far right has been cut just for the valve stem seal.

30. Screw-in studs were also installed—a must with a high-revving small-block. Head on bottom is stock with pressed-in studs, head on top has screw-ins.

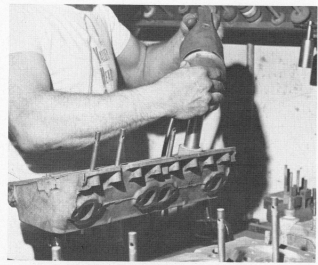

31. Chuck Prite, of Valley Head Service in Tarzana, Calif., wrapped up the cam swap by giving the heads a good valve job. Here, the seats are being ground.

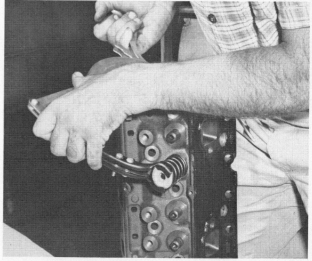

32. Head has been prepared and big valve springs are being compressed into position. Heavy duty, double-coiled springs are from the Howard cam kit.

Camming a 2-Liter Ford Pinto

If you plan a cam change for your 2-liter, you're going to need some special tools but we'll tell you where to get them and how to use them.

Cam changes on any ohc engine ought to be easy. With the cam and all the valve gear sitting right up on top of the engine, it should be a simple matter of undoing a few bolts and lifting the cam off—about as easy as changing a carburetor. On some overhead cam engines, it is that easy. On the Pinto 2000cc engine, it *isn't.*

The cam on this Pinto is removed by sliding it through the cam bearings to the back of the head. You have to do it that way because the front bearings are smaller than the rear. Cam changes with the cylinder head in the chassis are impossible, unless you want to cut a hole in the firewall and pull the cam out into the front seat of the car. Whether you remove the cylinder head only, or remove the whole engine in order to change the cam is up to you. In our photos we have the engine out and on a stand, but we remove the cylinder head anyway just to show you how it's done.

We have talked to a lot of Ford engineers, but so far, we haven't found one who has come up with a really good explanation of why the Pinto cylinder head and cam was designed with the small bearings to the front. We could think of a lot of reasons why the design might have been done that way, but they are pure speculation.

In February of '69, the Capri was introduced in Europe with a choice of several V-4's and V-6's. Several months later, the 2000 cc ohc inline four was introduced in the European Capri and in December of '70, production began on an emissions version for the U.S. market. Meanwhile, back in Detroit, the Pinto was going through final design and an economical, dependable engine was needed fast. The 1600 cc pushrod four and the 2000 cc ohc inline four were already available from Ford of Europe and any last-minute refinements, such as camshaft changes, would have held up final production and cost a lot of money. Therefore, the Pinto was introduced in '71 with either the British 1600 or the German 2000 engine. The deadline date was met and the 2000 worked well. However, because the entire cylinder head must be taken out for cam removal, warranty claims to Ford were quite a bit more expensive than they would have been if the cam were removable from the front. Nevertheless, it was much cheaper and less time consuming than tooling up for a new head design. And we figure that's why the Pinto 2000 has the small bearings to the front, but remember, it's just pure speculation.

The cog belt that drives the cam is printed with the words, *"Nicht Knicken, DO NOT CRIMP."* Maybe the designers were worried too much about putting a crimp in the belt, because they sure put a crimp in our cam change.

Most cam bearing removal tools are a simple shouldered plug with a long bar. Beat on the bar, and the plug pushes the cam bearing out of the hole in the block. Pinto cam bearings are mounted in tall towers that stick up from the head like the torch on the Statue of Liberty. The towers are cast in one piece with the cylinder head, so if you should break or crack one, you will have to scrap the whole head. Using the ordinary type cam bearing driver puts too much force on the towers resulting in a cracked head.

The tool that Ford dealers use is a special screw-type puller that gently pushes the cam bearing out without any danger of breaking the head. It's the same tool used by Ford dealers on other engines, with a couple of pieces added to adapt it for use on the Pinto. Owatonna Tool Co., Eisenhower Dr., Owatonna, Minn., 55060, makes the puller, and it should be available from them in their latest catalogs. If you are not going into the cam changing business, it would be cheaper to take your cylinder head down to your local Ford dealer and have him install new bearings. The main tool goes for $73.75 (January '74) and the adapter is $13.80.

Performance camshafts for the Pinto 2000 cc have just recently become available from some aftermarket grinders. Crane's '73 catalogue shows three different grinds for the 2000 each with valve springs, retainers and lube for approximately $150. Sig Erson sells a cam, springs and retainers for $102 (1973), but it's necessary to cut the head to accommodate the new springs and that's going to be a few extra bucks. However, these prices aren't really too bad for there's a lot of engineering that has to be done, because the Pinto cam is different than most. Each set of the lobe has a different profile which is necessary because of the leverage change in the cam follower.

In an ordinary camshaft, both sides of the lobe are the same, because all the lobe does is push a tappet up and down. There is no leverage change as the tip of the lobe wipes across the surface of the tappet. On the Pinto, the leverage and rate of opening changes as the tip of the lobe moves across the cam follower, because the distance from the lobe to the pivot point of the follower changes as the lobe rotates.

For example, when the cam opens an intake, the lobe is near the valve, which gives less leverage and a slower rate of opening. As the intake valve is closing, the lobe is close to the pivot point of the cam follower and the rate is greater. So the closing ramp on the lobe has to be ground differently than the opening ramp.

Another complication, to make life interesting for the cam grinder, is that the exhaust and intake valves are on opposite edges of the head. This means that an exhaust lobe has to have a contour exactly opposite to an intake lobe. We can all be glad that we don't have to make our living grinding cams.

Now let's take a look at how to put a cam in a Pinto, but first, you had better check out your finances because you're going to need a few special tools.

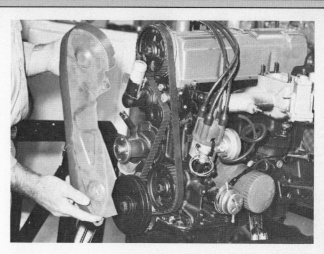

1. The clean floor and immaculate tool box at Ford Motor Co.'s training center is quite a change from our usual shade tree locations for making automotive repairs. But climbing in and out of that strange-looking engine stand is almost as difficult as working over the Pinto's fender.

2. Drain the cooling system into a bucket and remove the belt cover. The cover serves a purpose, but the engine can run fine without it. It's only a guard to keep out grease and to prevent inquisitive fingers from getting tangled up with the fast-moving cog-toothed belt.

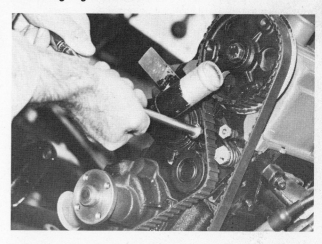

3. Loosen the camshaft bolt while the belt is in the installed position. Doing it this way will prevent the cam from turning. If you have already removed the belt, put it back on. Jamming a tool against the sprocket may keep it from moving, but it's likely to cause damage.

4. Located beneath the cog-toothed belt and next to the water outlet, is the locking bolt for the belt tensioner. Using a deep socket and extension, loosen the bolt. This will free the locking mechanism and allow the belt to be slackened enough for quick and easy removal.

5. Slackening the Pinto's belt is a two-handed job. Insert an extension bar as shown and pry the belt tensioner toward the slack side. While holding it in this position, tighten up the locking bolt. This will hold the belt in the loosened position and permit removal of the pry bar.

6. With the belt tensioner locked in the loose position, the belt can be easily removed without any trouble. This would also be a good time to disconnect the wires from the spark plugs. To ensure proper replacement of wires, mark them as to location before removing them.

HOW-TO: 2-Liter Pinto Cam Exchange

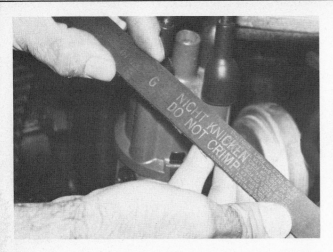

7. Work on the 2-liter engine long enough, and you will learn a little German. Most of the parts are made in Germany, but the engines are all assembled in England, which accounts for the mix of metric and American bolts. As a result, both kinds of wrenches are required.

8. Remove the cam cover bolts, lift off the cover and there's the cam right on top. It's hard to believe that the job has only just begun. If the cam could be removed from the front, the job would be an easy one but unfortunately, it can't, so prepare yourself for some work.

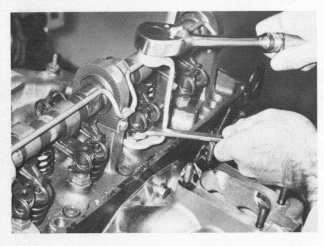

9. A special wrench is used to loosen adjuster lock nuts. If you lay both wrenches together as shown here, and put pressure on both of them at once, the stubborn lock nuts will come loose. Wrench is Owatonna No. 7012. Your friendly Ford mechanic can tell you where to get one.

10. After you have loosened the lock nuts, run them all the way up and then turn the adjusting studs all the way down. As you will notice, this changes the valve clearance (distance between follower and cam lobe) and makes it easier to remove the springs.

11. It takes strong fingers, but a good hard pull will snap the springs off the end of the cam followers. A screwdriver will save wear and tear on the fingers but if you choose to test your finger strength, brace yourself first to avoid doing backflips when spring releases.

12. If you emerged uninjured from the spring snapping, you're ready to remove the cam followers. The followers that are loose can be removed just by pushing them off the adjuster toward the valve. As you remove them, tag them as to location to ensure proper installation.

13. Some of the lobes will be against the followers so you will have to rotate the camshaft to free them. This is where we goofed. If we had left the belt on up to this point, it would have been a lot easier to turn the cam just by putting a large wrench on the crank pulley.

14. It isn't necessary to remove the springs from the adjusters so just let them hang there. Note the wear pattern on the cam lobes. This is the area that contacts the follower. Tube in background next to the cam is the oil supply pipe—its kind of fragile so be careful not to damage it.

15. Remove the bolt and sprocket from the cam. This is an easy job if you had loosened the bolt when the belt was still on; if not, shame on you. The only way to keep the cam from turning is by putting the belt back on or by using a cloth strap wrench to hold the sprocket.

16. Once you have removed the sprocket, remove the rear belt guide. You may have already removed it along with the sprocket; if not, it will slide easily from the end of the cam. In addition to keeping the belt straight, this guide also serves as a timing pointer for the camshaft.

17. Now it's time to remove the head; but, before you can begin, you must have a special tool to remove those weird head bolts. Ford of Europe sure made it tough for the do-it-yourselfer but it looks like Owatonna Tool Co. gets another sale—yours. Tool number is 7016.

18. As you remove the head bolts, tag them as to location so they can be returned to the same holes. Once removed, treat them like gold for you won't find them at your local hardware store. Ford's new 2300 engine, built in Ohio, improves things with more conventional bolts.

HOW-TO: 2-Liter Pinto Cam Exchange

19. We don't recommend this for hernia patients, but the head and manifold combination is light enough that one man can lift it right off the engine. However, that's on an engine stand. When working over a fender, lifting is tricky so you would probably need the help of another guy.

20. At last, the head is off. Fortunately, the exhaust and intake manifolds don't have to be removed from the head for they are all taken off as one unit. Nevertheless, seeing the cam right on top and so accessible-looking is pretty frustrating when you have to remove the head to get at it.

21. Now that you've got the head off, flip it over and take a closer look at what you've worked so hard to remove. Now's the time to check the valve faces for damage or excessive burning and carefully remove any carbon buildup from valves and combustion chambers.

22. Aluminum alloy pistons are of the conventional flat top design. What look like cylinder sleeves are actually the metal rings in the gasket lying on top of the head. Rust works quickly. If you expect the head to be off for more than an hour, make sure all parts are well oiled.

23. This strange apparatus, made by Owatonna, is necessary for removing and replacing the front cam bearing seal. However, the tools are expensive and we suggest that you save your money and take the head to your Ford dealer and have him install the new cam.

24. For those of you having access to the tools, we'll continue. For those choosing the dealership, read on and learn how to install the head. Work the puller fingers through the seal until they grasp the back side. The fingers are just springy enough to accomplish this.

25. Position the seal puller and gradually tighten the screw. This will pull the seal right out of the tower. Don't get overanxious and remove the cam prematurely because the camshaft must remain in position so that the puller can have something to push against.

26. Installing the new seal also requires that the camshaft remain in the cylinder head. Make sure that the seal is installed with its lip pointed toward the rear of the engine. If you're innovative and energetic, you could probably make this tool for just a few cents.

27. When positioned correctly, the front seal must be fully seated in its bore as shown. Note that the seal's lip is pointing toward the rear of the engine. Cam bearing surfaces are made of copper and lead and since they are soft, care must be taken not to damage them.

28. The camshaft thrust plate at the rear cam journal not only holds the cam in position but also controls the amount of camshaft end-play. Using a box wrench, remove the two cap screws from the plate. The cap screws must be used with washers so don't lose them.

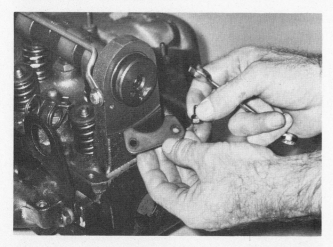

29. It sure doesn't look like much but this thrust plate affects the operation of the entire valve train. Without it, the camshaft will "walk" back and forth enough to cause damage but some end-play must exist, and this plate's thickness preserves the specified amount.

30. With the plate removed, the cam is ready to come out. However, if the same cam and bearings are to be reused, remove the cam very slowly and very carefully because the bearings and journals can be scratched very easily. If you damage the bearings they will have to be replaced.

HOW-TO: 2-Liter Pinto Cam Exchange

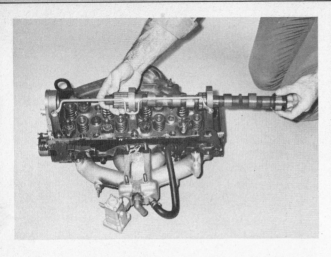

31. As you withdraw the cam, support and guide it through each cam bearing. In case you've been wondering, that gadget attached to the intake manifold is a decel. valve. The valve, found only on stick 2000's, draws extra gas from the carb to reduce deceleration emissions.

32. As you pull the cam through the rear bearing, notice the size difference between the front cam journal and the rear bearing. You can see that the front journal will slide through the rear bearing, but the rear journal is too large to be pulled out from the front of the engine.

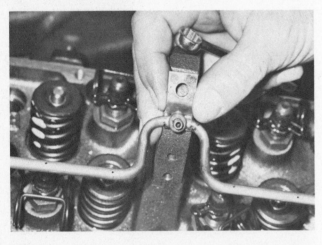

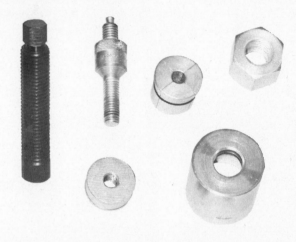

33. Remove the oil pipe. Note the holes in the bearing tower. The lower one is for the cap screw that holds the pipe and the upper supplies oil into the pipe. The small holes in the pipe (look closely) spray this oil onto the lobes, followers and valve stems—their only lubrication.

34. Are you ready for this? More special tools. This assortment of goodies is recommended for removing and replacing the camshaft bearings. The price is $87 and of course, Owatonna sells them. If you haven't already, take the head to your Ford dealer and have them do it.

35. However, if you're the stubborn type and you insist on doing the work yourself, you might sneak by with a conventional puller, but we don't recommend it. A conventional puller requires force for bearing removal and too much force just might crack that thin center tower.

36. If you should crack the bearing tower you're going to need a new head and that's expensive. So, if you are the stubborn type or you just dig owning special tools, then buy the tool. It fits perfectly and does a good job without any danger of damaging the cylinder head.

37. By using two wrenches—one on the big nut and one on the screw—you can push the cam bearings out in a few minutes. Once removed, clean and inspect each bearing saddle. If saddles are rough or burred, smooth out with crocus cloth and clean before installing new bearings.

38. Note the offset location of the oil holes in the cam bearings. Using the special tool, install each of the new bearings but take your time. The oil hole in each bearing must line up with the hole in each tower. To ensure initial lubrication, coat inner surface of bearings with STP.

39. Once the camshaft bearings are installed and lubricated, insert the cam in from the rear of the head. It's absolutely essential that cam installation be done slowly and very carefully. The bearings are quite soft and the hardened cam lobes can easily damage them.

40. Don't forget the thrust plate. It's back there at the rear where it could easily be left off. The cap screws include washers and, to ensure proper cam end-play, make sure they go back on. If the plate is too wide for the slot then the cam hasn't been fully seated.

41. Inspect the oil lubrication pipe. Check the small oil holes and the large oil entrance hole for blockage by dirty oil. If blocked or dirty, clean thoroughly with solvent before installing on cylinder head. Install the pipe in proper position and secure the appropriate cap screws.

42. There are no dowels or other locaters in the cylinder head or block, so it's a good idea to install a couple of long studs to guide the head into position on block. When working alone, that head gets pretty heavy and hard to handle. Install new gasket and then the head.

HOW-TO: 2-Liter Pinto Cam Exchange

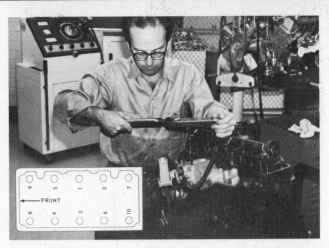

43. If you are installing a reground or new cam, be sure that the Woodruff key is in its place at the front of the shaft. If not, remove the key from the old cam and, using a soft hammer, tap into new shaft. Install belt guide and sprocket with three sprocket ribs to front.

44. Insert two head bolts, remove guide studs and install remaining bolts. Bolts must be clean, dry and torqued at 65-80 ft. lbs. according to the sequence shown. After the engine has been completed, started and warmed up, loosen one bolt at a time and retorque to specifications.

45. Put the belt on and time the engine before you insert the cam followers. By doing it this way, you'll find that it's a lot easier to turn over the engine. We tell you this because, as you can see, we installed the followers first and learned our lesson the hard way.

46. The 2-liter engine uses the same marks for ignition timing as for camshaft timing. Turn the front pulley clockwise until the "O" mark lines up with the pointer on the front of the engine. This indicates that No. 1 piston is at the top of its compression stroke (TDC).

47. This picture shows something we said earlier; that is, if the camshaft sprocket is on correctly, the three ribs should face outward. If they don't, then the sprocket is on backwards and must be corrected. Align the pointer on the sprocket with the ball on the belt guide.

48. Our distributor rotor is laying up there on the intake manifold but make sure your's is on the distributor shaft. Turn the cog wheel until rotor points to cap's No. 1 wire tower (if cap were in place) and points are just starting to open. This timing will be close enough to get engine started.

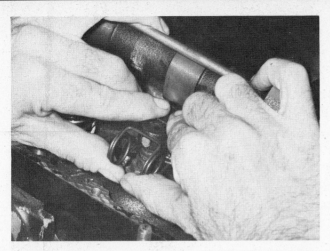

49. Now that you've initially timed the engine, you should install the cam followers. Some of the cam lobes will be in the way so the cam will have to be turned during follower installation. Snap on the springs and then be sure to realign the pointer on the cam sprocket.

50. Adjust the valves with engine cold and not running. Turn the crankshaft pulley until valves 1,2,3 and 5 are depressed and adjust the even numbered valves to .008-in. and the odds to .010-in. To get accurate reading, spring must be snapped off follower before adjusting.

51. After making the valve adjustment, don't forget to snap the follower springs back into place and then install the water outlet pipe. It mounts directly below the cam sprocket. Coat the cam lobes, followers and valve tips with STP to ensure initial lubrication when the engine is first started.

52. The belt tensioner works by itself. All you have to do is loosen the bolt, and the spring will push it over against the belt for just the right amount of tension. Once that is accomplished, you must lock it in position with the smaller bolt so that it will stay there.

53. After you have tightened the belt, connect the smog equipment. Deceleration valve has an air-fuel line connecting it to the carburetor. Make sure this line is connected and the fittings tight. Clean off top of cylinder head and scrape the old gasket from the valve cover.

54. Install the valve cover with a new gasket and check cam sprocket bolt for tightness. Install carb, hook up all wires and start it up. If it starts OK, shut it off and mark the timing pointer and the 8° mark at the crank pulley with chalk and, using a timing light, set timing at 8°BTDC.

Camming Ford's V-6's

Virtually overnight, our automotive industry has entered a new age of production—one that should be welcomed by all. The age of the small car is here and none-too-soon. For too long, Americans have been attracted by huge, resource-wasting, gas-gulping barges and unfortunately, nothing less than an energy crisis could have discouraged them. The American car maker makes a bundle on luxury car sales. If the energy was available, he would continue to woo the public with status symbol bait and go right on wasting iron and materials on those 20 foot monsters. Fortunately, there's no longer enough gas to make the big car practical and the factories have been forced by consumer demand to convert to small car production. Chrysler Corporation has been working overtime to convert and by May of '74, they'll be equipped to devote 60% of their production to Valiants, Dusters and Darts. To American Motors, the small car people, the crisis has brought great success. As of March, '74, they had filled all orders for '74 cars because they couldn't possibly produce any more. Import sales are the best ever bringing increased production, but fuel shortages have brought shipping reductions and long waiting lines for customers.

Many people are switching to smaller cars, but the big-car owners are the hardest to convince. They're a rather snobbish bunch, and for years they have been blindly opposed to small cars. Now even this has begun to change. The energy crisis has opened some eyes and the rich man sees the little car in a different light. He humbles himself and moves in for a closer look discovering that maybe the smaller car isn't so bad after all. And now, it's no longer such a stigma to be a rich man driving an economy car because waiting in long gas lines has become an even greater stigma for the big car owner.

Detroit sympathizes with the rich and to ease the pain of his small car transition, they have combined status with economy into a new luxury small car. A long list of options including air conditioning, plush interiors and full powers have produced a $5000+ compact. Surprizingly, a large number of people are paying those prices and discovering that a smaller car can be nearly as luxurious and roomy as their Eldos or Mark IV's. This makes Detroit happy for they have held onto a wealthy customer and at the same time sold a $5000 car.

The point has been made. The big-car driver experiencing the little car just might find it a lot more acceptable than expected. Perhaps so much so that once the shortage is over, he'll find it difficult returning to the larger car. As a further persuasion, Ford has just decided to introduce two all new small luxury sedans for '75—a great expense for Ford but justified if the demand increases as we expect it to. As Ford's President, Lee Iacocca has said: "The essence of these new cars is luxury in a small size . . . Although smaller, there will be no compromise of comfort and convenience." Yes, it took a gas shortage, but it looks like the 20 foot monster may be on its way out—replaced by a smaller car in the Mercedes-BMW tradition. We hope so, for who needs all that iron when the job can be done with fewer materials without sacrificing usable room, power or luxury?

FORD'S V-6

It looks like small cars are becoming the rule rather than the exception, and cars like the Capri and Mustang II will be around for awhile. Gazing into our crystal ball, it looks as if the V-6 will eventually become the popular Capri/Mustang engine and, in time, it'll find its way into junkyards and classified ads. V-6 speed equipment is being developed now and conversion kits may appear resulting in new power for Capris, Mustang II's, Pintos and lots of street rods. As one Ford service manager said: "The V-6 is really a sweetheart," and we'll have to agree.

Ford's V-6 is built by Ford of Europe in Cologne, Germany. The first V-6, a 2.6 liter, made its European debut in 1971 as an option for their Capri. The car sold well and in one year of service, the 2.6 proved to be a fine German engine. In '72, the 2.6 Capri arrived on American shores as a welcome addition to the underpowered four-banger. The engine dis-

HOW-TO: V-6 Cam Installation

1. The 2.6 and 2.8 appear to be the same engines, until you take a closer look. Most obvious difference is carburetor position—gas flow between cylinders is improved on 2.6 by mounting the carburetor at an angle (à la Edelbrock) while mounting is straight on 2.8.

2. Remove valve covers and alternator and mark location of plug wires before removing distributor. V-6 operates so smoothly that a dampener is not used. You'll need a bucket because you'll have to drain the cooling system before removing radiator, fan, and front pulley.

places 2540cc's (2.6 liters) or, in more familiar terms, 156 cu. ins. Compression ratio is 8.2:1 and a Holley/Weber 2-bbl. distributes the air and fuel. Net horsepower is rated at 107. For '74, the 2.6 has been replaced by a new 2.8 (171 cu. ins.) V-6. Carburetion and compression remain the same, but bore and stroke (3.54x2.62 vs. 3.66x2.70) are larger in an attempt to offset additional smog equipment. With the exception of the fuel pump lobe location, the camshafts are the same for both engines. Valve head diameters on the 2.8 have changed a tad from the 2.6 with a slight increase on the intake and a bit smaller exhaust valve. The 2.8 heads are a great improvement—they each have three exhaust ports while the 2.6 is restricted with only two. Breathing has improved as a result but with the addition of a smog pump and refinements to EGR and IMCO, hp has dropped to 105. The V-6 has made a big hit with everyone except the mechanics—it's been so troublefree that its absence has rusted their metrics.

MODIFYING THE V-6

Engine swappers take heed! The V-6 is small, lightweight and open to modifications. At only 305 lbs., it's quite a bit lighter than Chevy's small-block (580 lbs.) or Ford's 289/302 (406 lbs.) and because its cylinders are in a 60° rather than a 90°V, it's very narrow. The valve lifters are solid and since the cam is located so high in the block. the pushrods are very short and combining the two (lifters and short pushrods) has produced a high-revving machine. Seven

grand can be squeezed from a stock 2.6-liter Capri and with modifications, nine can be fine. However, this isn't the case with the 2.8. Due to very lean mixtures, the smog pump and additional emissions changes, maximum engine rpm on the larger engine is only 5500, and it's difficult achieving that. Gear drive replaces the usual timing chains on all V-6's resulting in minimal timing wander, no more chain stretch and higher rpm capability. The gears are ideal for competition.

As we've said, the three port heads of the 2.8 are much freer breathing than the restrictive two port design of the 2.6. We placed the new head on the 2.6 and it appeared to fit perfectly. The cylinder bore of the 2.8 is just slightly different but probably not enough to affect the head switch. We've heard that the switch is possible, but a gasket change and/or a water jacket modification might be required. The swap, if possible, should bring some improvement to the 2.6 but check with a reputable machine shop before buying the heads.

Speed equipment for the V-6 is a little scarce at this writing; however, some things are available and others are well into the design stages. Performance cams can be bought from Isky, Crower, Crane and others but only regrinds. You send them your cam and they'll grind it to specs or sell you a new stocker that's been reground. Hooker will have headers, but only for the 2.8. Others have tried making them for the 2.6 but the two port head created too much heat and vibration and the headers cracked. Interpart is aware of the problems but

they seem to have gotten around them. Their new headers (for both engines) will be out soon. Manifolds are not yet available but Weiand makes an adaptor for installing Weber sidedrafts. Ak Miller Enterprises of Pico Rivera, Calif., has a turbocharger for the 2.6 but they avoid the 2.8 because of the smog pump. Law says that the pump must stay but using it with the turbo creates problems, like explosions within the turbo pipe.

REMOVING CAMSHAFT

Our cam change was performed at Ford's Pico Rivera training center. As we took notes and pictures, Charlie Camp, chief instructor and veteran hot rodder, turned the wrenches. As we've said, the V-6 has been a stranger to the repair shops and trying to find a sick engine is like looking for a tailor in a nudist camp. We wanted to show you a cam change with the engine in the car but after searching the L.A. area, we had to settle for an engine stand job. To make room for cam removal, you have to remove everything in the way including radiator, fan and on air conditioned models, the condenser. To remove the distributor, you'll probably need a distributor wrench, but remember that you'll need metric sizes. The rest of the information is with the pictures so take your time and follow instructions. To avoid duplication of pictures, we didn't show you how to install the cam but since it's only a reversal of removal, just follow the pictures back to the beginning and note the instructions pertaining to installation. The rest is up to you so get out your metrics and begin. ☬

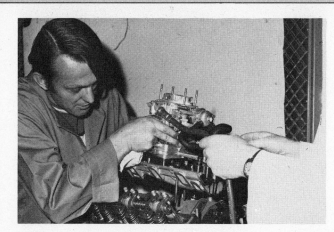

3. Mike, a local Ford mechanic, assists Charlie on manifold removal. Carburetor and aluminum manifold are small and light, but don't rush things because those long bolts just might ruin a perfectly good gasket. Angled carb mounting is more visible here.

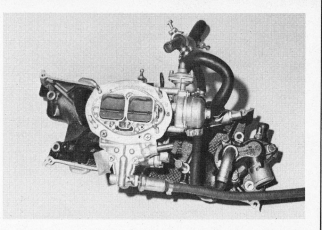

4. The V-6 has a 60°V of cylinders compared to V-8's 90°. This makes for a narrow engine and a skinny intake manifold. Carburetor is Weber/Holley 2 bbl. with water heated choke, in case you're puzzled by all those hoses. At only 305 lbs., engine has great street rod potential.

HOW-TO: V-6 Cam Installation

5. Check out that neat gasket. Its design certainly saves a lot of Permatex and a good many dirty words. Gasket is one piece including those small end pieces which on other cars always seem to slip out of place at the last minute, bringing untold grief and aggravation.

6. Don't panic! Removing valve springs is not required for this job. Springs were removed for previous class and not replaced. Also note that corner studs on head (arrows) also anchor manifold, making it appear that heads can be removed without removing manifold.

7. Remove rocker arm and shaft assemblies, but remove bolts in sequence two turns at a time to equalize stress on the shaft. During installation, tighten them in same manner. Remove pushrods and tag each according to location, so it can be returned to same rocker arm.

8. Even in stock form, the 2.6 is capable of high rpm's and, apparently, Ford of Germany anticipated some problems and prepared for them. At high rpm, some MoPars have been known to loosen shaft oil plugs and ruin engines, but the Germans install a roll pin and take no chances.

9. Remove the oil baffle and, when assembly time comes, don't forget to put it back. Baffle looks unimportant enough to leave off, but its presence prevents oil from flooding seals and guides. Oil is supplied to rocker shaft from hole in shaft's central mounting hole.

10. Monolithic timing slot on front pulley is used by the factory to get ¼° accurate ignition timing. Magnetic sensor plugged into sleeve (arrow) on timing tab picks up signal created by slot. Only factories have sensors, dealers and others must use conventional methods.

11. Using a wrench, remove front pulley. As you can see, we've removed the water pump from the front cover to show you that pump removal is not necessary for cover removal. They are removed as an assembly. Thermostat location is unusual—it attaches to lower part of pump.

12. Drain oil pan and remove front cover with pump attached. On our 2.6, we had to loosen front pan bolts, but the 2.8 shop manual requires pan removal. The manual may be correct, but we can't find anyone who's done one. If you're doing the 2.8, you'll find out soon enough.

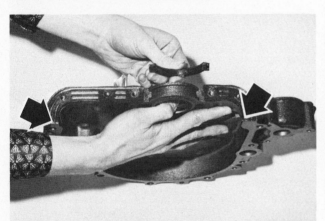

13. This seal cements cover to pan and it's the reason you had to loosen pan bolts. When you removed the cover, you took front of pan gasket (arrows) with it. If gasket looks good, you can reuse it but, before installing, coat it with a gel-type sealer and replace seal.

14. What, no timing chain? V-6 eliminates the slack and wear of a chain with a gear-driven camshaft. Arrows indicate small timing marks that must be aligned after installing cam. Mark on cam gear must be at a 6 o'clock position and mark on crank gear at 12.

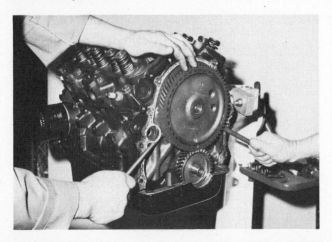

15. Using two pry bars, you can next remove cam sprocket with a wobbling motion rather than a prying motion. Note the huge size of the cam sprocket. The crank sprocket must also be larger than usual in order to maintain a half-size relationship with the cam gear.

16. Timing mark is hard to spot, but if you remove the bolt and follow the keyway straight down, you will find a small punch mark (arrow) in fiber portion of gear—that's it. Cam sprocket is metal with fiber teeth and plenty of tooth contact area—great for racing.

HOW-TO: V-6 Cam Installation

17. Remove camshaft thrust plate and note oil groove on back of plate. As you can see, an oil gallery direct from the oil pump extends to the hole behind the plate. Oil exits the hole, enters the groove and lubricates plate and cam nose. Assemble with plate covering hole.

18. When replacing a cam, the lifters should also be replaced, but, unfortunately, heads must be removed to free last four lifters. So, off with the heads and gaskets but be sure that you tag each head bolt as to location so that it can be returned to exactly the same hole.

19. Since these heads are separated by distance, they appear to be quite different in size; however, they are actually the same. The head in the background is from the 2600 V-6 while the other is from the 2800. The 2.8 has improved breathing from extra exhaust port.

20. To cope with lower octane ratings and increased heat, the valve seats on the 2.8 (background) are induction hardened to a depth of .060-in.—deep enough to endure a great many valve jobs. Induction seats can be identified as dark circles around valve heads.

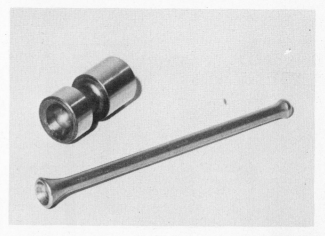

21. Using a magnet, you can now remove the lifters and, if you plan to reuse them, be sure to tag them as to location so they can be returned to the same bores. Present block design permits only solid lifters because there's no upper oil gallery to supply hydraulics.

22. The V-6 valvetrain is very light and efficient. Even the lifters have been lightened by removing sizable chunks. Cam sits high in engine, so pushrods are quite short, and shorter pushrods mean less travel and higher rpm. Charlie claims seven grand from his stock 2.6 Capri.

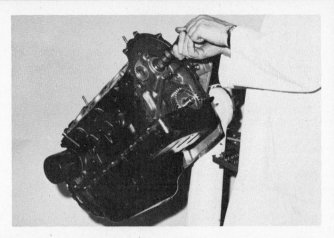

23. Place a bolt in the end of cam and gently, very gently, withdraw it from engine. Cam bearings are soft and the lobes are hard and sharp and, unless you're careful, you can easily gouge bearings. If you could tilt the engine as we did, the risk would be much less.

24. With the cam now removed, take a look at the oil hole in the front bearing. Bearing receives oil from oil gallery below. Coolant transfer tubes (arrows) also act as locating dowels for the front cover. They insure that the crankshaft seal is properly aligned.

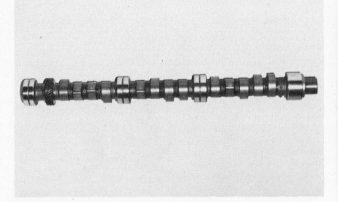

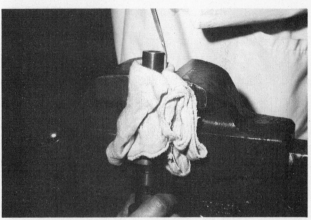

25. German attention to detail shows up repeatedly in the V-6. The camshaft is an example. Note the journals—they include oil grooves for better lubrication and chamfered (beveled) edges to reduce the risks of bearing damage during removal and installation.

26. Wrap the cam in rags and place in a vise. Using a screwdriver, carefully remove the Woodruff key. New cams generally don't include key, so try not to damage it for you're going to use it again. To reduce chances of damage, we recommend a dull screwdriver.

27. Install spacer washer on new cam with chamfered side toward cam. Coat cam bearings, journals, and lobes with STP and gently insert in engine. Install thrust plate, cam sprocket, and align timing marks. Lubricate and install lifters followed by heads with new gaskets.

28. Torque head bolts from 65 to 80 ft.-lbs. and manifold bolts from 15 to 18 ft.-lbs. in sequence shown. Install front cover and lubricate and install pushrods, rocker arms, and baffle. Install pulley, exhaust and intake manifolds. Adjust valves and set timing to 12° BTDC.

Camming a Small-Block Ford

Performance or economy—install a new cam in your Ford and get either or both.

The little Mustang took the nation by storm when it was introduced in the spring of 1964. The basic powerplant was a Ford 6 engine, and there were a few 260-in. V-8's sold, but most came with the '289. A factory high-performance engine was available in '66 and '67 for the Mustang and Fairlane. Recognized by a gold "high performance" crest over the 289 fender emblem, they put out 271 ponies.

The 289 was a popular engine but in '68, Ford saw the need for a change. The 289 phase-out began in '68 with the introduction of the new 302. The two engines ran together for that one year and in '69, the 289 did not return to Ford. The 302 was a 289 block with the same bore dimen-

sions but a longer stroke—from 2.87 ins. to 3.00 ins. Horsepower was rated at 210 with a 2-bbl. and 235 with the quad. A high-performance version, the BOSS 302, appeared as a limited-production option for the '69 Mustang. The car, complete with special trim, H.D. suspension and brakes, was Ford's answer to the Z28. Like the Camaro, the BOSS was underrated at 290 hp. It lasted for one more year when it was replaced with the BOSS 351. A 2-bbl. version of the 302 is still being produced for some of Ford's intermediates.

Cam installations are the same for all of the small-blocks—260, 289 and 302—with the only differences arising from accessory placement. A car with

air conditioning and power steering is naturally going to be harder to work on than a car without. Once you've cleared away the pumps and belts and reached the water pump, then the rest of the operation is the same for all three engines.

Eddie Virant, a Mustang enthusiast from Arleta, Calif., decided to install a new cam in his 289 Mustang and we were on the scene recording the project. Eddie's Mustang was equipped with headers, a Mallory distributor and a 4-speed but it needed something more. For this extra little something, he selected an Engle high-lift cam, grind number 56. Included with the cam were solid lifters, dual springs with aluminum retainers,

HOW-TO: Ford Camshaft Exchange

1. Drain radiator and disconnect oil cooler lines (auto. trans.) from radiator. Remove radiator, fan, pulley, air pump and, using a puller, remove harmonic balancer.

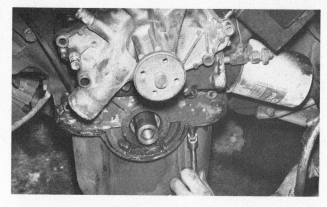

2. Drain the crankcase of oil and, while it's draining, you can remove the front bolts from the oil pan to permit the removal of the timing chain cover.

3. Using a ratchet and extension, loosen the water pump bolts and then disconnect the heater hose from the water pump and the water pump bypass from the block.

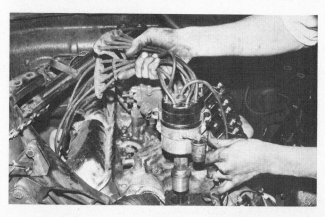

4. Remove the No. 1 spark plug, turn engine until pressure is felt from plug hole, then turn pulley until "TDC" aligns with timing pointer. Mark rotor and pull distributor.

keepers, spring shims and tubular pushrods. Today, with our present gas situation, you might want to choose a milder cam and for the late-model ('72-'74) 302's, it would be wise to go to an Isky or a Crower mileage cam—one having less overlap for improved economy, driveability and more low-end torque. However, whatever cam you may select, the installation procedure is the same.

We have shown you how to remove the cam and how to install the new one but our last picture shows Eddie inserting lifters. Of course, the installation process doesn't stop there—it includes mounting the water pump, the carburetor, radiator, etc. However, installation is merely a reversal of removal, so just work backward through the photos for direction.

Before you pick up that wrench, there are a few points to remember. To ensure that the engine will start when you finish, follow the directions on distributor removal. If the distributor is returned to the same position, then engine timing will not be disturbed and the car will start right up. Remove the No. 1 spark plug (first plug on passenger's side of engine) and crank the engine by turning the fan clockwise by hand or electrically with the starter motor. Place a thumb or a piece of paper over the plug hole and when No. 1 piston reaches the top of its compression stroke, you can feel the air pressure. When you do, stop and then slowly turn the fan until the timing pointer aligns with the "TDC" (top dead center) mark on the harmonic balancer. Remove the distributor cap and note the direction of the rotor pointer and make a mark on the distributor housing to ensure that the rotor can be returned to the same position. Okay, you can go ahead and remove the distributor, and if you don't turn the crankshaft again, you can count on correct installation. Later, if you must turn the crank to align the cam timing marks, then you will have to repeat this procedure before inserting the distributor.

One more thing—don't ignore the instructions on aligning those little marks on the cam and crankshaft sprockets. The cam must be installed with its dowel pin down at a 6 o'clock position. When you install the cam sprocket, its timing mark will align with the pin and the mark on the crank gear should align with the Woodruff key on the crank with both at 12 o'clock. If not, then the crank will have to be rotated until they do and that means that the engine will have to be retimed (as explained above) before distributor installation. When everything is back together, adjust the valves according to the specs for your cam and then, using a timing light, set the timing to 6° BTDC (289 and 302) or 16° BTDC on the BOSS 302.

To facilitate installation of all parts, make little notes, tag parts as to location (especially if the lifters and/or pushrods are being reused) and keep bolts and nuts together with the parts they hold. You've been made aware of the dangers, the rest is up to you. The job is really pretty easy, so get right to it.

5. Disconnect throttle linkage and fuel line from the carburetor and any vacuum hoses from intake manifold. Remove the carburetor and manifold as an assembly.

6. Remove the valve covers and loosen the rocker arm nuts. Eddie had previously installed rocker arm lock nuts making it necessary to use an Allen wrench for removal.

7. Pivot the rocker arms out of the way and remove the push-rods. If you plan on reusing the pushrods, tag them as to location to ensure a return to the same rocker arms.

8. The lifters may be a bit sticky but a magnet or a pair of needle-nose pliers will get them out. Remember, if you're replacing the cam, you must install new lifters.

9. The dipstick tube protrudes up through the generator bracket and runs into the timing chain housing and that means you must remove the generator.

10. Remove the fuel pump and using a long screwdriver; pry between the timing chain housing and the block. Remove the water pump and housing as an assembly.

11. Remove the bolt, washer and fuel pump eccentric from the front of the cam sprocket. Using a screwdriver, carefully pry the sprocket and chain from the camshaft.

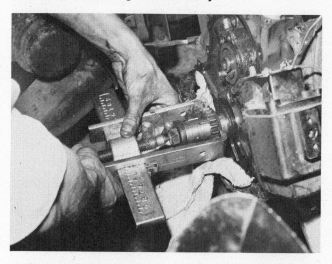

12. Remove the thrust plate from the cam and if old chain has seen a few miles, replace it along with cam sprocket and crank gear. Use a puller to remove gear.

13. Slowly and carefully remove the camshaft from the block. Camshaft bearings are pretty soft and sharp cam lobes can easily damage them so handle with care.

14. Lay a few clean shop towels in the valley area of block before scraping old gasket material from head surfaces. Stuff ports with tissue, too.

15. Wash your new cam in solvent to remove any dust, dirt or grease. Then apply cam lube or STP to the lobes, journals and the first cam bearing in the block.

16. Install the new camshaft into the engine but easy does it. Once the cam is in place, don't forget to bolt down the camshaft thrust plate.

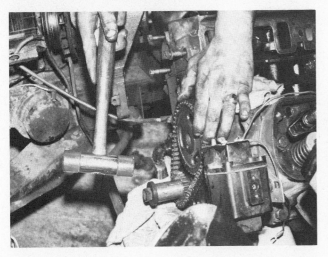

17. Turn cam so dowel pin is at 6 o'clock and Woodruff key on crank is at 12 o'clock. Marks on both gears should then align. Gently tap gear and chain into place.

18. Once you've aligned the timing marks on the gears, install the fuel pump eccentric to the cam and tighten down with the bolt and large flat washer.

19. Using solvent, clean up new lifters and then smear cam lube or STP to the base of each to ensure lubrication when the car is first started.

20. Install the lifters into bores with the flat ends down. Lube ends of pushrods and insert into place. Install the remaining parts and adjust the valves.

Camming a Small-Block Plymouth

Install a special cam in your 340 and turn on the Mopar power.
Watch your Duster live up to its name.

The "small-block" MoPar engines are pretty dependable in stock form, relatively speaking, but they lack the suds commonly found in their rival down the street—Chevrolet. Still, with a little help these engines can perform better than when they left the showroom floor.

A typical example can be found in the '70 Plymouth Duster portrayed within the following pages. However, the way it is set up by the factory, if you own a later model Duster 340 ('71 through '73) or its replacement, the Duster 360, don't be disappointed because the pictures apply to you too. Our '70 Duster was equipped with a 340-in. engine with 4-barrel, 3-speed on the floor, stock gearing and air conditioning. Nothing fancy. Just a plain car for getting back and forth to work. It so happens this particular package runs the full complement of anti-pollution equipment, and the best gasoline in town won't prevent detonation under load during normal driving conditions. But this is something we have to live with.

On a couple of occasions the car has been run at the digs, and with exception of severe spring wrap-up (the housing wants to do a 360°) during shifting, ran fairly well. A set of Lakewood Industries traction bars were acquired and installed, and this took care of the rear end situation. Next, a set of Doug Thorley headers was installed to allow the engine to breathe better and to improve gas economy. The duals were routed through the twin stock mufflers so as to hold the noise down, and keep the fuzz off our backs. The car was not drag tested after these installations,

HOW-TO: Plymouth Camshaft Exchange

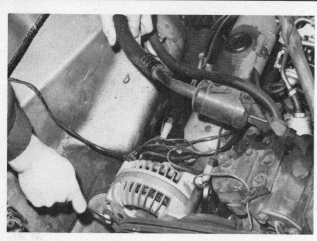

1. Everything up front has to come off, and the alternator follows the hoses. Remove all the hold-down nuts and bolts, but remember where they go for later replacement.

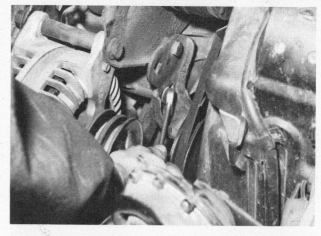

2. Same thing for the air conditioning compressor; all nuts and bolts have to come out of the brackets. If you feel you'll forget where they go back, use a labeled can.

3. You'll note as you really dig into things, that some of alternator and air conditioning compressor nuts and bolts are common to both units.

4. Hate to do it, but A/C Freon gas has to be let out, but use extreme caution. Freon liquid boils at -21°F. so precautions must be taken to prevent frostbite.

but there was no appreciable "seat of the pants" performance gain that could be bragged about. An Accel ignition kit was installed to assist in firing the fuel, something was missing.

Another component was needed that would help the engine run better. Naturally this was a camshaft. There are a lot of different cams available for the 340 engine, but like a lot of shafts, they just sport more lift and additional timing duration. We went to a cam grinder that is well known for grinding shafts for both stock and super stock engines. Not that he specializes in these shafts, he doesn't (Ray Godman runs one in his Bo-Weevil AA/Fuel digger), he just got his start in this area and still spends considerable time developing cams for these cars. After all, if you can grind a shaft that will give a virtual stocker a big boost, what do you think will probably happen with a full-blown engine?

Anyway, a camshaft, spring, and lifter kit were obtained from Lunati Cams (3271 Chelsea, Memphis, Tenn.), for the Duster 340. The Lunati cam selected for our 340 is interchangeable with the 360 and goes by the trade name of SPI 1-285-300. This shaft is a hydraulic grind, as the car is basically a street machine, and the driver is typical of so many others: He loves the feel of a "heavy" engine under the hood but seldom goes drag racing with serious intent.

However, if you consider a Lunati cam for your 340, be sure to specify exact model year, engine output, modifications, etc. Just because you also have a 340 don't rush out and buy a 285—300. It was suited for our engine but maybe not yours, so choose carefully.

The Lunati cam installed in our 340 sports a total of 285° intake duration, and 300° during the exhaust cycle. Valve lift at both intake and exhaust

valves is .462-in., with checking clearance at the lifters being .006-in. Installation was very easy once all of the hardware was removed from the block. Since this particular car is air-conditioned, additional time was involved in making the cam swap with the block in the car. If your MoPar isn't so equipped, you can figure on spending a good short working day, taking your time, to produce the same results. The pictures accompanying this text involve only the cam installation bit . . . another chapter within these covers concerns valve spring pressures, shims, etc.

Off-hand, the car seemed to perform far better than it did in the past and it sure sounds healthier than it did the day before. Runs better, too, because the Lunati shaft is an ideal companion for the other goodies installed beforehand. In conclusion, we can only say that this is one Duster that has finally come alive.

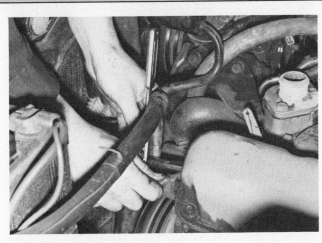

5. On our Duster the battery ground cable connects to the front of the lefthand cylinder head. Remove it, then also remove the other battery cable.

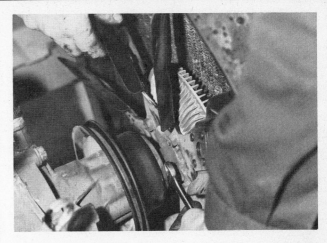

6. Now the fan assembly has to go. Get a good grip on one of the blades and remove the four hold-down bolts that hold the fan to the fan clutch hub.

7. Next for removal is the radiator, and if your car is equipped with air conditioning, the condenser will also have to be removed. Remove all radiator and shroud bolts.

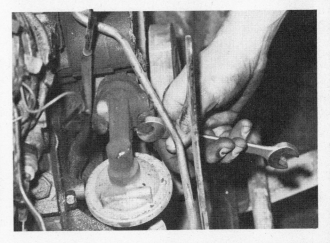

8. The fuel pump is held in place with two cap screws. After they're out, you may have to wiggle the fuel pump a little to break it loose. Fuel line can be left on.

HOW-TO: Plymouth Camshaft Exchange

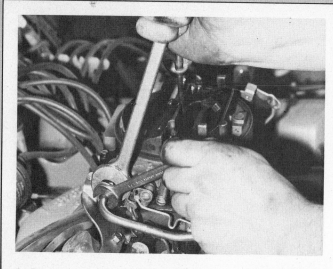

9. For the moment we'll move topside on the 340. Hold the fitting in the carburetor with one proper-size end wrench, then remove line fitting with another wrench.

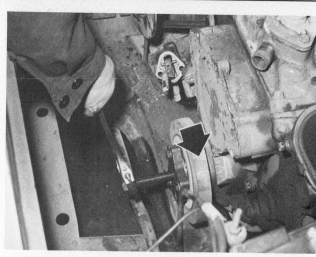

10. After rotating engine until timing mark (arrow) on harmonic balancer is at Top Dead Center (on No. 1 cylinder), use puller to remove balancer from crank.

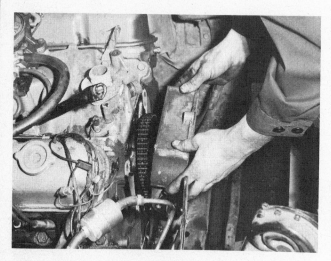

11. Now you can unwind the bolts that hold the water pump in place, then carefully remove both the water pump and the timing cover housing.

12. That off-center round thing on the front of the cam is the eccentric that drives the fuel pump. Remove the single bolt that secures eccentric in place.

13. Now we're getting down to the nitty-gritty. The cam and crankshaft gears, with the timing chain attached, can both be removed from the engine as a unit.

14. Incidentally, Steven Hassler is the fella doing the 340 cam job, and he's fairly typical of the young breed running the popular pony cars.

15. Slated for removal next are the rocker covers. The quickest way to get all the hold-down bolts off is to use a speed handle; it saves knuckles.

16. If the engine has a lot of miles on it, the chances are pretty good the rocker covers will need a bit of wiggling to bust 'em free. Leave smog hoses attached.

17. The rocker shafts have to come off. Steve uses a ratchet wrench to break loose the hold-down bolts. These should be torqued down fairly tight, so watch knuckles.

18. Speed handle is brought back into action to remove the hold-down screws on rocker arm shafts. Loosen them just a half-turn at a time to prevent unequal loads from open valves.

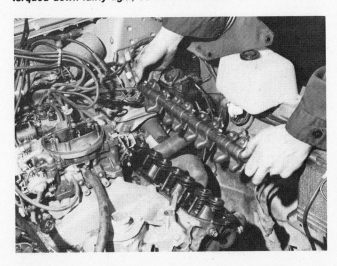

19. When valve spring pressures have all been released, wind the hold-down bolts the rest of the way out, then lift the complete rocker assembly off.

20. Lift the stock tubular pushrods out of their holes. The Lunati kit includes new ones, but keep the old ones around "just in case."

HOW-TO: Plymouth Camshaft Exchange

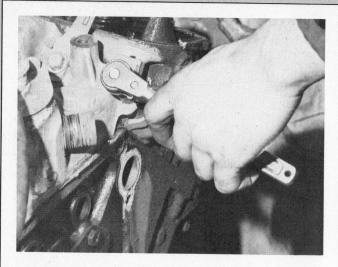

21. Disconnect the various pieces of the carburetor throttle linkage, then remove all the cap screws that hold the intake manifold in place.

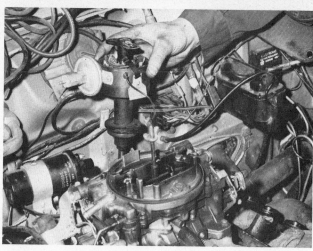

22. The distributor has to come off next. Notice which way the distributor rotor is pointing, remove the clamp bolt, then lift distributor out of its hole.

23. The chances are pretty good that the intake manifold has taken a "permanent" set against its gasket. Reach across the manifold, get a good hold, then give it a mighty tug.

24. Remove the stock lifters from the valley. Use clean shop towels to plug holes in cylinder heads, and stuff some into the valley before scraping old gasket off.

25. Go back to the front of the engine again and remove the bolts that hold the camshaft thrust plate to the front of the block. Remember how it goes back on.

26. At long, long last the stock camshaft can be slipped out from the front of the block. Extreme caution must be used so the sharp cam lobe edges won't score cam bearings.

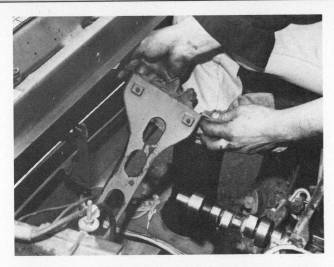

27. Nobody knows everything, and we're no exception. At this point we discovered cam wouldn't come all the way out since it hit the hood latch bracket. It had to be removed.

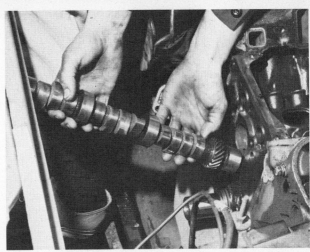

28. Even with supposedly all the clearance in the world, the cam still had to be withdrawn carefully at an angle. We wonder why engineers and body designers don't get together.

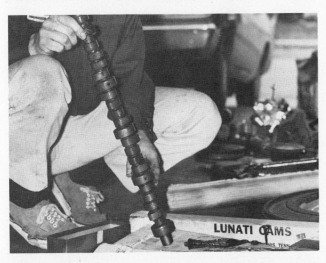

29. Even though the new cam was carefully boxed and wasn't opened until this stage, it's still necessary to wash cam in solvent to remove dust, etc. Use moly lube on journals.

30. With a sizeable pile of engine parts behind him, Steve has finally reached the point where the cam has been lubed and is ready to be slid into place in the block.

31. The Lunati cam slipped in as easily as the stocker came out. Again, take care to prevent galling the cam bearings. Rear cam journal is small, allowing shaft to be angled in.

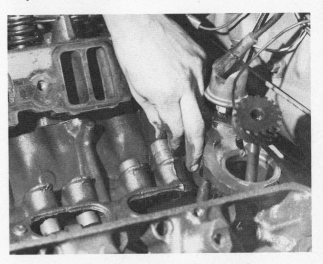

32. New Lunati lifters are rinsed in solvent, then lubed with moly lube. Each is dropped in its respective hole, then reassembly from this point is reverse of disassembly.

Timing Your Cam

This is one step that many shy away from because it appears difficult, but it's really quite simple—and very important.

Why check a camshaft for proper timing? That's a question a lot of people ask. They know of a lot of engine builders, probably thousands, who never check the cam timing once the camshaft has been installed in an engine, and yet they go on winning races. Still these same people tend to overlook the many advantages that can be had from checking the cam at the time of installation.

The primary reason for checking the cam in the engine is to be sure that the valves open and close at the proper time in relation to piston travel. Although the chances of the cam timing being within tolerance as installed are quite good, the engine builder cannot be sure of the cam timing if it isn't checked.

Another advantage of knowing the actual valve timing is that it gives an accurate starting point if subsequent testing shows cam phasing must be changed to alter engine characteristics. In addition, it is invaluable to have this data, should the engine be damaged. If these facts are on hand, it will then be easy to duplicate the original setup and performance. Knowing the actual valve timing gives a valuable reference point for tuning and maintaining the engine.

The steps performed here were accomplished by Fred Badberg, who runs a small-block Chevy in a B/Street Roadster. Fitted with a Jackson fuel injection and gear drive setup, Fred's car has been running consist-

1

2

3

ently near the record. He decided to change cams at the same time he jumped to a 427-in. Chevy engine (added weight to stay in same class), and chose one of Sig Erson's shafts. Erson, located at 20925 Brant Ave., Long Beach, Calif., has a complete line of cams, kits and related products. Following factory recommendations, Fred checked and altered his cam timing as shown in the accompanying photos. Most cams are ground with a couple of degrees of advance "built in," but to make things easier to read, we bumped it one more degree, producing a cam that is 3° advanced.

WHAT'S WITH A CAM?

Briefly, a camshaft has a "cam" for each valve in an engine (intake and exhaust). It has journals which allow it to rotate in bearings located in the cylinder block, or if of the overhead cam type, in the head. The camshaft itself is called a "core" and each cam has what is called a "base circle" and a "lobe." The lobe consists of a nose, two clearance ramps and two flanks. When the valve is closed, the lifter or tappet rests on the base circle, and when the valve is fully open, the lifter is directly on top of the nose. The flanks control the speed of lifter or valve movement in relation to piston position, and the clearance ramps take up the valve lash. The lifter rides on the cam to convert rotary motion to up-and-down movement for the valve.

1. If you're worried about timing your cam, feel sorry for this man!

2. Though it's not necessary to perform this step—miking the cam bushing bore—when timing your cam, it's wise to do it if you're building an engine designed for all-out power.

3. The telescoping gauge used in miking the cam bushing bore is now checked with a regular micrometer.

4. Cam journals should be miked to check clearances, then checked for runout with a dial indicator.

5. Each cam lobe should be liberally coated with moly lube before sliding the shaft into the block.

6. The camshaft is carefully slid into the cylinder block. Care must be exercised so the lobes do not cut the soft surface of the bushings.

7. Rotate the camshaft until the dowel pin points in the direction of 3 o'clock. Rotate the crankshaft until the keyway is pointing to about a 45° angle to the right (between 1 and 2 o'clock). At this point the cam gear can be slid on the cam with the timing chain, and the gear timing marks will be lined up right.

8. A couple of cam bolts can now be driven in place, securing the gear.

4

5

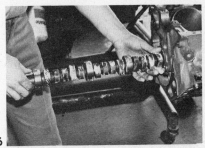

6

7

8

Timing Your Cam

Valve opening and closing times are measured by the number of degrees of crankshaft rotation that takes place before or after what is called the piston's Top Dead Center (TDC) or Bottom Dead Center (BDC) positions. A piston is at TDC when it is at its highest point in the cylinder and at BDC when at its lowest point. Intake valves open *before* the piston reaches TDC (BTDC) on the exhaust stroke and close *after* the piston passes BDC (ABDC) on the intake stroke. While exhaust valves open *before* the piston reaches BDC (BBDC) on the power stroke, they close *after* the piston passes TDC (ATDC) on the exhaust stroke.

The amount of crankshaft rotation as expressed in degrees between the time a valve opens and the time it closes is called "duration." Intake duration can easily be figured by adding together the number of degrees the intake valve is open BTDC, the 180° of the intake stroke, and the number of degrees the valve is open ABDC. To figure exhaust valve duration, add the number of degrees the valve is open BBDC, the 180° of the exhaust stroke, and the number of degrees the valve is open ATDC. If the intake valve opens 52° BTDC and closes 88° ABDC, you would add together 52°, 180°, and 88° to come up with total of 320° in intake valve duration. Exhaust duration is figured in the same manner.

A "degree wheel" is used to measure crankshaft rotation in degrees, and it's a necessary tool to accurately phase the camshaft with the crankshaft to achieve perfect valve timing.

1. This front view shows the gears and chain in place. Arrows point out dowel pin and key on shafts.

2. A simple positive stop bar is attached across the top of the front cylinder to aid in finding TDC.

3. A degree wheel is bolted to face of crankshaft and a pointer is attached nearby on the cylinder block.

4. Engine is rotated in one direction until piston contacts the positive stop bar attached above that bore.

5. In this instance, the pointer was aiming at 45° before top dead center (BTDC) of the piston.

6. This view shows the piston up against the positive stop bar.

7. Now the engine is rotated in the opposite direction until the piston again contacts the positive stop bar.

8. The pointer is at 30° after top dead (ATDC) on the degree wheel now. This indicates the degree wheel must be moved on the crank to a position midway between the 30° and 45° readings.

The degree wheel is a round disc (usually made of metal), and its facing edge is marked off in degrees similar to the markings on a protractor. When in use, a degree wheel is bolted to the front end of the crank.

A "pointer," which can be nothing more than a piece of heavy gauge wire or metal strap filed to a point, is attached to the engine block and is used to indicate the degrees. Iskenderian Racing Cams has a very easy-to-read degree wheel because it's marked off in four 90° increments. TDC and BDC are indicated, as well as instructions for finding TDC—the starting place for checking valve timing.

A "dial indicator" is also necessary to check valve timing, to tell precisely when a valve starts to open and the moment it closes. This opening and closing is very critical and cannot be done by feel or by sight if you intend to accurately check your camshaft. Along with the dial indicator you'll need a simple "piston stop" to accurately find TDC. The piston stop should be made of ¼-steel plate, drilled with a couple holes so that it can be bolted to the top of the block directly over one cylinder.

This should help you understand something about cam terminology, so that when we get into the explanation of proper valve timing you'll know what area we're referring to and the parts mentioned.

IMPORTANCE OF CAM TIMING

Regardless of how many cylinders your engine has—4, 6, or 8—if it's to develop maximum power, every factor that has an influence on the power potential of each cylinder must be correct. Thus every valve in the engine must have correct timing so it will open and close at the exact times in relation to the positions of the pistons. Simply put, valve timing is controlled by the camshaft and its phasing with the crankshaft.

Most engine builders take the camshaft for granted; that is, they expect it to be absolutely perfect. And this is easy to assume because it is supposed to be a piece of precision equipment. Certainly manufacturers advertise great care and precision, and the price tag on a "good" cam is not a small one. However, a cam that is absolutely perfect is as rare as any other supposedly perfect engine part(s). While you probably wouldn't go to a lot of trouble checking a replacement camshaft for grandma's

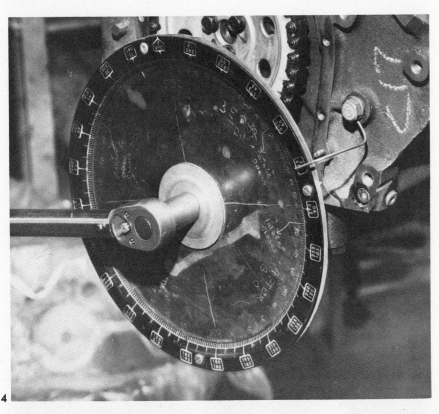

4

5

6

7

8

Timing Your Cam

go-to-the-market car, any serious engine builder looking for performance can determine if a camshaft is machined within a usable tolerance only by actually double checking the specifications of each of its lobes. These specifications are supplied by the manufacturer, and then, if it is found usable, it must be phased to the crankshaft correctly so the valve opening and closing times in relation to piston position will be correct.

There are several causes of phasing errors: The keyway in the crankshaft for the camshaft drive gear or sprocket may be incorrectly located, the keyway in the drive sprocket or gear may also be incorrectly located, the dowel pin or keyway in the camshaft may be located incorrectly, and the dowel pin hole or keyway in the cam drive gear or sprocket may be incorrectly located. This type of manufacturing error can be corrected easily, but it's up to the engine builder to determine the amount of out-of-phase, and then make the necessary correction. The only time this can't be done is when all of the intake or all of the exhaust cams do not have the same opening and closing times. This is why it's very important to check the opening and closing of every valve and not just the No. 1 cylinder. Then you can be sure that each cylinder is producing maximum power.

The first step in timing a camshaft is to find top dead center. And this first step, as well as the procedures to follow, is critical. If your TDC marking isn't correct, you've bombed out, because none of the valve timing checks can be accurate.

Assuming that you're ready for valve timing, you should have the crankshaft, rods and pistons, camshaft and drive mechanism, and lifters in place. The degree wheel is on the crank snout, and a pointer is attached to the block alongside it. You begin by rotating the crank until the No. 1 piston is at TDC on the compression stroke. You'll know this because both lifters for that cylinder will be on the base circle of the camshaft (both valves would be closed).

Install the degree wheel on the crankshaft nose and the pointer on the block. Set the degree wheel at TDC marking with the pointer and tighten the degree wheel to the crankshaft. Now, by turning the flywheel end, rotate the crank opposite its normal direction to lower the piston sufficiently to install the piston stop. Install the stop and rotate the crank in a normal direction until the piston is against the stop. Make a pencil note of the position of the degree wheel in relation to the pointer,

and then rotate the crank opposite its normal direction until the piston again touches the stop. Read the degree wheel and make note of its position. Now remove the piston stop and rotate the crank so that the pointer is exactly aligned on the degree wheel between the two readings—this is TDC. Very carefully, and without disturbing the crank, loosen the degree wheel and adjust it so that the pointer aligns with the TDC marking—then lock it in place.

To double-check your work, rotate the crank to pull the piston down and install the piston stop again. Repeat the TDC procedure, and if you have correctly found TDC, the number of degrees at which the piston touches the stop *before* and *after* TDC will be identical. Remove the stop if this check is perfectly correct. A word of caution from here on out: bumping or relocating the wheel or pointer will throw off the TDC adjustment, making any check of the cams inaccurate. If this happens, you will have to start all over again—so be careful.

CHECKING VALVE TIMING

After you have TDC, you're ready to check duration and camshaft phasing with the crankshaft. For this oper-

ation you'll need the manufacturer's specification card which comes with the cam. The card tells you the exact intake and exhaust valve openings and closings and the amount of lift at the lifter. Without this specification card you can't install the camshaft correctly, so be sure it's included with your cam when you buy it.

The first step in checking the accuracy of a camshaft is to compute the accuracy of each lobe's duration according to the spec sheet. Besides the degree wheel, which is now in position at TDC, we're going to use the dial indicator. The dial indicator you use should be one which has a measurement range of about 1 in. This is necessary for accurate checks, otherwise you will have to rotate the engine in both directions, and this can result in inaccuracies.

On an "L"-head engine the valves must be installed and their lash adjusted to zero. On an overhead valve engine, just the lifters are installed. However, in both engines the dial indicator must be mounted securely to the block and in a vertical centerline with the valve or lifter. An angle in the indicator's plunger can result in inaccurate readings. Also, the plunger should not be located in the pushrod

radius in the lifter as there is a chance of your getting inaccurate readings. Instead, take an old lifter and braze a rod to its top that will bring the tappet up to about the proximity of the head gasket surface so the indicator can be positioned easily.

To begin your check of the camshaft, rotate the crankshaft until the dial indicator, set up over the No. 1 intake lifter, reads .050-in. lift. Stop rotating the crankshaft and read the degree wheel opposite the stationary pointer. Using the 320° duration cam mentioned earlier (the one Badberg is installing here), the wheel should show that the intake is opening 31° BTDC. Record your reading and con-

tinue rotating the crankshaft, watching the lifter reach full lift and begin to descend, and stop the crankshaft's movement at .050-in. dial indicator reading before zero. The reading opposite the pointer should show the intake closing at 67° ABDC. Record your reading and repeat your check of the opening and closing points of the lobes on the camshaft. It would be wise to double-check many of the lobes to insure against human error

in reading the indicator or degree wheel.

After you have finished checking all the cam lobes, compare your figures with the timing tag provided with your camshaft. The readings you have taken on the intake and exhaust lobes may very well be off 2° to 4° (crankshaft degrees) from timing tag figures. If this is the case, the cause is probably slight errors in keyway location of the crankshaft or crank

1. The degree wheel is moved until the pointer aims at 37½°. Now you should rotate the crank in both directions again to double check on where the pointer indicates.

2. Fred took an old Chevy lifter and welded a rod to its top for use in timing the cam. The dial indicator sits on top of the block, its finger resting on the lifter rod. It should be installed so that the indicator reads zero lift when the lifter is on the heel of the cam. Remove the positive stop bar and rotate the engine a couple of times. The indicator should always stop at zero when the lifter is on the cam heel.

3. On this particular Sig Erson cam, a 2500x for big-block Chevys, the exhaust opens at 88° BBDC. In checking out the cam, however, it is checked at .050 in. lift. So the crank and cam were rotated until the indicator shows the lifter has traveled .050-in. If the cam is "right on," the degree wheel pointer should be at 67°. It points at 70° in this photo, indicating the cam is advanced 3°, standard for most cams.

4. Continue rotating cam in same direction, with valve opening full amount, stopping movement on the down side of the lobe .050-in. before the valve closes. Now check the degree wheel reading. It would read 31°, but because the cam has already proven to be advanced 3°, the dial indicator pointer reads at 28°.

5. Because this cam shows a full 3° advance, Fred felt it wise to install a cam advance/retard bushing. So he drills all four holes in the cam gear. The bushing fits in but one hole, but the others must be drilled too to allow the gear to be rotated the amount required.

6. This view shows the gear back in place, drilled and with a bushing in place to correct the cam timing.

7. Quite a few firms manufacture degree wheels. This unit is by Crane Cams, is of heavy die cast aluminum, 7½ ins. in diameter, with permanent 1° markings on a 45° bevel face. Degree wheels are something every engine builder should possess if he's going to build his engines in a proper manner.

4

5

6

7

Timing Your Cam

sprocket, or in the keyway or dowel pin hole location of the cam sprocket. These slight errors may be corrected by the use of offset cam bushings or offset cam or crank keys, which will offset the camshaft with relation to the crank to bring the cam into phase with the crankshaft. They may also be used however, to either further advance or retard the cam to obtain the desired results.

It can be stated very simply that advancing the camshaft raises the cylinder pressure due to the earlier closing of the valves and consequently increases the mid-range power at the expense of top-end. Retarding the cam has the reverse effect and within limits, will help the top-end power while hurting mid-range.

It has been found over many years of experimenting with all types of engines that most engines perform best with the camshaft in an advanced po-sition. Usually 2° to 6° (crank degrees) advance provides the best overall performance and has been found in many applications to also help power at peak rpm and above.

When advancing or retarding the camshaft in an effort to improve performance or to alter performance characteristics, it is important to know the actual valve timing of the engine before making the changes. To move the camshaft indiscriminately with no knowledge of the starting point is a waste of time and can cause serious damage to the engine—which is our reason for explaining how to go about checking and altering camshaft timing in relation to the crankshaft.

An important thing to remember when altering the cam-to-crank relationship is that this also changes the piston-to-valve relationship. Whenever valve-to-piston timing is changed in an overhead valve engine, one valve or the other is moved closer to the piston and the clearance should be checked before running the engine.

1. If you're planning on building more than one engine you'll find a set of micrometers, like this 5-piece set from Manley Performance Engineering, Bloomfield, N.J., indispensable. They run from 1 to 5 ins. in size, can be used for miking journals, rods, valve stems, and telescoping gauges.

2. Iskenderian Racing Cams, Gardena, Calif., offers the race engine builder this cam timing kit. It contains everything you need to properly check the timing of your camshaft and the valve-to-piston clearance. Kit includes an Isky degree wheel, two light valve springs and clay (to check clearance).

3. Combination of high-speed valve train components gives any Chevy semi-hemi 8000 rpm potential. Of course, the engines with shorter crank stroke might have the upper hand at top end, but the 454 is ready to deliver gobs of torque with just about any cam you choose.

4. All racing cams from reputable manufacturers include a timing tag. This tag should give the recommended valve clearance, gross lift at the valve, and a timing diagram which represents one complete cycle, two revolutions (720°) of the engine.

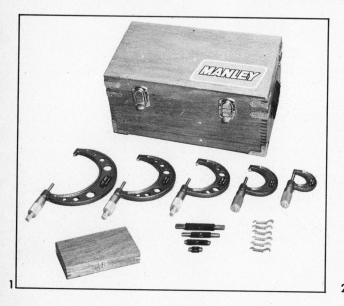

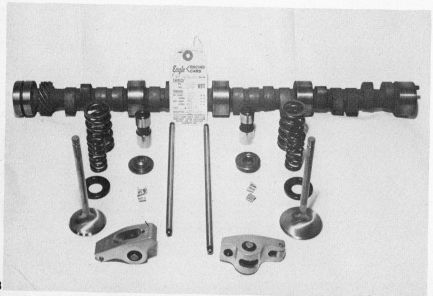

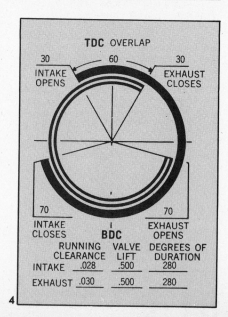

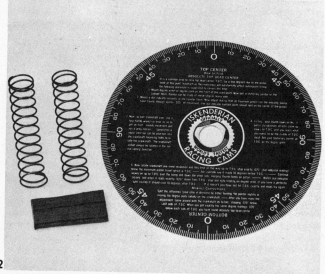

	RUNNING CLEARANCE	VALVE LIFT	DEGREES OF DURATION
INTAKE	.028	.500	280
EXHAUST	.030	.500	280

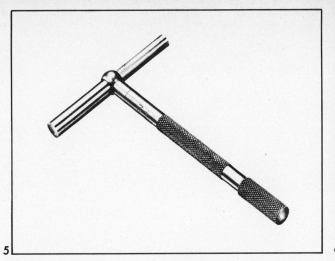

5

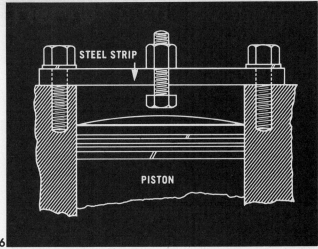

STEEL STRIP

PISTON

6

Also, remember that any time the camshaft timing is changed, the ignition timing is changed a like amount. The ignition timing must be reset whenever the camshaft is moved.

So there you have cam timing. Your engine may be new and so might be all of the parts, but remember that timing chains stretch and gears wear, so they should be checked from time-to-time and heavy-duty parts used wherever possible. This is all part of the game to maintain ''racer''-sharp timing, so necessary on today's drag strips . . . especially if you want to wind up in the winner's circle.

5. This Manley telescoping gauge allows accurate measuring of engine components between 1¼ and 2⅛ ins. Constant spring tension gives uniform feel. Hardened tool steel contact point ends prevent undue wear. This gauge also has a double-action self-centering feature.

6. This illustration defines more clearly the principle of using a positive stop (steel bar with bolt) to find top dead center of one cylinder without using an indicator.

7. This illustration is used for degreeing the cam only. This Erson timing tag gives the following information: the gross valve lift measured at the cam, the timing diagram with timing points checked at .050-in. rise off base circle.

8. The perfect tool for degreeing camshafts is this Manley dial indicator. Unit has an easy-to-read face, contact point of hardened, ground and chrome-plated tool steel, accuracy to .0001-in. and a revolution counter hand, in addition to 0-100 readings in .001-in. units.

9. This timing illustration by Isky clearly demonstrates how cam timing is affected by either an advance or retard situation, quite likely caused by any one or more of a number of built-in errors, such as errors in keyway locations, timing chain stretch and the slight amount of advance built into the camshaft.

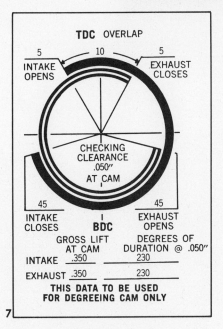

TDC OVERLAP

5   10   5

INTAKE OPENS

EXHAUST CLOSES

CHECKING CLEARANCE .050'' AT CAM

45   45

INTAKE CLOSES   **BDC**   EXHAUST OPENS

	GROSS LIFT AT CAM	DEGREES OF DURATION @ .050''
INTAKE	.350	230
EXHAUST	.350	230

THIS DATA TO BE USED FOR DEGREEING CAM ONLY

7

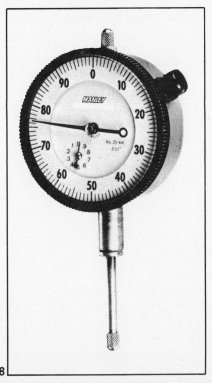

8

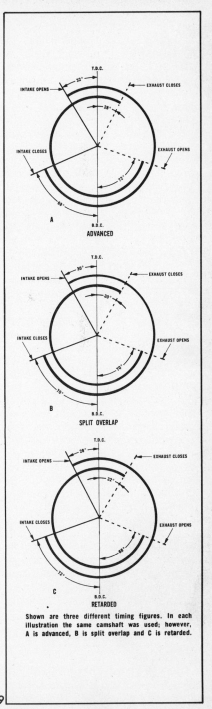

A ADVANCED

B SPLIT OVERLAP

C RETARDED

Shown are three different timing figures. In each illustration the same camshaft was used; however, A is advanced, B is split overlap and C is retarded.

9

Fingerprinting Cams

Checking and comparing cam profiles can be educational and fun. Here's how easy it is.

When you buy a piece of aftermarket equipment, you usually know what you're buying. You can check a custom wheel for defects or cracks, see if a piston is well made or whether a traction bar is going to fit your chassis, but what about camshafts? When you buy one of these engine ''hearts'' all you have to go on is what the guy behind the counter tells you and what's written by the manufacturer on the timing tag that comes with the assembly. Normally you have no way to tell whether the cam is well made, serves your purpose or even whether it has the specs that the tag says it does. It's really a caveat emptor situation when you have to just stick it in the engine and hope it does the job. Remember back when some people used to actually counterfeit cams and sell them like dirty postcards? You never knew what you were getting.

Fortunately, there is a way of not only checking out the basic specs of a cam, at home *sans* expensive tools, but also of delving into its actual profile, or fingerprint. Without any prior experience, you can learn all you need to know about a particular cam right on your kitchen table. What's involved is holding the cam in a lathe, between machinist's centers, or simply resting in a set of V-blocks. A dial indicator is then attached to one of the lobes, a degree wheel bolted to the cam nose and now the exact lift for every degree of rotation can be determined. Plotting all your findings out and doing a little math provides you with an accurate profile.

Believe it or not, cams are not always smooth. In fact, cams are commonly rough, even though the variations are too small to pick out with your eye. By what we're going to call ''fingerprinting'' a cam, you can determine if a cam is improperly ground (chatter marks from poor grinding wheels, sloppy machining, etc.), or if it is even too violent in action for your valvetrain components. The simple procedure outlined here will tell you about the cam's rates, lifts, lobe centers, and acceleration specs, and all without the use of a cam comparator machine. The only computer necessary is the one in your skull.

COMPILING DATA

With the cam set up so that it can rotate between centers on a lathe or between V-blocks and with the $4

speedshop degree wheel bolted up to the nose, you set a fixed pointer next to the degree wheel and position your dial indicator stand so the indicator can read off the lobes. A stiff section of hacksaw blade (polished smooth) can be used to ride on the lobe, but it's *best* if you make a fixture to hold an actual lifter on the lobe and read from it, since many lifters are radiused to fit the cam. With roller cams you'll be obliged to use a roller lifter, of course. If you don't have access to a lathe or V-blocks, you can stick the cam in your engine and check it there, but be sure the degree wheel is bolted to the cam and not the crankshaft (which runs at twice cam speed). You can check a cam for every degree of rotation, but this is time-consuming and not really necessary. For most purposes, you can check the cam every .005-.010-in. of lift, and in our example we checked it every .010-in. Grab a notebook and

start taking down figures. Start from the base circle (heel) of the cam and turn until you register .010-in. of lift, then write down the degree wheel location where this occurred. Keep turning and mark down the degree location for every succeeding increment of .010-in. lift. These two columns of figures are your basics. With these figures you can determine if the timing tag specs for lift and duration are correct, and indeed if all the lobes on a cam even read the same. Some poorly-ground cams can vary lobe-to-lobe as much as .040-in. in lift and be different for all 16 lobes, while some exceptionally-good ones are as close as .0003-in., which is ''right on.''

RATE AND ACCELERATION

Now you can start four more columns of figures, these placed on your notebook *between* your basic readings. The third column will be the

2

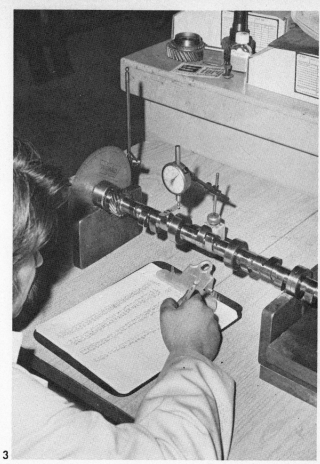

3

1. Top Fuel racer Tony Nancy (left) and rear-end expert Pepe Estrada check out one of Tony's fueler cams in the lathe via fingerprint method described in the text. With just a dial indicator and a degree wheel, you too can check and compare cams.

2. The most accurate method to check a cam profile is with the actual lifter that belongs on that cam, and that means roller lifters for roller cams, but don't use a hydraulic one even for a hydraulic cam. Pepe made this fixture to hold the lifter in line with the dial indicator.

3. If you have a strong math/physics background like Pepe, you'll enjoy the discoveries in checking a cam, but anyone can take the readings and note down the figures. If you don't have access to a lathe, you can use a set of V-blocks like this.

change in degrees (for each .010-in. of lift). In our sample the difference between our first two readings was 7.9 camshaft degrees. The fourth column will be important, this is the *rate* of lift, expressed in TPD, or thousandths per degree of rotation. To find the TPD figures, you simply divide the 7.9° into 10 (the .010-in. we are using for increments), and you come up with 1.3 thousandths per degree. Obviously the figures you come up with in this fourth column are of great importance to the way a camshaft behaves in an engine. If the figures are excessively high or jerky,

this lets us know that we may have a faulty cam, but we'll have to go a little further to be sure.

The fifth column is the change in TPD, our second column of differences. In this case these are the differences in successive TPD figures from the fourth column. This tells us the amount that the rate of lift is changing for each .010-in. of lift, and we know a little more about the cam's roughness or smoothness. The last column is for *acceleration,* which is called TPDD, or thousandths per degree, per degree. These figures provide even greater sensitivity than the other columns in determining if the cam is properly ground. If the figures jump all over the place, even from positive to negative and back, this may indicate grinder's chatter marks or a deliberate "polydyne" correction factor introduced by the cam designer.

POLYDYNE CORRECTIONS

What this means is a polynomial design correction factor has been planned into the cam profile to correct for some deficiency of the valvetrain. As you know, for every minute detail of the cam lobe to be transferred to the valve head, you have to have an extremely *stiff* valve train. It is because most valve trains are not

stiff enough (pushrod flex, etc.) that the polydyne correction is used. Basically, the lift rate may be going right along when it suddenly slips back for a bit and then continues on, this is to keep from overstressing the valve train and give it a chance to "catch its breath" as it accelerates. If the bumps or irregularities you find in your rate and acceleration figures are similar and consistent, like only three or four times in a full rotation, then you can assume these are legitimate corrections. But if the figures jump around all through the profile and are different every time, these are most likely chatter marks or poor grinding. Take the cam back if it's defective!

LOBE CENTER ANGLES

There are as many different profiles as there are engines to put them in. Dozens of companies grind cams for various purposes from all-out racing profiles to gas mileage and emissions cams, and there are some basics to understand before examining different types and comparing their specs. One of the most important considerations of cam design is the *lobe center angle,* yet most hot rodders don't know what this means. Simply put, it is just another way of expressing the opening and closing points of the valves. For instance, a cam timing

Fingerprinting Cams

SAMPLE DIFFERENCE TABLE					
CAM LIFT (INS.)	@ IN POSITION DEGREES	△ DEGREES	TPD	△TPD	TPDD
.010"	@ 41.3				
.020"	@ 33.4	7.9	1.3	1.0	.12
.030"	@ 29.0	4.4	2.3	.7	.16
.040"	@ 25.7	3.3	3.0	.6	.18
.050"	@ 22.9	2.8	3.6	.6	.21
.060"	@ 20.5	2.4	4.2	.7	.29

card may tell you that the exhaust valve will open at 70° before BDC and close at 50° after TDC. If the cam is a single-profile, symmetrical cam (both intake and exhaust have the same profile) then the 70° and 50° figures apply to the intake as well. Taking 180° (half of a full circle), we add the 70°, subtract the 50° figure, and divide the total by two. This gives us 100°, which in our example is the lobe center angle. If we had only the 50° figure but knew the cam's duration, we could still find the angle. Dividing the 300° duration figure by two, we get 150° and subtracting the 50° we are back to 100° as the lobe center angle. You can figure this angle from your timing figures, or work back to the timing figures if you know the lobe center angle. Another way of expressing the formular is: the difference in degrees between the time when the exhaust valve opens and the intake valve opens is twice the lobe center angle.

To give you some insight into why this angle is an important and easy way to compare various cams, let's look at the lobe centers for some current cam designs. Most cam lobe centers are between 104° and 114° (since cranks turn twice for every one camshaft rotation, this would be 208° -228° at the crankshaft). When you *increase* the lobe center angle, you *decrease* the overlap period (when both valves are open). On a racing cam there will be lots of overlap, causing the charateristic rough idle, to completely scavenge the cylinders. The overlap period is when both valves are open at the top of the stroke. On a racing profile, the exhaust valve is kept open for a while, while the intake valve is beginning to open, allowing the rush of exhaust gasses passing out to help "suck" in the new intake charge and better fill the chamber. Because the overlap is so great on racing cams, all of the exhaust gasses may be out of the cylinder before the valve closes. This actually allows some of the new, unburned intake charge to go out the exhaust port, but this is intentional since the new charge of air/fuel will cool down the exhaust valve. The main consideration in any racing cam is *building area under the valve curve,* meaning that the idea is to get the valve open as soon as possible, lift it up as high as possible and as long as possible. This feeds the maximum charge to the cylinders.

As a direct contrast, let's now look at some of the current "gas mileage" profiles offered by most of the major aftermarket grinders. Isky has the

"Mile-A-Mor," Crower calls his the "Gas-Stretcher," and Racer Brown, Engle and the others have similar designs or are working on them, all with varying claims as to the mileage improvements. You wouldn't ordinarily think of a camshaft as a mileage increaser, in fact, just the opposite. While these cams have the same lift and duration of a stock or very mild aftermarket cam, their lobe center angle is right up around 112°-114° with only 30°-60° of overlap. This is *very* little overlap for a V-8 engine, and for a good reason. These cams are designed purposely to have very little scavenging of the cylinders, meaning that residual gases from combustion will be left in the chamber when the exhaust valve closes. This works much like the exhaust gas recirculation (EGR) devices seen on new cars, in that these residual gases left in the chamber dilute the new intake charge, reduce the reactivity of the mixture and slow down the burning. The low overlap keeps any raw fuel from going out the exhaust port and makes more economical use of the fuel/air the engine takes in. This increase in economy oddly enough brings with it an increase in bottom end torque on the street, more driveability than a stock factory cam, and better emissions, too. All this is not without a drawback, which is lower top speed, but who gets even close to top speeds on the street anymore?

WHAT IS A PROFILE?

Besides the basic factors of lobe center angle, overlap and duration, there are a lot of subtleties that go into the full profile of a camshaft. You could line up 10 camshafts from different manufacturers and, although they featured the same lift and duration specs, they would have entirely different profiles or fingerprints. That's because even though they're all taking the valve the same distance, the routes they take can be as different as Route 66 and the Autobahn. These routes differ basically in their rates and acceleration, which is

1. Here's a portion of the figures we got from checking Tony's cam. You can get an idea here of the relation of the measured figures to those you derive from them. Don't worry about where the degree indications start, because this depends on where you attach the degree wheel. What counts are the differences and lifts.

2. If you're handy with graph paper, you can draw your own true profile. These are the acceleration points and deceleration points you'll find on any camshaft, but there will be no clearance ramp for a hydraulic.

3. The lobe center angle is one of the keys to a cam's design, usually a good indication of valve timing and overlap. Increasing the angle will always decrease the overlap.

why the fingerprinting method we've discussed should prove interesting in checking out a cam design.

It's hard for some people to correctly understand the difference between rate and acceleration, so let's talk about these two terms for a minute. Rate is often used synonymously with *velocity* or *speed* which is OK, but think of rate and acceleration as they apply to a complete car. While it can travel at a *rate* of 60 mph all day, it can also *accelerate* from 0-60 mph in 10 seconds. When you're talking about camshafts, the only difference is that speed or rate is expressed as TPD rather than mph, and acceleration is TPDD. Acceleration is simply the change in rate (from the Latin foundations of the word, it means to speed up the rate), while deceleration is the reverse, or slowing down the rate.

The rate and acceleration of a lifter riding on a cam lobe changes throughout its profile many times. At the base of a cam, called the base circle or heel, there is no lift at all and the rate is zero. When looking at a lobe you really can't tell just where it starts moving the lifter, but with our fingerprinting setup, you can assume that a rate (TPD) of one constitutes where valve action begins. At a rate lower than this, the valve is not opening yet, and at one and above, there *is* flow occurring at the valve.

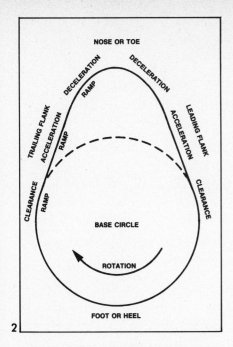

2

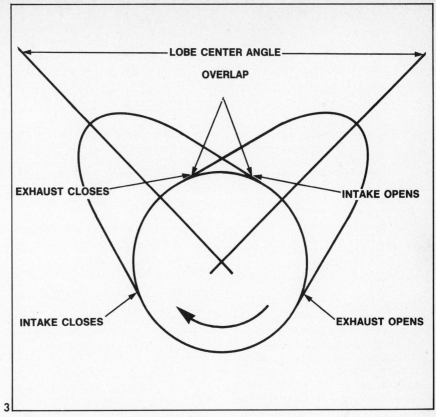

3

Moving off the base circle, all mechanical cams have a "clearance ramp," which is a section where the lifter moves at a steady, slow speed (.00035-in. to .00055-in. per degree) to take up slack in the valve train caused by the valve lash. This ramp is some .010-in. to .030-in. high, and it is in the middle of this ramp that most camshaft duration figures begin (usually .017-in. off the heel). After the clearance ramp, there is the acceleration ramp which is the key to breathing. How fast the lifter is moving and accelerating determines how much area there will be under the valve curve and how much mixture will be let in and out of the cylinder. Then the lifter must slow down as it approaches the toe or top of the lobe, where again the velocity may come down to zero, just like a ball thrown into the air will momentarily stop before it starts coming back down again from gravity. If you check a number of cams, you'll find that most reach a peak rate at around .180-.200-in. lift (at the cam). The fueler cam we tested peaked out at .250-in. at 9.1 TPD, which is fairly fast. For flat-tappet cams you can figure that 10-12 TPD is the maximum, as this is severe velocity. A roller cam may exhibit as much as 15 TPD, while a "soft" and gentle grind may only peak at 6 or 7 TPD.

While what we've shown you *is* an easy way to compare different cams, it should be stressed that accuracy in measuring is the key to an accurate picture of a profile. When you get to measuring the acceleration or TPDD figures, every bit of measuring accuracy counts. If you check only every .010-in. of lift, the readings will certainly not be as accurate as if you checked at every .001-in., but this re-

quires good measuring equipment and a large and precise degree wheel. Also, the rate maximum of 10-12 TPD may vary from grinder to grinder. One who has poor equipment can't get away with as quick a rate without error. Those with the best equipment may use rates of 10-12 without any problems because they can still grind the profile *smooth,* which is such an important consideration for the valve train life.

ADJUSTING VALVES

While we're on the subject of smoothness, there are a few tips on valve adjusting that may help you. As most of you readers know, you can juggle the low end and top end power of a car by advancing or retarding the cam timing (by drilling out the cam sprocket for an offset bushing to go over the cam dowel), and that the same effect can be accomplished to a lesser degree by changing the lash setting. Changing the lash setting can also provide more smoothness and perhaps increase valve train life by eliminating violent lash takeup. Sometimes an engine that the book says needs .028-in. lash can be run with only .018-in. lash and operate smoother without any problems.

You've probably seen valves adjusted many times or read about the several ways to go through this procedure, but most systems are not really accurate. The only way to be *sure* that the lifter is on the base cir-

cle of the cam, where it should be for lash adjustments, is to watch the opposite valve. Looking at the rocker arms with the valve cover off, you can see which rocker and valve is next to an exhaust port or an intake port. To adjust an exhaust valve, turn the engine over and watch the intake valve for that same cylinder. When the intake valve goes all the way down, comes back up and just about closes again, this is the point to adjust that exhaust valve. For an intake, turn the engine until the adjacent exhaust valve just starts to open, this means the intake is on the heel of the cam and can be adjusted. By the way, we're talking about solid lifters.

Another little tip for racers only is backing off your rockers when you let your race car sit for any length of time. Most racers run extremely high spring pressures, and when you shut off the engine after a run there are always four valves that are open against this spring pressure. Since valve spring fatigue can occur just as easily when the spring "takes a set" when held open for a long time (a week between races), it's a good idea to back off those four rockers between races and save your springs.

Hopefully, this brief exposure to the ramifications of a camshaft profile hasn't been confusing, and our simple way of checking out a cam with a dial indicator has stimulated you to want to check out your own and come to a new understanding of how the heart of your engine beats. ♛

Springing the Valve

In the glamorous cam and valve train setup, the lowly spring is often overlooked, but it's a vitally important member of the team.

A valve spring is no less a vital part than any other component in the valve train system. And on a modern high-speed, high-performance engine it becomes a very significant factor in efficiency and power output. To emphasize this point further, it must be remembered that while the cam is a positive means for *opening* the valve at a precise time, the *valve spring* must perform the *closing* operation with the same sort of precision.

The actual design of a valve spring is very restrictive and depends on several factors: material, cam lift, valve length, and spring diameter. Engineers must work in a very confined area of the block or head(s) and yet produce a spring that will perform its function according to cam and engine requirements. Of major consideration is the reciprocating valve motion which is extremely rapid at high rpm. It produces an inertia effect on reciprocating parts, and under these conditions spring tension may not be sufficient for the lifter to follow the cam contour. When this happens, we have what is called "valve float." At this point, Joe Lunchbox is apt to quip:

"Install the heaviest springs you can find." But you can't; too stiff a spring will accelerate wear on the whole valve train—cam, lifters, pushrods, rocker arms, and valve stem tips. It's always a compromise which the engineer must be content with—just enough spring pressure to do the job, but not enough to accelerate wear.

VALVE FLOAT

As mentioned, valve float is caused by the inability of the lifter to follow the cam lobe. In simple terms, you might say the lifter is left behind as engine rpm increases. When this happens (lifter not on the cam), there is an abrupt seating of the valve on its seat and the lifter smacks the cam lobe. You can see right away this means—heavy wear on the valve seat, cam and lifter, and possible breakage of the valve itself. Moreover, valve float can cause early spring fatigue—a common reference with valve springs that have lost their tension. This is not to say that they then feel like a wet sponge, but just a 10% loss in required tension means they should be replaced. Usually

there is a much greater loss in tension, however.

As bad as valve float may be in a stock engine, this condition is disastrous in any kind of high-performance mill. Moreover, valve float is especially noticeable in the pushrod overhead valve-type engine—the kind most of us use today.

Still another problem area related to valve float is the combustion chamber. With compression ratios running up to 12:1 and higher, the operating room for the valves suddenly becomes very small. Valve-to-piston clearance is very tight when a high-lift, long-duration cam is installed. Clearance notches are usually milled into the tops of the pistons, but even so, serious valve float can cause the piston to hit a valve that is "hung-out" and hasn't returned to its seat quickly enough. When this happens, a valve can be broken or bent or the piston severely damaged.

While these are some of the problems of valve float found in pushrod ohv engines, the "L"-head engine does not suffer on an equal basis. Usually the whole valve train is considerably lighter, as well as being

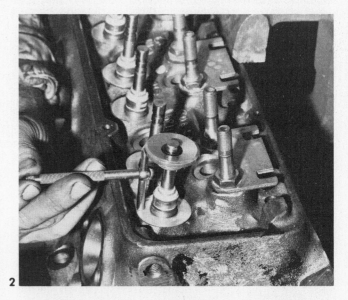

be purchased outright, if you want to invest a little money.

The counterboring tool is a hollow shell mill with a pilot shaft that slip-fits the valve guide bore. It can be operated with a ½-in. electric drill with a speed range of 400-700 rpm, but no faster. The use of a drill press would even be better if one is available to you. This way, drill speed can be regulated to just the right amount, and you have a level table to work on which is 90 degrees to the counter-bore tool. Before and during counter-boring, the valve guides must be well lubricated to prevent galling.

But before starting to counterbore, we must first determine if the "fitted dimension" is correct. This measurement can also be found on the camshaft specification card. You can measure the fitted dimension by installing a valve in the guide and holding it firmly against the seat. Now install the valve-retaining washer and its keepers. Pull the retaining washer up tight and measure with a steel rule or inside micrometer between the spring seat in the head and the underside of the retaining washer where the outer spring makes contact. Say the fitted length is 1-13/16 ins. If

5

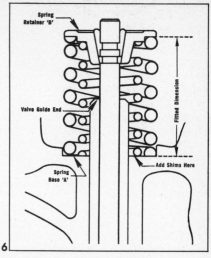

6

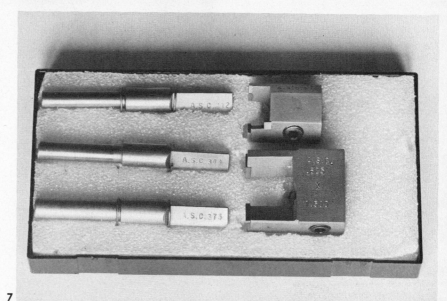

7

8

1. Most pros install valves with an air-operated, C-type spring compressor.

2. Shown is another method of checking for possible coil bind. With valve train installed, rotate crankshaft until valve is fully open. Slip .010-in. feeler between each coil.

3. Valve spring surge chart as measured at the Iskenderian testing facility shows the dampening effect of the dual-spring combination.

4. Illustration shows the relationship of the valve guide to valve spring retainer. Any contact would be disastrous to valve train. Allow about 1/16 to 1/8-in. clearance. Machine top of guide to get clearance.

5. When using an inner-outer valve spring assembly there is always that possibility of spring bind . . . when the coils come together and stack up, thus ruining your valve train. At "full open" you should be able to insert a .010-.012-in. feeler gauge between each coil. Repeat this on all springs.

6. Shown is an illustration of the fitted dimension between the valve spring seat and the valve spring retainer. Note that the measuring height is at the outside edge of the retainer where the outer spring seats.

7. Valve guides have a tendency to wear on a modern ohv which allows oil to pass down the valve stem and into the combustion chamber. Seals are a must, and this is the tool needed to prepare a stock guide for them.

8. The stock guide is given its initial cut and the end is reshaped for better oil runoff.

Springing the Valve

your measurement was *less,* then you will have to counterbore the difference in depth. If the measurement was *more* than 1-13/16 ins., then do not go any deeper—just open up the spring seats and slim the valve guides as you will have to use spacer washers to build up the difference. Usually the determining factor in counterboring for depth is whether or not you have reworked the combustion chamber and seated the valves deeper into the head.

Spring pressure is measured at the two lengths at which the spring operates: valve open and valve closed. Pressure at full open is called "open" pressure and valve on seat (fitted dimension) is called "seat" pressure. Again seat and open pressure should be listed on the camshaft specification card, and all springs must be checked before installation. Most speed shops and automotive machine shops have a spring tester.

To check outer spring tension at seat pressure, install the spring in the tester, compress the spring to its fitted dimension and check the pressure—do not include any spacer washers. Now increase spring compression to maximum cam lift. If the fitted dimension was 1-13/16 ins. and lift is 7/16 in., then the scale should read 1-⅜ ins.—so note the open spring pressure, everything should check out. At this time (while spring is at open pressure) check for "coil bind." When coil bind occurs, the individual spring coils come together and stack up with no more compressibility—this can ruin your valve train. You should be able to fit a .010 to .012-in. feeler gauge between each coil at full open. This means you will end up with about .060-in. safety margin at full lift.

Repeat the same test on *all* the *outer* and *inner* springs. However, take into consideration that the inner spring rides on a stepped portion of the spring retainer and you'll have to allow for this. For example, if the step measures ⅛-in., the spring must be compressed ⅛-in. *more* than the outer spring.

The next check is for interference between the spring retainer and the valve guide. But this must be done with the head on the engine and the valve train assembled and adjusted to specifications. Rotate the crankshaft very slowly until the lifter is on the cam nose, then check for retainer-to-guide clearance. Allow 1/16 to ⅛-in. safety margin. If you do not have this, the top of the guides will have to be machined off accordingly.

Basically these are the things with which we must contend when modify-

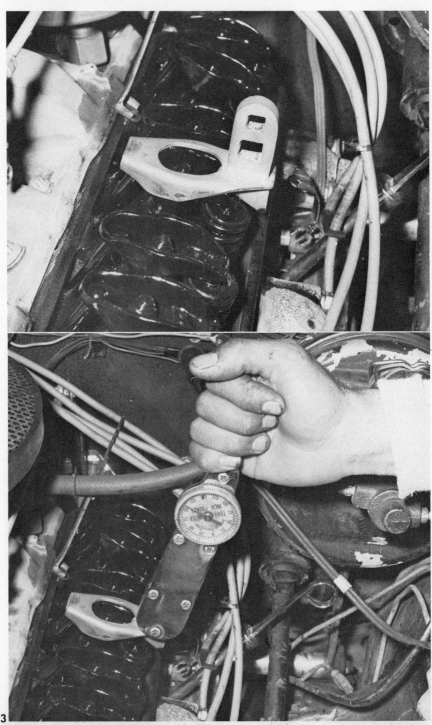

ing an ohv engine with a special camshaft. However, there is still another way in which we can minimize valve float, increase effective rpm and thereby gain more power, and that is to use a "rev kit." Rev kits can be used only with roller lifters but they do three things: increase usable rpm, take the strain off pushrods and rocker arms, and help keep the roller square with the cam lobe. A rev kit consists of two aluminum plates which fit under each head and hold an extra set of springs between the plate and lifter.

While springs aren't the only way to close a valve in an automotive engine, they have been used extensively because they are able to get the job done, are very uncomplicated, and are inexpensive. Recently, Honda unveiled a torsion bar setup to close the valves; it works extremely well. Before that, they designed a desmodromic setup which is a fully mechanical means of opening and closing the valves—using no springs at all. But it's a very complicated, as well as costly, system.

So there you have it! If you're not satisfied with using valve springs, which must be constantly checked for proper pressure when used in competition, then come up with a new way—there's room for improvement. ♛

1. The second cut is to provide a shoulder on which the seal rests.

2. This is usually how a valve guide is modified to accept the seal.
(1) Stock guide with no machine work. (2) The first pass with the end tapered from better oil control. (3) The second pass showing the shoulder cut for the seal to rest and the enlargement of the flat area on which the shim(s) and dual springs will seat.

3. Now here's a handy-dandy way of checking your valve spring tension without removing same. Bandimere Mfg. Co. (Denver, Colo.) has come up with this little gizmo which fits over the rocker and accepts the business end of a torque wrench. The dial indicator on the wrench allows you to see just how much pressure it takes to fully compress the spring.

4. Shown is another form of helper spring as used on Chrysler Hemi.

5. Another method used to return the valve to its seat is a torsion bar setup as used by Honda on their 450cc motorcycle engine and which could be applied to automotive use. Components are (1) cam follower, (2) cam follower shaft, (3) torsion bar valve spring, (4) outer torsion bar, and (5) outer arm.

6. Iskenderian rev kit for small-block Chevy puts spring between lifter and special plate which fits under head.

7. Crower rev kit for 396, 427 Chevy places extra springs on special retainer attached to pushrod.

4

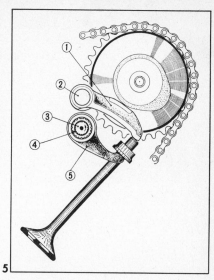

5

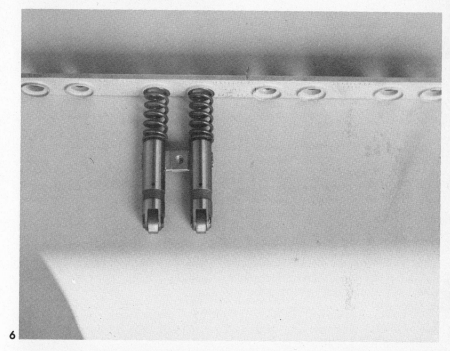

6

7

Lifters and Tappets

Solid, hydraulic, or roller tappets.
Which to use? Select the right type
for the specific application. It's as
important as picking the proper cam grind.

When it comes time to choose a camshaft for your engine—street, street-and-strip, or all-out competition—you must also make a decision as to which type of lifter, or tappet, you intend to run (solid, hydraulic, or roller) because camshafts are ground to be used with one of the types of lifters mentioned. Lifters cannot be interchanged at a later date. As you inquire about several different makes of camshafts to suit your needs, you'll discover that in most cases the manufacturer has already made the decision because he knows what his product will do. Depending on the year and make of your engine, in the milder street or street-and-strip grinds you usually have a lifter choice between solid or hydraulic, but in the wilder grinds most camshafts are matched with the solid or roller lifter. For the popular Ford, GM, and Chrysler engines there's lots to choose from.

If this is your first engine modification job, or you're not exactly sure of the type of camshaft and lifter set you should buy, consult a manufacturer. All leading cam manufacturers offer advice free of charge and can make the best recommendation based on the information you supply—engine usage, car type and all other engine modifications and specs.

LIFTER INSTALLATION

While installation of lifters is simple, it's not so simple as "just dropping them in a hole." There are a few items which must first be checked to insure proper cam timing and satisfactory operation.

To begin with, every lifter must move *freely* in its own bore in the cylinder block throughout its range of operation. Before installing the camshaft, lubricate the lifters and the lifter bores with a light engine oil and operate them up and down by hand over their full travel. If there is any sticking or hesitation, find out what the trouble is and correct it! It may only be a small scratch or burr in the bore or on the lifter body. If every lifter moves freely, install the camshaft and the lifters.

Now notice if the lifters follow the cam contour by themselves, especially on the closing side of the cam lobe. The lifters' own weight and gravity are enough to do this if everything is working freely. Besides the obvious reason for a smooth running engine that will put out peak power, all lifters must work freely so that each cam may be checked with a dial indicator for proper timing. If a lifter "sticks," then the dial indicator will be unable to read the closing movement of the valve. Morever, the lifters that come with the camshaft as a kit or the ones that will be used in actual engine operation must be the same ones used in checking cam timing. It is also good engine-building practice to mark the lifters so that they will be returned to the same lifter bore in the cylinder block when tearing down and reassembling an engine. Through the hours of engine operation, the lifters have lapped themselves to their respective bores and have become compatible (wear hardened) with the cam lobes.

SOLID LIFTER

The solid lifter may be used with all grinds of camshafts—street, street-and-strip, drag only, or track racing—except for the very radical high-rpm grinds.

One misconception about solid lifters is that they are generally thought of as not being able to rev as high as a roller lifter. In a sense, this is not true. If a roller camshaft and a solid lifter camshaft were ground with the same profile they would rev equally. However, because the roller lifter may be used with much wilder cam designs, we can pull more rpm from a roller cam and kit.

Other factors in determining whether a solid lifter is best for your use are the modifications that have been made to the engine and drive train. Will the engine modifications and low rear end gears keep rpm in a high range—say, from 3500 up to 8000 rpm? This could be for street-and-highway, drags, or track racing. Thus, according to the bucks you want to spend, the solid lifter may be your bag. However, remember that the solid lifter needs periodic adjustment, or on a more frequent basis if you drive

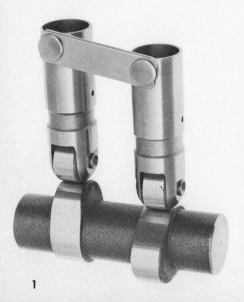

1

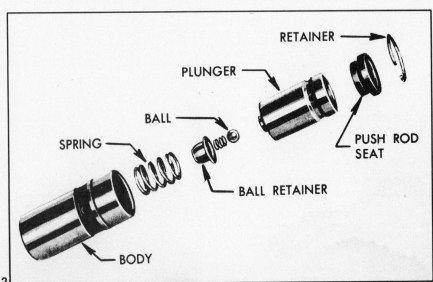

2

RETAINER

PLUNGER

BALL

SPRING

BALL RETAINER

PUSH ROD SEAT

BODY

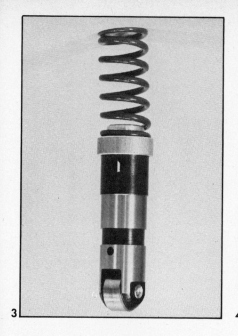

3

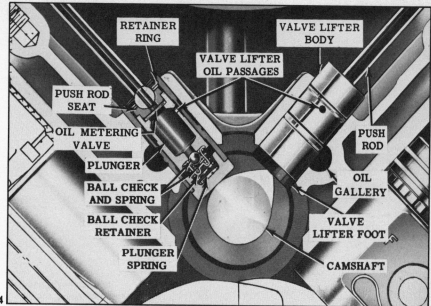

RETAINER RING

VALVE LIFTER BODY

VALVE LIFTER OIL PASSAGES

PUSH ROD SEAT

OIL METERING VALVE

PLUNGER

BALL CHECK AND SPRING

BALL CHECK RETAINER

PLUNGER SPRING

PUSH ROD

OIL GALLERY

VALVE LIFTER FOOT

CAMSHAFT

4

a lot of street miles, but this can be minimized with a rigid valve train.

HYDRAULIC LIFTER

The hydraulic lifter has really come into its own recently and is being used more and more in cars that must serve a dual purpose: high-performance street and street-and-strip. And on the air cooled engine—VW and Corvair, and on the older aluminum Buick and Olds V-8's—they're

the only way to go because of the high degree of operating clearance variations encountered.

But a note here: The VW has never come from the factory with hydraulic lifters. Apparently a max expansion of some .004-in. under high load has been sufficently accommodated with a .006-in. valve lash clearance, now advised for VW late model pancake 4's. And, of course, cost looms as another factor, although factory

1. One of Racer Brown's more popular roller lifters uses this simple connecting link to prevent rollers from turning. Roller types are easy drop-in; no machining is needed.

2. Exploded hydraulic lifter. A hydraulic lifter needs no periodic valve lash adjustment because it senses the operating clearance and automatically makes up the difference.

3. Norris roller tappets are available in numerous variety of designs, the difference being in the methods used to lock the roller tappet in place and prevent it from turning in the tappet boss.

4. Hydraulic lifters are gaining widespread acceptance with the hot rod set. Hydraulics provide near perfect cam timing at all times because they operate at zero lash.

5. Crane roller tappet has stock oil metering control, which prevents excessive oil from reaching the rocker arms and starving the engine bearings.

6. Hydraulic lifter is more complex than 1-piece mechanical type. Hydraulic lifter has found favor due to quietness of operation and elimination of periodic adjustment.

7. Valve lifters come in a whole variety of sizes, shapes, and styles. Shown here are several types available from Crane.

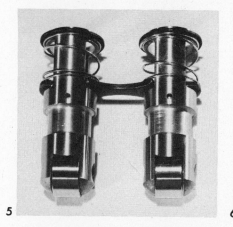

5

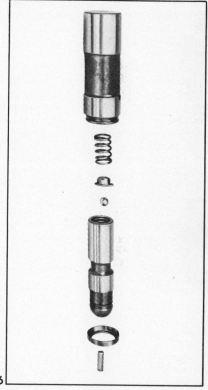

6

7

Lifters and Tappets

spokesmen will neither confirm nor deny economic reasons. But back to our story.

The hydraulic lifter needs no lash adjustment other than an original setting because its tiny piston senses the operating clearance and makes up the difference. This feature makes it ideal for street use—it's quiet and needs no periodic adjustment.

But this wasn't always the case. It used to be that the first item on the agenda for building up a high-performance engine was to get rid of the hydraulic camshaft and lifters and install a solid lifter set and camshaft. Now everything is reversed; a hydraulic camshaft and lifter set actually produces more power and rpm than the solid lifters in street-driven cars. This is because they provide near-perfect cam timing at all times, due to the simple fact that they operate at zero lash. Thermal expansion and contraction are automatically compensated for by the piston in the hydraulic lifter.

To gain the higher revs needed in competition, Iskenderian Racing Cams has developed a patented "anti-pump-up" lifter that eliminates pump-up, a condition usually associated with hydraulic lifters at high rpm. When pump-up occurs it holds the valves off their seats if an engine is over-revved, causing a loss of power. To eliminate pump-up due to over-revving, a second hole in the lifter unmasks (opens) to allow immediate release of excessive oil trapped in the body, thereby maintaining peak power in a higher rpm range and eliminating the dangers of valve-to-piston contact.

Today's hydraulic lifters and camshaft combinations can rev to 7500 rpm plus—this may be the way for you to go dual-purpose racing.

ROLLER LIFTER

The roller tappets are usually run with the ultra-high-performance camshafts. More camshaft grinds are possible with the roller because of its ability to follow a radical cam profile that would ordinarily be impossible for a solid lifter to follow. The roller by its very nature allows it to merely "roll over" the cam without scuffing. This also means a longer life for both camshaft and lifter—an important factor in competition as well as street driving.

With a roller camshaft and kit, over-8000 rpm is no problem and the small-block Chevy V-8's have cranked as high as 10,000 rpm. To get this high rpm, greater valve spring pressures are required, not only at the valve but in the form of a

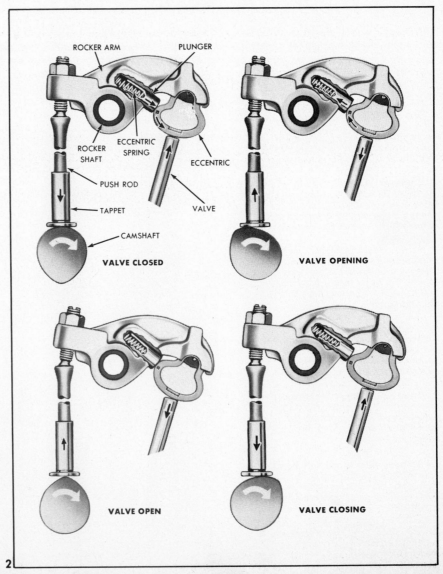

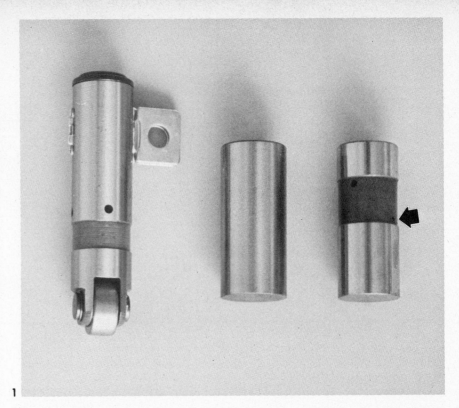

VALVE CLOSED

VALVE OPENING

VALVE OPEN

VALVE CLOSING

ROCKER ARM — PLUNGER — ECCENTRIC SPRING — ROCKER SHAFT — PUSH ROD — TAPPET — CAMSHAFT — ECCENTRIC — VALVE

rev kit. The rev kit consists of an extra set of springs that fit between the lifter and the head, and exert direct pressure on the lifter. This does two things: helps to keep the lifter in constant contact with the cam, and takes some of the strain off the upper valve train.

All the popular roller lifters slip into place without special tools or machine work and use some type of simple guide arm or interlocking device to keep the roller squarely in line with the cam so that there is no chance of its rotating and ruining the camshaft.

While the roller camshaft and kit costs more money than either the solid or hydraulic combinations, the roller grinds are considered necessary by the racers who need durability and maximum rpm. Then too, the roller can be used on the street for those who want a high-performance street machine. As is the case with many roller grinds, idle smoothness and idle speed are not objectionable.

So there you have it—you make the choice, or let a camshaft manufacturer help reach the correct decision. ⚑

3

4

1. Iskenderian lifters shown left to right are: roller, solid and hydraulic. Roller uses needle bearings and is held straight by interlocking tab of next lifter. Note second hole in hydraulic lifter to bleed off extra trapped oil and prevent pump-up.

2. Silent lash rocker arms for Ford 6 have hardened steel eccentric which presses against plunger to take up lash clearance. Novel rocker has same silencing effect as do the hydraulic lifters.

3. One of Racer Brown's designs for holding roller lifter "straight" on cam is this straddle type.

4. Crower Surelock roller lifter and locking device for holding lifter square with cam for 396- and 427-cu.-in. Chevy engines.

5. Crower offers two basic types of Linc-Lock rollers: heat treated (case hardened) lightweight steel rollers (right) or the rugged lightweight aluminum alloy roller (left). Installation is drop-in, and design prevents twisting of the lifters and eliminates drilling, machining, welding, or block modifications of any kind.

6. Pick a lifter, any lifter, for almost any engine. It's a good bet Crower has it in stock.

7. Crower Linc-Lock rollers hold no oil that would add to the weight of the lifter. An oil pulse valve eliminates the oil control problems that are normally associated with roller tappets.

8. Crowned roller bearing which eliminates edge riding or tracking on cam lobes is visible in this exploded view of Crower roller tappet.

5

6

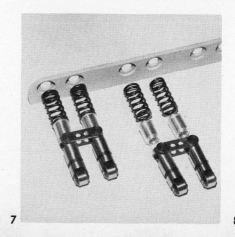

7

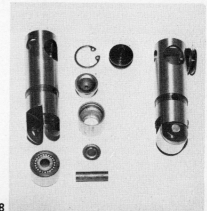

8

Rockerarms and Pushrods

In valve train action, it's the rocking and the pushing that gets the work done. Any weakness here can cost you dearly.

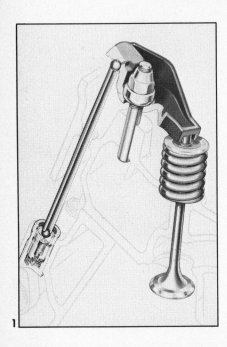

So you've got the *hot* setup: ported and polished heads, big valves, a hairy intake system, the best camshaft, and valve springs that will open and close the valves for peak power when you need it. But wait—aren't you forgetting something? How about those two goodies between the cam's lifter and the valve stem—the rocker arm and pushrod! Even with all your good engine work and the best camshaft and valve gear available, they can't function properly if there is a weak link in the chain. The ohv engine's valve train by its own nature is very flexible, and at much higher rpm it can actually change cam timing or fail completely.

Two requirements for an efficiently operating valve train are *light weight and rigidity*. In a modified engine you need the light weight to increase rpm, and rigid parts that will take the increased rpm, as well as insure accurate operation through the intended performance range. This is why you must make sure that if you replace any original reciprocating parts with lighter ones (light alloy pushrods or rocker arms), you don't end up with a valve train that lacks rigidity. It's better to have slightly heavier parts than ones which cannot keep up with other components, thereby offsetting any actual engine improvements.

In the early days of the ohv engine, builders had to be content with stock rockers and pushrods. While attempts

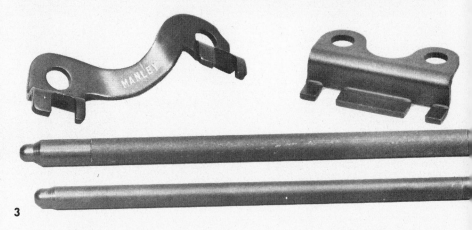

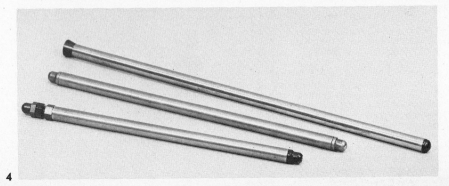

were made to lighten the cast steel rocker arms, not enough material could be removed to make a significant difference in performance without affecting longevity. Aluminum rocker arms patterned after the stock design were tried, and while there was a noticeable gain in rpm, two or three ¼-mile runs usually found at least one rocker broken and the steel inserts (tip and adjusting screw end) badly worn.

1. Ford 289 valve train showing the valve in wide open position. Rocker arm has ball seat adjustable with self-locking nut. Oil for lubrication comes through hollow pushrod, through hole in rocker arm.

2. The rocker arm studs on A&W's 340 mount on a thick steel plate attached to the head, and rockers are stabilized on sides by pins riding in bolt-on support slots attached to the plate.

3. Manley pushrods are made of chrome moly steel, have hardened tips to prevent wear in the rocker or lifter. Pushrod guide plates for small- and large-block Chevys are designed for use with Manley pushrods.

4. Norris pushrods are made from either chrome-moly tubing, aluminum alloy tubing, titanium tubing or heat treated chrome-moly tubing. Pushrods are available in stock lengths with special lengths made to order.

5. Crower pushrods are available for almost every engine application. All pushrods can be used as a replacement pushrod with any cam lifter combination.

6. Crane high-performance needle bearing, roller tip aluminum rocker arms are furnished with heat-treated Adjusto-lock adjusting nuts for precise lash adjustment.

7. Valve train components for the BME Boss 351 consist of Ford 3-piece springs, Crane aluminum roller rockers, and lightweight Ford racing valves. At lower right the valve spring seat "buckets" (arrows) are visible.

8. Needle bearing rocker arms are coated in white and fabricated to suit the special needs of racing.

9. Isky rockers of billet aluminum come with needle bearing trunnions and roller tips.

Pushrods also went through this trial-and-error period, with the chrome-moly tubular steel design being the most effective both in the rpm and rigidity categories.

The big breakthrough in rocker arm design came in 1955 when Chevrolet introduced their new V-8 which incorporated a lightweight, stamped steel rocker arm that operated on a pivot ball and a single stud. The new Chevy arrangement eliminated the heretofore standard rocker arm shaft and 16 heavy cast-steel rocker arms that required expensive machining. Over the years, the Chevy pattern

has proven itself both in reliability and performance, so that today you'll find many factory stock engines running this type of setup. But with it, the ball-type rocker arm has presented a new problem to the engine builder: rocker arm geometry.

ROCKER ARM GEOMETRY

Basically, rocker arm geometry is correct when the center of the rocker arm tip radius coincides *exactly* with the centerline of the valve stem, with the valve positioned from 40% to 50% of total lift. If this is *not* the case, the valve guide will become egg-shaped

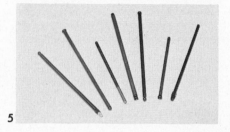

5

6

7

8

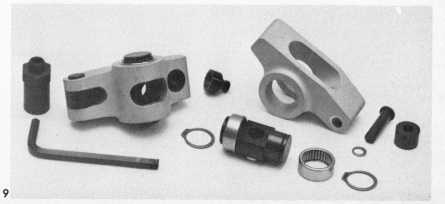

9

Rockerarms

very quickly, causing oil consumption which can lead to fouled plugs and loss of power. Simply put, if the rocker arm tip does *not* meet the valve stem just right, excessive side thrust causes guide bore wear.

In a stock engine with a stock camshaft and valve springs, rocker arm geometry may be off slightly due to "factory tolerances" but will not cause any problems until a high-lift camshaft with stiff springs is installed. Then this problem will become apparent. If the two centerlines coincide with the valve tip at *less* than 40% of total lift, you must shorten the pushrod the amount of the difference between the two centerlines, usually about 1/16 to 3/32-in. Correcting your rocker arm geometry will eliminate rapid and excessive guide bore wear as well as enable a few more rpm in the top range. So if you're looking for every little bit of perfor-

mance, it will pay to perform this check during engine assembly.

Incorrect rocker arm geometry can also exist in engines that use rocker arms where the pivot point is fixed by a rocker shaft. This happens with the adjustable rocker arms when the adjusting screw is screwed in to the limit of its travel. A longer pushrod is the cure here, with the adjusting screw set at about one-fourth of its total travel.

ROCKER ARM-TO-STUD CLEARANCE

Another important area to check on all engines equipped with the ball-type rocker arms is the clearance between the end of the slot in the rocker arm and the rocker arm stud. Interference between the rocker arm slot and stud will usually occur when a camshaft with a lift of more than .450-in. is installed. Any interference at this point can be as harmful as "coil bind" or "valve-to-piston con-

tact." It can occur at either end of the slot (valve open or valve closed), but it's most likely to occur just before the valve opens fully.

You can easily determine if there is contact, or near contact, at either end of the slot by using a piece of 1/16-in.-diameter solder about 6 inches long, with one end (¼-in.) bent at 90°. Use this as a "hook" and fit it up between the rocker (at one end of the slot) and the stud. Now, slowly rotate the crankshaft through a valve opening and valve closing cycle, moving the solder wire from one end of the slot to the other on every rocker arm. If you have sufficient operating clearance, the rocker arm should *not* make an impression in the solder. However, if the rocker arm *does* pinch the solder or squeeze off the end, then this indicates very close or actual rocker arm contact with the stud, and it must be corrected before proceeding with any other cam timing checks or assembly.

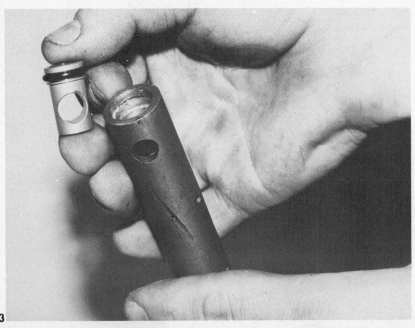

1

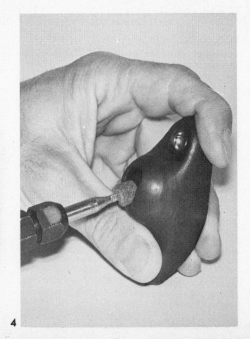

2

3

4

Before starting to correct this condition, remember that this type of rocker arm depends on the width of the slot in relation to the rocker stud diameter for guidance during movement. Therefore, you must be careful only to elongate the slot and not widen it. Also, these rockers are *hard* and cannot be filed, so the best method of lengthening the slot is with a small high-speed hand grinder. Only open up the slots as much as necessary so that you will have about 1/16-in. clearance on both ends. For an example: If the 1/16-in. solder wire was pinched in half, you will have to grind out 1/32-in. After grinding be sure to radius the ends of the slots as they were in their stock condition.

If you have checked or adjusted your rocker arm geometry and rocker-to-stud clearance, the ball-type rocker arms will give as long and dependable service as the rocker shaft type—and with more usable rpm.

PERFORMANCE ROCKER ARMS

The next step up in valve train performance is through the use of

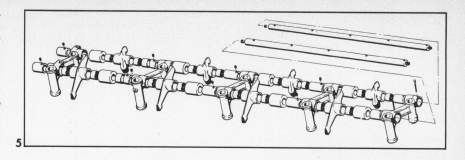

5

7

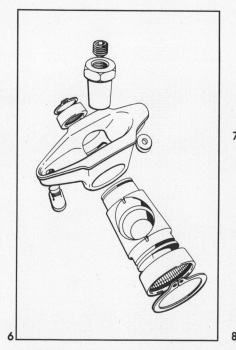

6

8

1. Gotha produces three types of rocker arms: a forged steel unit fitted with needle bearing trunnion, forged rocker with steel-backed bronze bushing and adjustment screw, and a cast iron rocker with adjustment screw (left to right).

2. Cast iron adjustable rocker arms are available from A&W Performance Products, Santa Fe Springs, Calif. for use with stock shafts on MoPar's small-block.

3. When using stock or A&W's hard-chromed rocker arm shafts, aluminum plugs with O-rings are used instead of stock press-in plugs, as was done on this shaft. If a stock plug comes out at 8500 rpm, the oil runs out and your valve train "goes away."

4. On ball-type rocker arms, interference between rocker arm slot and stud may occur when cam with more than .450-in. lift is installed. If you do not have enough clearance, use a high-speed grinder and lengthen slot as shown.

5. Exploded view of Donovan Engineering Chrysler rockers shows use of needle bearings. Stock rocker arms and rocker stands are used with the needle bearings being pressed into the rocker arms.

6. Exploded view of Thompson needle-bearing rocker—this one has the flat or solid tip.

7. Long slot rocker arms from Manley prevent the rockers from binding on the studs.

8. Chrysler Hemi rockers are made of forged steel and use bronze rocker shaft bushings.

9. An under-the-valve-cover peek shows the rocker arm arrangement on an Ed Pink drag Hemi.

9

Rockerarms

needle-bearing, roller rocker arms. So far, these super aluminum rocker arms have shown an increase in rpm, reduction in valve float and oil temperature, increases in cam and valve spring life, and a further reduction in valve guide wear. Assuming that your rocker arm geometry is correct, these new roller rockers reduce valve guide wear to the absolute minimum by "rolling" over the valve stem as it pushes the valve open instead of scuffing the stem to the side when it opens the valve, as with a standard setup. Another important feature of

the roller rocker is that it takes only about *half* the horsepower to operate the valve train.

When you first pick up one of these aluminum roller rockers, the weight doesn't seem much lighter than that of the stamped steel variety. In most cases your first assumption is correct; the *total* weight difference isn't much. However you must consider that the majority of the weight of the aluminum roller rocker is concentrated at the point of pivot—the steel insert and the needle bearing making up this weight. And because this weight is at the point of pivot and only the outer bearing race oscillates,

the mass of weight which falls on the valve and pushrod is far less than that of the original steel rocker.

Reliability of the aluminum roller rocker has greatly increased since they were first introduced, and now all the engine builder has to consider is the cost—are the added features worth the $160 to $220 per set for a V-8? If you're a serious racer (any class) or you want ultimate street performance, then the answer must be "yes"!

TIMING CHANGES

Since our discussion deals mainly with ohv engines where valve adjustment is made at the rocker arm or

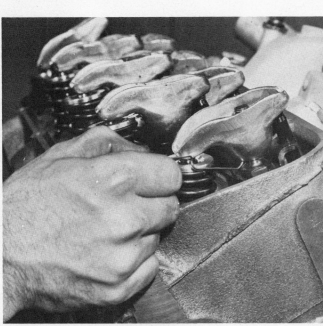

pushrod, it might be well to mention here that slight cam timing changes can be made by opening up or closing down the lash adjustment from that specified on the cam operating card.

By closing down the lash we can increase the duration, valve overlap and lift, as well as make the lifters quieter. The effective result of the cam at a close setting would be higher torque and bhp in the top range, but less torque in the lower speeds. This combination would aid you on a track that is slick and where high rpm is important. You could also use this at the drags by keeping engine rpm high.

By opening up the lash we can shorten the duration, overlap and valve lift. While the valves will tend to be on the noisy side, the slight loss of lift is insignificant. Characteristics of this setting would be less torque and bhp in the top range, but more torque at the lower speeds. Also, wider clearances will make the point of valve float occur at a lower rpm, so care must be taken not to over-rev the engine. Remember, too, that increased clearances are harder on the valve train but will not be harmful if the engine is not run for long periods.

Always get the best quality parts for your valve train. Keep them light but rigid, for only when one component can rely on the other, can your engine put out peak power. ✠

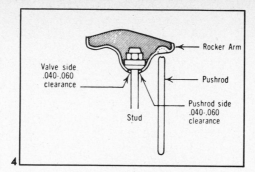

4

5

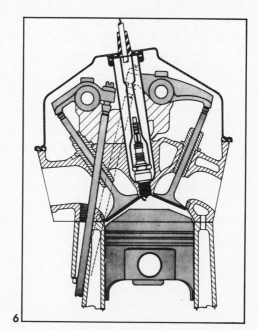

6

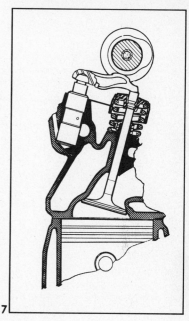

7

1. Opened paper clip can be slipped into the slot of a Manley rocker when valve is fully opened with a high lift cam (left). Same engine with stock rocker installed (right). Clip is bound up between the rocker slot and stud, emphasizing clearance need.

2. For high-performance applications, screw-in rocker studs are highly recommended. Most heads can be tapped to accept screw-in studs.

3. View of cylinder head shows difference between stock pushrod (rear) and .100-in. shorter Manley pushrod when used with a high-lift cam. Long rod is already in an opening position, although valve is closed.

4. When checking rocker-to-stud clearance, use a 1/16-in. diameter piece of solder wire. You should have .040 to .060 to be safe.

5. Small-block Ford uses pushrod guide plates.

6. The late Chrysler Hemi has the most involved valve mechanism with an unusually heavy exhaust rocker arm. Any increase in valve train weight ups the chance of valve float.

7. Direct-acting rocker arm setup is used in the overhead cam Pontiac Tempest engine.

8. Crower pushrods are made of 4130 seamless steel tubing. Notice the different pushrod ends that are used for various engine applications.

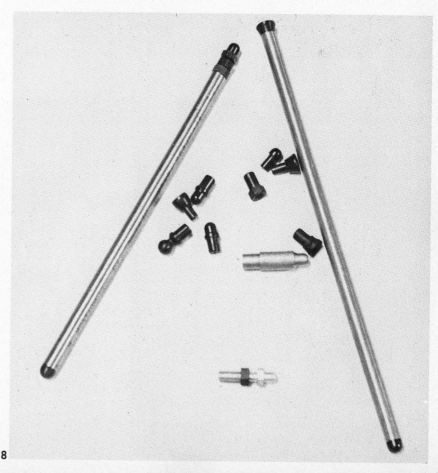

8

How to do a Valve Job

There are two ways to do it—fast or right.
Follow these tips for the proper way—and best results.

If your share of family chores has included irrigating the front lawn, and in the course of hooking up last year's garden hose to a water faucet you discovered some sizable leaks, you probably also discovered that water pressure on the squirtin' end left something to be desired. Well, consider what happens when valves fail to seat properly: Combustion chamber pressures ooze out during the combustion process, and compression is diminished. It may take a bit of imagination-stretching to relate these two situations, but in any event, the leaky hose and the leaky valves have this in common: They interfere with power delivery.

Curing the valve ailment is the subject at hand. The following discussion of valve-job procedures, tips on maintenance between trips to the grinder and shortcuts that save money without sacrificing quality will hopefully be of assistance when your vehicle's valves require attention.

Let's first consider the function of a valve. We've already indicated a relationship to the combustion process; specifically, a valve permits entry of fresh fuel and exit of spent fuel mixture. At the same time, valves also seal the chamber to facilitate buildup of combustion pressures. So why don't they just perform these functions efficiently with a squirt of oil now and then for good measure? Heat is one reason. Exhaust valve heads operate at temperatures greater than any other engine component—as high as 1400° F. In fact, valves operate in an extreme "climate," alternately being subjected to cold blasts of incoming fuel and hot combustion gases leaving the chamber, as well as being slammed onto their respective seats by high-pressure valve springs. They must withstand tremendous pressure loads; piston loads in excess of three tons are created during high-rpm, open-throttle engine operation. And even during normal driving, pressure increases fourfold from the psi (pounds per square inch) figure when the spark plug fires (say 150 psi) to the combustion peak psi (600). The flame generated in the process travels over 100 mph. Meanwhile, the scrawny valves are expected to be keepers of the seal to prevent power loss. Have we convinced you that the valve/valve-seat combination is vitally important for optimum performance? OK, let's try to determine whether or not there's malfunctioning in the valve department.

When pressures vary more than 10-12 psi between high and low readings of all cylinders, a determination derived from a compression check of each cylinder, "valve job" time is at hand.

The first step is removal of the head. As it's disassembled, valves should be arranged in the order in which they were installed in the head, unless you've already decided to put in new guides; if so, it isn't necessary to be sure valves are returned to their original spots. Keeping up with which valve goes where is simplified by using a valve-holding board. You can impress your friends with your garage setup by building such a board. Just drill a series of holes in a reasonably straight line in a piece of board ¼ x 3¼ x 30 ins. Now, let's get back to the discussion at hand.

Plop the head (or block, if the engine in question has its valves positioned there) in a suitable hot tank or solvent and let it soak while the valve components are being carefully inspected for bent or scratched stems; unusually pounded faces where valve head margin may have been removed (1/32-in. is required for proper functioning); and warped, cracked or burned valve heads. Valves with chipped stems or those whose spring-retainer lock grooves are enlarged should be discarded or used only as pounding tools to assist in carbon-removal from otherwise good

1

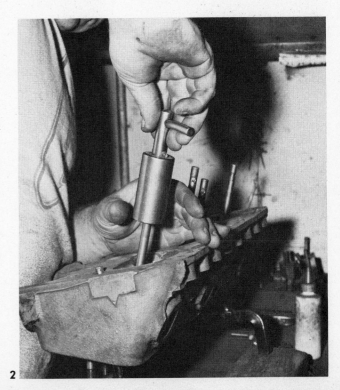

2

3

4

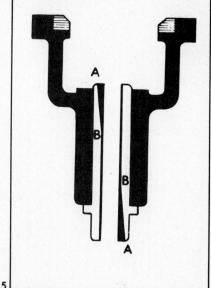

5

valve guides. To remove the carbon, first soak the valves in a solvent to remove varnish and oil. Use of a bench-mounted wire wheel is the best method of removing carbon deposits. If one is available for your use, be sure to adequately protect your eyes, hands and face during the process. Next? Back to the solvent bath (the valves, we mean) for another session

1. Chuck Prite, of Valley Head Service, 18422 Topham, Tarzana, Calif., uses a Sioux seat grinder on this customer's Chevy head.

2. Four pilot shafts are installed in the head at once to speed up valve jobs. Here a special tool is used to remove pilots.

3. When grinding valve seats it's a waste of time and money if the guides are shot, since the pilot will wobble and give you an eccentric valve seat.

4. From the left: a low-cost P-C valve stem seal made of neoprene with teflon insert, a good all-teflon P-C seal (used by most engine builders), and a simple stock valve stem seal.

5. This illustration is of a valve guide cross section, showing how guides can wear. "A," or the black area in the guide, is where metal is worn away.

6. Valve springs must be installed to a specific "installed height" and shims can accomplish this. Of course, where shims are used, valve spring pressure is boosted, but don't use shims as a cure for weak valve springs.

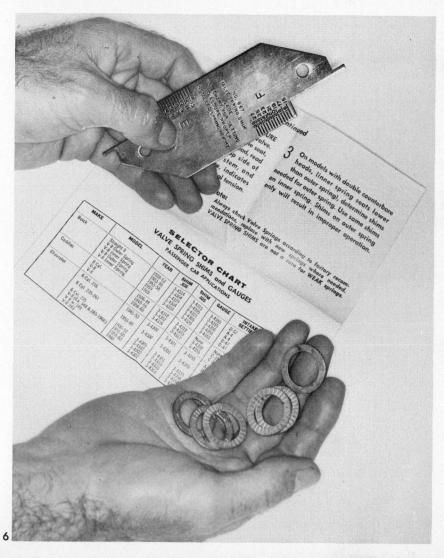

6

How to do a Valve Job

before face-cutting begins. Take another close look for tiny flaws that may have been missed earlier.

VALVE FACING EQUIPMENT

Valve-facing equipment includes proper stone grit, coolant and cutting speeds. Face-cutting is therefore ordinarily a job for a "pro." An amateurish grind session will result in warped heads, improper face finish and poorly sealing valves after reinstallation—and that's what we're trying to eliminate. Any overlooked bent valve stems can be spotted by the experienced grinder as they turn in the machine. It's also possible that a rejected valve will result if obtaining a suitable valve face is at the expense of the valve head margin. For these reasons, you'll be bucks ahead to visit your local machinist and let him do the facing operation.

Assuming you now have a complete set of ready-to-install valves, we'd better haul the head or block out of the hot tank and get it ready. You'll need a flat file or some coarse-grit paper attached to a block of wood (or some such holder) to re-

move bits of gasket and other substances which have found a resting place on the head or block surface. Once the surface has been smoothed and cleaned, it must be checked for trueness. Place a level bar or comparable tool on the surface in a lengthwise direction. Use a .004-in. strip gauge to test for clearance. Head torquing will normally take care of variations up to this limit; deviations greater than this necessitate mill-cutting or surface-grinding. Repeat this trueness test procedure at three other positions: crosswise and at two diagonal locations on the head or block surface. Even though it may not affect the trueness, any etching on the surface (caused by corroded steel head gaskets) should be removed.

The next task is to check for cracks. There are numerous methods of making the seemingly invisible cracks visible, including spray-on metal products and Magnafluxing. This step is a vital one, so don't just "eyeball" the head or block for obvious cracks. Make sure "scientifically" that none exist. Now let's look at the valve guides.

Guides may be removable or stationary, and in either case, bores can

be knurled to restore them to proper specifications. The machinist you approach on this particular subject may not favor the knurling procedure, but the process has been used for years on extremely costly racing engines such as the blown Offy. Guide/stem clearances as low as .001-in. have been run successfully in these engines.

GUIDES AND SEAT RECONDITIONING

Before measurements and wobble checks are attempted, valve guides should be subjected to the scrub treatment to eliminate carbon or other deposits. The wobble test is best performed when the valve is raised to near-maximum camshaft lift. Wear is caused by rocker arm scrub in overhead valve engines, and the amount of "damage" is what needs checking. If no more than .005-.006-in. wobble is present, you're home free. If the figure is greater than this, an oversize valve stem, guide replacement or knurling is called for. The results of worn guides and the attendant excess wobble are highly undesirable—"wandering" of valves on their seats, warped heads, pounding of seat met-

1

2

3

4

5

6

1. Some shops still use tapered reamers to clean up the area below the valve seat, but most head service shops don't rely on them.

2. When the seat is blued with Dykem-Blue (or Red), the new valve seat width will stand out sharply after grinding. A 15° stone is used for top angle.

3. A 45° stone is normally used in cutting valve seats in most cylinder heads. Be sure stone is sharpened frequently, thereby insuring accuracy.

4. The angle below the valve seat is usually 60°, cut with another stone. This improves breathing and reduces seat width to that desired by the head serviceman.

5. After you finish grinding the seats (1), clean the water ports (3) and check the head for grooves (2) or flaws that might require surfacing the head.

6. Here the valve stem is being radiused for smoother, more even air flow. Any imperfections that might deflect flow are being removed.

al and seats that are incapable of being reconditioned. Let's assume that these harmful conditions haven't prevailed and the seats can be saved.

Once again, we'll call on our friendly machinist to lend a hand for this operation. Like the facing procedure, reconditioning of valve seats requires specific tools and know-how which is difficult to assimilate through the pages of a book chapter. It's true that tools which utilize emery paper and special holders are for sale for the recut purpose, but the problems that can result from botched seat work—alteration of seat size, etc.—are a great deal more costly and unsatisfactory in the long run than the expense incurred at the professional machinist's establishment. The valve/

valve seat fit is crucial for efficient functioning. If the seat's too wide, carbon deposits will form in valve pockets; if the seat's too narrow, valve head heat won't dissipate adequately. A seat width of 1/16-in. has been proven satisfactory for stock-type applications.

Some valve seats are removable (such as those on aluminum heads and blocks and even on some cast iron counterparts), and badly damaged seats can be replaced with little difficulty. Slight breaks in the metal don't absolutely necessitate replacement. There are a number of crack repair materials and methods in use today, and any of them can restore the insert seat to performance condition. Consider the crack location and likely stresses involved after it's repaired and returned to use in deciding whether to make a repair or replacement.

Whether the replacement screws in or is pressed or shrunk into place, it's important that insert seats fit all the way to the bottom of the respective receptacle. Air space left below the inserted seat will interfere with heat dissipation and cause a too-hot seat condition. Incidentally, if you're installing a press-fit insert seat and find it tough going, put the piece in the deep freeze for a little while; it'll shrink enough to slip in more readily. Dry ice will accomplish the shrink job in even faster time, but care must be taken in handling the pieces afterward (regardless of cold-storage method used); accidental breakage is more likely with the icy metal.

Valve guide bore axis and corresponding valve seats should be concentric. Total allowable error in this regard is .001-in., and a dial indicator mounted on a valve guide pilot shaft should be used to perform this checking operation.

Our pile of scrubbed, checked, reworked (if necessary) equipment now includes the head or block, attendant valve seats and guides and the set of valves. Before checking valve fit on the newly reconditioned seats, let's complete the unwinding of components; the springs make up the next go-around.

Valve life and the maintenance of uniform cylinder pressures throughout an engine's rpm range depend on the valve springs, so look 'em over carefully. Any that are rusted or etched should be added to your collection of "useless but ornamental" paraphernalia. Using a straightedge and the block side of the head or some other level surface, check each spring's perpendicularity; that is, its amount of variance from a straight up and down line. If deviation at the top of the spring next to the straightedge is no more than 1/16-in., the spring can move along to the next inspection station. Otherwise, discard it. Two measurements take place next and are compared with factory (or spring-maker) specs: free length of spring and compressed spring tension. If you have the notion a spring is a spring is a spring, consider what can result if a spring breaks or collapses during engine operation and allows a valve to join the piston's travels. Treat 'em kindly.

By now we know you're getting anxious to start putting things back together; just can't wait to see how compression is improved, can you? Wait long enough for us to hash over the schools of thought on valve lapping and we'll start the reinstallation process.

LAPPING THOSE VALVES

Valve lapping involves putting an abrasive coating between valve and seat surfaces and rotating the valve.

How to do a Valve Job

Those favoring the procedure feel that it will indicate any bad valve-seat fits, which, they believe, can be expected from any machining operation. The valve lapping compensates for these irregularities and insures conformity of seats and valves. The "no-lappers" veto the process because the lapping compounds become *permanently* embedded in pores of seat/valve metals. These folks recommend use of Prussian blue paste or a similar fit-checking substance which is removable once it's served its purpose. The reason for checking is to make certain a seat has been formed via the grinding operation throughout the full width and circumference of the valve. Otherwise, all this scrubbing, grinding and checking is another Saturday down the drain.

Now it's bolt-up time. Don't toss away the inspector's badge yet. Throughout the put-together process, we'll be doing some more checking. First target is the spring seating surfaces, and you should look for nicks or burrs that need attention and check spring retainers and keepers for cracks and wear spots. Also coat valve guide bores with a dab of oil and don't forget to return valves to their original places. If springs have one end with a closed coil, put that end next to the cylinder head (or block). Secondary valve springs (or anti-surge coils) should be given the same inspection as primary springs. The valve/spring assembly is installed with the assistance of a spring-compression tool. Be sure to use new valve stem or guide oil seals and to watch out for your fingers in the installation process. That 160-lb. spring has a bite!

Look over the rocker arms (and make corrections, if required), especially at the valve contact point, and check the pushrods to make sure

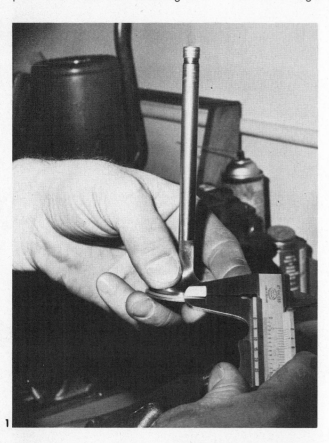

1

2

3

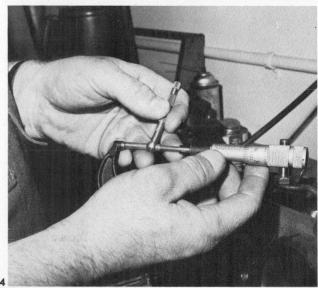

4

5

6

1. After the valve seats have been faced, you can lightly lap the valves, just enough to leave their faces dull where they contact the seats, then check the contact area with calipers. This will tell you exactly how wide the valve seats are.

2. An indication as to how true the guide and new valve seat are can be determined with a dial indicator, such as used by Racing Head Service in Memphis.

3. After installing a valve, slip a valve spring retainer over it and hold same with a pair of keepers. With the valve tight against the seat, use a tele-scoping gauge to accurately measure the installed spring height. This will tell you if shims will be required.

4. A micrometer is then used on the telescoping gauge to give you an accurate reading of the height the spring will be when installed.

5. Or, springs can be installed in a spring tester, then brought down to installed height found by the telescoping gauge. If springs are very weak, they should be replaced with new units.

6. Most high-performance engines are equipped with dual valve springs to fight valve spring surge, or float, at high speed. The inner springs, whether coil (1) or ribbon (2), are counterwound (that is, in opposite directions) and, of course, are of lesser tension, thus cancelling out main spring float.

7. Valve-to-piston clearance is assured by attaching a dial indicator to register against the valve stem. If clearance is insufficient, piston must be relieved.

8. A valve spring compressor is an indispensable tool if you're going to do much head work.

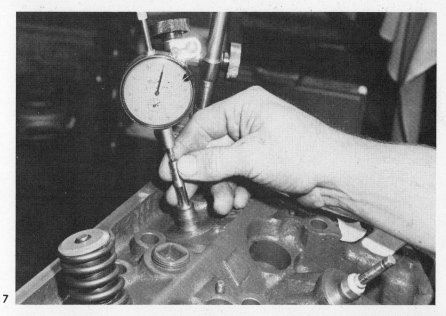

7

8

How to do a Valve Job

they're straight. See if the pushrod side of the rocker arm shows any smeared metal spots. They could mean trouble.

Valve springs frequently tend to stand taller when installed on ground valve seats, and shims are needed to restore proper height and tension. Measure the springs after installation and add the shims if necessary. Serrated-surface shims can be used to compensate for metal set or "torsion relax" which accompanies spring flexing and heat during the break-in period of new springs. The smooth side of the serrated shim should be placed toward the *valve* spring (not the head). Use a new gasket and a proper sealer when re-installing the head and keep in mind required torque patterns and pulls.

In the category of things in general and installation-maintenance tips in particular, we'll include the following. Valve guide damage can be prevented when valve-removal time occurs by carefully filing the tips of valve stems. Guides positioned near the front of an engine require careful checking, because these valve components (and like-positioned cylinder parts) ordinarily run cooler than in other locations and are apt to wear faster.

If you're determined to try your hand at cutting-grinding operations, keep these things in mind: Don't let any oil get on valve seats during cutting. You'll have slippin' and slidin' from the seat stone if you do—and no cutting. The metal used in insert seats is very hard; special stones are required to face them (don't try to get

by with using the same stone as for integral seats).

Oil can accumulate and subsequently run down a valve stem, past the guide and into a combustion chamber in an OHV engine if the tops of valve guides aren't either tapered slightly with a suitable tool or else (preferred but more expensive) P.C. valve seals are used. The latter eliminates oil-contamination fuel-mix charges that stem from oil entry past guides in these engines. The P.C. valve seals are doughnut-shaped and are installed after counterboring has rendered guides small enough in diameter to accept the seals. Get the opinion of the machinist who performed the face-cutting and seat-grinding operations on your heads.

We have intentionally slanted our discussion toward stock-type valve jobs. Performance-type valve work may include alteration of valve-pocket attack angles and seat location or width, such alterations being made with hand-operated reamers. We won't launch into a discussion of valve seat theories, but it is true that a reamer can sometimes be used to save a stock head that was seemingly destined to become a newfangled flowerpot.

A first-class valve job includes even more checking than we've mentioned—rocker shafts, valve stem side of rocker arms, pushrod ends . . . you get the idea.

If you've absorbed the contents of the foregoing paragraphs, you should now be all set to save some greenbacks when a compression check indicates that a valve job is in order. ♔

5

1. If P-C valve stem seals are going to be installed, the tops of the guides must be cut. Valley Head Service uses a special guide cutter for this.

2. A plastic seal protector must be slipped over the valve stem before seals are installed. It comes with the kit.

3. A deep socket can be used to press seal over the guide.

4. Now that seal is in place, it's best to install valve spring and retainer, to prevent chance of valve slipping through seal and valve guide.

5. P-C seals, double-coil valve springs, aluminum retainers and screw-in studs ensure minimum oil leakage and high engine speeds.

6. With valve job completed, head undergoes ccing. This determines combustion chamber volume in cubic centimeters. The smaller chambers are enlarged with a grinder until they are all equal to the volume of the largest. This equalizes compression in the head. A waste of money for the street machine but a good investment for the hard-core race car.

6

How the Valve Operates

It takes one of the worst beatings of any engine part, yet it must maintain its shape and adjustment to do its critical job.

Today's modern passenger car engine, as well as the all-out racing engine, makes extremely critical demands on the operating conditions of the valve. The basic operation of the valve is to admit the air/fuel mixture into the cylinder, seal it off, and ultimately release the burned gases to the exhaust port. When these valves are to open, the height to which they are lifted, the length of time they are held open, and when they are closed is directed by the camshaft and its related gear (pushrods, lifters, rocker arms, etc.). To successfully complete this seemingly simple job, the valves must withstand the most diverse circumstances imaginable.

Let's look at a typical exhaust valve during a single cycle for a case in point. At the beginning of the intake stroke during the overlap period, it's subjected to a chilling blast of fuel-laden air, then it is excessively slammed down with a force of from 300 to 400 lbs., perhaps bouncing a time or two on a seat that may or may not have imbedded carbon granules. Then it is blasted with a hot flame, hot enough to melt aluminum, yanked off the seat while this inferno is still at its height and brought to a temperature ranging from 1300° to 1800°F.—depending upon where you measure it—and then suddenly hit with the chilling blast of fuel again. This whole cycle of events occurs in a high-performance engine anywhere from 500 to 4000 times a minute and during roughly three-quarters of this time this poor abused piece of metal is expected to form a gas seal that will successfully contain pressures ranging from 150 to as much as 1800 psi. *It's a heavy scene.*

An intake valve is expected to do much the same thing except that it doesn't get as hot. A spark plug may get the same temperature treatment but it doesn't get slammed up and down while it's getting it. It also gets looked at more often. The duty imposed on even the simplest valve head when compared to that imposed upon any other part of the engine you care to name is positively mind-bending. As mentioned, it must withstand temperatures in welding range, and resist pounding, creep, fatigue and corrosion from the various lead, sulphur and nitrogen compounds released in the combustion process. And the stem must remain compatible with its guide.

When the valve is prevented from contacting the seat in such a case, there must be enough of a thermal safety factor in the material to prevent the valve head from being quickly destroyed by heat. Proper lubrication of the valve stem, while sometimes quite difficult to effect, is necessary to a certain degree to prevent rapid wear of the valve stem and guide. Consequently metallurgical compatibility between the stem and the guide must be good under boundary or nonexistent lubrication conditions. The valve stem tip, being subjected to repetitive whacks from the rocker arm, must be sufficiently hard to resist the impact loads without rapid wear, cracking, chipping, mushrooming, splitting or galling.

VALVE OPERATING TEMPERATURES

Unfortunately valves cannot be directly cooled by contact with the engine coolant. They do, however, indirectly transfer their heat to the coolant by direct contact with the valve seat and the valve guides. The heat thus transferred eventually finds its way to the coolant, but only after a sizable portion has been absorbed by the necessary masses of metal surrounding the seats and guides. While the foregoing applies generally to both the intake and exhaust valves, the problem becomes acute with the exhaust due to the heat involved. The intake is governed by a much less severe set of temperature regulations, under sustained full load conditions. With a modern high-output automotive engine, tests have shown that the exhaust valve temperature can reach 1500°F., which as far as color is concerned, is a bright cherry red. The points of the valve that reach the highest temperature are at the center of the head and at the juncture of the fillet radius and the stem with a difference in temperature between the two points of less than 2%. With a 1500°F. maximum temperature, the area close to the outer edge of the valve head will be about 1350°F., while the valve face will be around 1300°F. The stem, away from the fil-

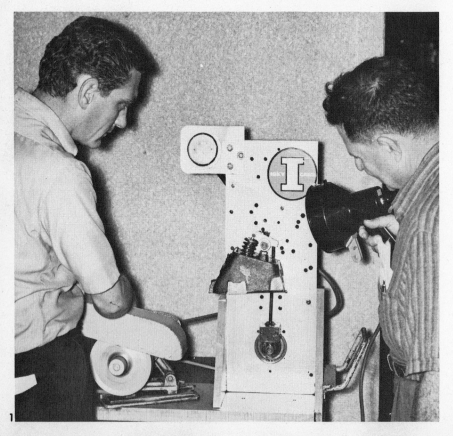

let radius junction, will be around 1380°F.

Heat is not the only problem with the exhaust valve, since we have the additional factors of corrosion and fatigue to consider, which result from repetitive mechanical stresses combined with the high corrosive action of unconsumed hot oxygen and other combustion products. In the past, corrosive fatigue has caused exhaust valves to break at the juncture of the fillet radius and the stem, the point at which the working temperature is the highest. The most exacting operating conditions of the exhaust valve in the high-performance engine have called for specialized metallurgical applications and manufacturing processes. This, plus the fact that in all recent engines the intake valve head diameter is larger than that of the exhaust, has precluded the possibility of using intake valves for exhaust, or vice versa.

VALVE CONSTRUCTION: MATERIALS & DESIGN

Modern exhaust valves are usually forged from steel alloy containing fairly large percentages of chromium and nickel, and smaller percentages of carbon, manganese, silicone, and molybdenum. Such valves have good resistance to warping, a high scaling temperature, and good hot strength. But the mechanical ability is only fair. Late engines use exhaust valves that are forged from austenitic or stainless steels. In other words, steel alloys that are not responsive to heat treatment are nonmagnetic, and they contain quite high percentages of chromium nickel. These alloys are considerably better than the other valve steels with respect to hot strength, impact, and resistance to oxidation and corrosion. However, the coefficient of heat expansion of the stainless group is about 40% higher than normal alloys, which necessitates larger clearances between the valve and rocker arm and the stem to guide. Also the stainless group does not resist valve stem wear as well as other alloys. Flash-chroming the stems solves this problem nicely. In spite of these drawbacks, stainless exhaust valves have proved to be excellent companions to the high-output engines as have the more recent chromium nickel steels.

Modern welding techniques and welding inspection methods have resulted in the development of valves of welded composite construction. Such valves were considered impossible or impractical 20 years ago, but they are currently being used in several of the late model engines as exhaust valves. They possess an advantage in that the head material can be chosen for high hot strength and to resist warping, scaling, cracking, etc., without regard to the wearing qualities of the stem and tip.

The stem material is chosen for good wearing qualities with poor lubrication. An impact and abrasion-resistant material can then be welded to the stem top. While the operating conditions of the intake valve are not nearly as severe as the exhaust, the intake heads are nevertheless subjected to the heat of combustion. Accordingly, the material must have most of the qualities of an exhaust valve material but the higher hot strength is not as important. However, the intake valve must resist the corrosive actions of tetraethyl lead found in most gasolines.

Valve stem diameter for both intake and exhaust valves has been fairly consistent at the nominal fractions of 11/32- or ⅜-in. Actually the stems measure from .0005- to .0040-in. smaller in diameter than the above fractions to allow a certain amount of clearance from the stem to the guide. This permits the valve guide bores to be machine-finished with standard fractional reamer sizes. The outside diameter of the valve head, the valve seat face, the stem and the keeper and the seal grooves are all ground for accuracy and dimensional consistency, the remainder of the valve surface

1. If you have the right test rig, you don't have to take anybody's word for it—you can actually see how the valve operates. Dave Carpenter handles the "gas pedal" while Ed Iskenderian points the strobe light.

2. The sodium-filled valve shown is from a Norton Manx motorcycle. These valves run up to 10% cooler than solid valves, but are rather expensive.

3. Stainless steel Donovan valves used in most blown fuel Chrysler engines have a relief cut in the stem which retains oil to lubricate the stem.

4. Improved valve design has led to more meat in the fillet radius where the heat concentration is said to be the greatest. An additional advantage to this design is increased flow of gases both in and out of the head.

5. Flow through a normally faced and seated valve is less than originally calculated due to turbulence caused by sharp breakaways.

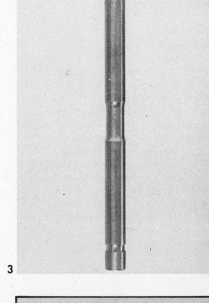
2

3

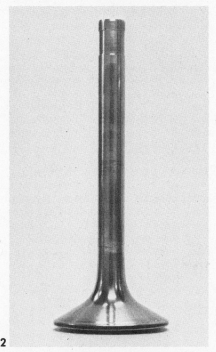
4

ORIGINAL

REVISED

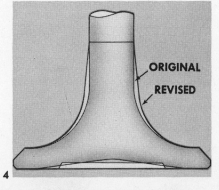
5

How the Valve Operates

being in the "as-forged" condition.

There are currently three types of valve head designs in use; the SAE standard, the flat top head, and the tulip head. Head dimensions are made with minimum strength requirements in mind, with a safety factor of at least 200% to prevent fatigue failures. The SAE standard head is formed with a spherical convex radius which results in the increase of head thickness at the center. The purpose of this is to increase the beam strength of the head at the center where the bending moment is the greatest. In this type, the surface below the seat face is conical in form and is blended into the stem by a fairly small fillet radius.

The most common type of valve now in use is the flat top design. No further definition is required except that the fillet radius joining the head and stem is usually quite large, extending just short of the valve seat on the head, which in terms of beam strength compensates to a degree for the absence of a convex head.

A valve head type that is being found more frequently in automotive engines today is the so-called tulip head, which has a concave head and a large radius under the head where it joins the stem. The purpose of the radius is to facilitate the flow of gases through the port opening, past the valve and into the combustion chamber. With a large fillet radius, the area of the port gets smaller as the valve seat is approached, resulting in a venturi effect to give the gases a last-minute boost in velocity before entering the chamber. The most common of the tulip-type valves is now being used in the late Chrysler Hemi with a huge increase in breathing.

The valve seat and face receive a good deal of attention elsewhere in this book, so we won't elaborate here except to point out that valves transfer by far the greatest amount of heat to the engine coolant by way of the valve seat. This, of course, calls for valve seats of the proper diameter and width in relation to the valve face. Also, the seats must be concentric with the valve guide bores within very close limits in order to form effective seals against the loss of cylinder pressure. Modern design practices favor the use of integral valve seats—that is, to seat the valves directly upon the head, without the use of removable seat inserts. This practice has a very definite advantage in that valve head temperatures can be reduced by as much as 250°F. The temperature reduction is due to a thermal barrier (head dam) that exists when two metals are in direct contact, even if a very tight force fit is used, as in the case of the valve seat inserts. Integral valve seats also make it practical to bring the engine coolant closer to the seat than would be possible with inserts.

VALVE SEAT ANGLES

Raising the question of valve seat angle will nearly always result in at least a good argument. The primary purpose of any seat angle aside from being perpendicular to the valve axis, is to center the valve on its seat. As the seat angle increases—that is, as it falls away from being perpendicular to the valve axis and approaches being parallel with the axis—the more effective the self-centering action will be. However, if the angle is too great there's a good chance that the valve will become tightly and immovably wedged in its seat. On the other hand, the smaller angles have, in theory, better gas flow values past the seat and the valve due to an actual increase in effective valve opening area, but only if the valve seat and valve lift dimensions are the same in both cases.

By far the most common nominal seat angle is 45° and if a smaller angle is used, it is almost always 30° and is specified for the intake valve and not the exhaust. At 30°, the exhaust seat angle would result in a rather thin section around the edge of the valve which could lead to overheating. As far as gas flow past the seat and valve is concerned, the seat angle means very little if the seats are properly spaced in relation to the valve face and are not too wide. Usually an interference angle of from 0.5° to 1° is specified between the seat and the valve face. That is, the seat may be ground to an angle of 45° and the valve face ground to an angle of from 44° to 44.5° so that initially the valve seats only on the outer edge. This assures a tight seal until the valve and seat become matched to each other.

VALVE GUIDES

There are two types of valve guides; one is the removal bushing type and the other is the integral valve guide, or cast-in valve guide. The purpose of the integral valve guide is to eliminate the undesirable effects of a thermal barrier between the two similar metals in close contact, and to bring the coolant closer to the valve guide bore. One of the advantages of the integral-type guide is that it is cheaper to make. The disadvantage is that the guide bore must be carefully reamed, and new valves with oversized stems must be fitted in the case of the exhaust stem or guide wear. Knurling the guides is a partial solution to the problem. How-

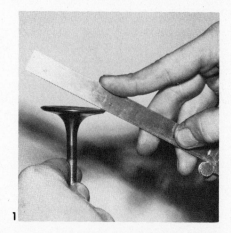

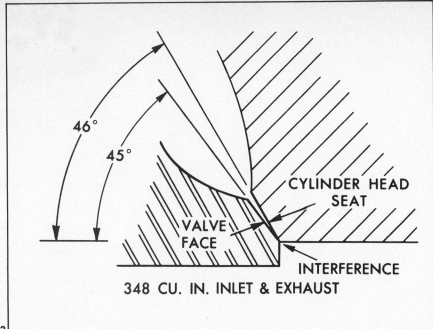

46°
45°

CYLINDER HEAD SEAT

VALVE FACE

INTERFERENCE

348 CU. IN. INLET & EXHAUST

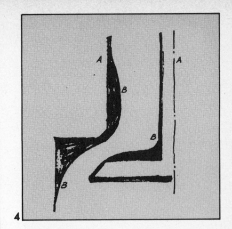

4

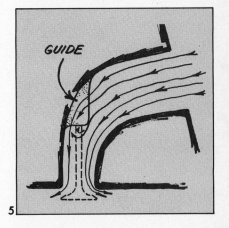

GUIDE

5

ever, this can only be done once. Then you must install bronze or steel valve guides, which is also explained in another chapter in this book.

In the process of engine modification many builders arbitrarily install larger-diameter valves without knowing if the result will be beneficial to power output, or without thinking of the consequences. Apparently they have yet to learn that larger valves run hotter than smaller ones due to an increase in the valve mass, and that valve temperatures increase with engine speed, and the larger valves are heavier as well. In an engine with a borderline exhaust valve condition, this is asking for trouble. A far more satisfactory method is to closely ex-

1. The primary purpose of any valve seat angle is to center the valve on its seat. The most common nominal seat angle is 45%.

2. Removable valve seat inserts have lost favor with modern engine designers. When the valve seats directly against the head, valve head temperatures can be reduced as much as 250° F.

3. An interference angle of from ½° to 1° is usually specified between the seat and the valve face. This assures a tight seal until the valves and seat become matched to each other.

4. A simple valve and seat (A) contrasted to a contoured valve and seat, dark portion (B). The modified valve and seat have been shown to increase flow up to 50%.

5. Size, shape and location of the valve guide have a great bearing upon airflow through head port. If the guide is large, it tends to change the actual airflow pattern, so that much of the air is restricted (shaded area).

amine the valves, seats, and ports to determine if any better use can be made of the existing valve size. In other words, if the ports were cleaned up, the valve pockets taper-reamed to a larger diameter, the seats narrowed and the valves properly modified, the results could easily be more satisfactory than the installation of larger valves.

Modifying valves and seats is a process that can result in better overall engine performance, provided that the original purpose of the valve and seat is not overlooked. In other words, the major seat diameter should be located so that it contacts the valve face within 1/64-in. from the edge of the face. In most cases a seat width of 1/16-in. is enough to satisfy the demands of heat transfer, yet narrow enough to permit a good gas flow pattern past the valve and seat. Once the outside seat diameter has been determined, the inside seat diameter should be established by reaming the valve pocket with a 60°-70° pilot hand reamer, a practice that is much more consistent and accurate than hand grinding. All intake seats should be as close to identical as possible; so should the exhaust seats.

SODIUM-FILLED VALVES

One type valve we haven't mentioned yet is the sodium-filled exhaust valve. In this type the stem—or the stem and head—is hollow and the cavity is half filled with metallic sodium. This substance has a low melting point of 207°F., and a high boiling point of 1616°F. The operating principle is that as the valve is heated, the metallic sodium melts, becoming a

liquid, and in the process of normal valve operation the liquid sodium is violently sloshed from one end of the cavity to the other. While at the valve head the sodium absorbs heat from the head and fillet and carries the heat further up the stem, giving it up to the valve guide. Some sodium-cooled valves have the internal cavity copper-plated, which has four times the heat conductivity of valve steels.

There can be little doubt as to the advantages of sodium-filled valves over the conventional type. Comparative tests under identical conditions have shown that an exhaust valve with a sodium-filled stem will reduce valve head temperatures by 10%, while a valve with a sodium-filled head and stem will lower the maximum valve head temperature by as much as 25%. About the only factor that has thus far precluded the use of sodium-filled valves in automotive engines is cost, the valve being quite expensive to manufacture. They are available in a great variety of head and stem diameters and overall lengths for use in popular makes of automobiles and commercial engines for extra heavy-duty applications. These exhaust valves do a real good job in blown engines, too, by reducing the likelihood of detonation under sustained full load.

Yes, the valve has a "simple" job all right. "Simply impossible" would be closer to the truth!

Installing Big Valves

If cam, carburetion and compression won't do the trick, then maybe you're ready for some deep-breathing exercises with bigger valves.

So you have a Chevy and you plan to make the little jewel fly even faster than it does stock? Well, there are a number of ways to more horsepower, but if you boil them all down you will find that increased horsepower is a direct result of increased engine breathing ability. Some ways to make an engine breathe better are to add carburetion, install a camshaft with more timing, increase compression and add cubic inches by boring or stroking.

Suppose you have the extra carburetion, more inches, a hot cam, head-

ers and the rest—you still might not be reaping the benefits of all these extras unless you have increased the size of the trap doors that let intake and exhaust gases in and out of the cylinder. These trap doors, better known as valves, have a lot to do with the way your engine runs. Just remember that these little steel lids open less than a half-inch off their seats and it is easy to see how they can be so important in determining final results.

The logical way to get more flow through an opening is to enlarge the

opening, and this, of course, then requires a larger door to close the hole when it's not being used. So, we come to the problem of installing oversize valves and, in particular, how to install them in the popular 283/327-in. Chevy V-8.

One thing you must realize when installing larger valves in an overhead valve engine is that the big valves naturally take up more room in the combustion chamber and, therefore, will come closer to the side of the chamber than the stock valves. In most cases, this closer proximity to

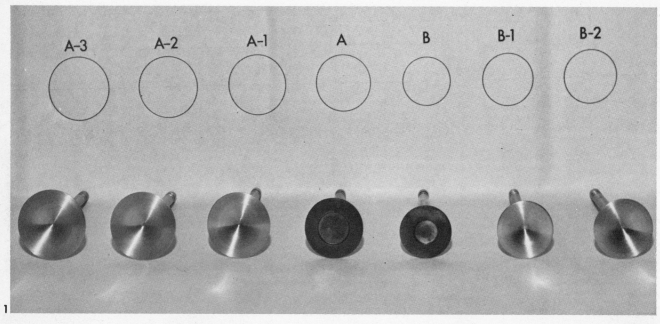

A-3 A-2 A-1 A B B-1 B-2

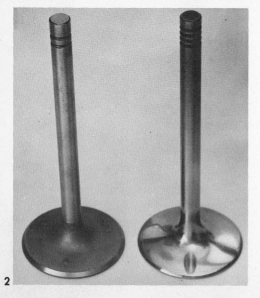

5

6

1. There are some pretty large valves for Chevys available right from your dealer. At center are stock items, at left are oversize intakes, and those on the right are the larger exhausts.

2. When installing bigger valves, it is not unusual to take big valves from another type engine and cut them down to fit. To the right of the Chevy is a Cadillac that has been polished and undercut to take its place.

3. Putting Prussian blue on the seat and dropping the valve in place will tell you where the valve is hitting. Here the seat is at the edge of the valve, which would be OK on an intake but not an exhaust, because the edge of the valve gets red-hot.

4. Here shown on a Chrysler Hemi head, machinist's blue is applied to valve area to outline reaming work.

5. A finer finish grinding, done with a stone, smoothes the undervalve area and provides a machined surface for the valve seat to be cut.

6. A special reamer is used to make the rough cut of the seat area. Some additional grinding of the port area will then be needed to smooth it out.

7. When the diameter of the reamed hole equals the smallest diameter of the valve face, it's big enough. Take measurements as you go along so you won't cut the seat area too big.

7

Installing Big Valves

the sides of the chamber means that the chamber walls will shroud a portion of the valve and restrict airflow. So, if the big valve is to prove advantageous and not hinder the flow of gases, the chamber too must be modified to meet the occasion. Enlarging the chamber to remove restrictions around the valve will result in a lower compression ratio. Unless you are increasing displacement at the same time or desire low compression for use with a blower, you will have to install new pistons with a dome or deflector type head to regain the lost compression. If you installed a reground camshaft and extra carburetion, chances are that you can stand a lot more compression than the engine had originally.

The how-to-do-it picture story on these pages gives a good rundown on how to rework the Chevy heads so that they will give maximum efficiency. If you own or can obtain a portable grinder, this operation can be done at home with the exception of having the big valves cut down and regrooved for keepers. If you have spent a lot of money on speed equipment and still don't get the results you expect, this could be the answer.

1

2

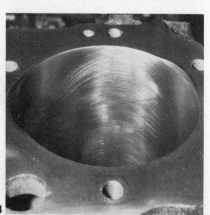

3

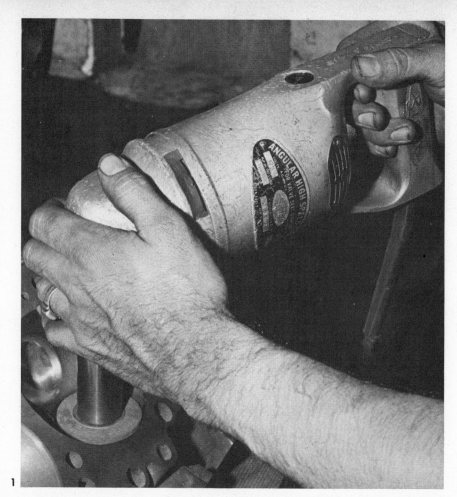

4

1. With major machine work completed, the actual seat can be ground. It is usually a combination of three angles, perhaps 30° on the inside, 45° on the seat, and then a 70° cut to flare the opening.

2. Area marked in white on this Chevy head is material that must be removed to reduce shrouding around the bigger valves. Care must be taken to keep combustion chamber volumes equal.

3. The cylinders on this block have been notched to clear big valves. This is often necessary with engines having a canted valve layout.

4. Shaping the underside of the head not only lightens up the valve, but provides for better mixture flow.

5. A closeup of the valves in No. 6, the stocker on the left, shows the extra stem groove still on the 427 valve.

6. Compared with the swirl-polished Chevy hi-perf intake on the left, the Gurney Eagle Ford valve at right is only .010-inch bigger, but has more tulip for better flow. It also has the same stem length and diameter.

7. For all you small-block Ford fans, at left are two stock Boss 302 valves, and at right are two 427 valves whose stems have been cut down to fit a 302. The block had to be cut to clear them and special pistons were required.

8. How's that for a "boss" combustion chamber? These Doug Nash 427 valves are just about the biggest you can get into the Boss 302's chamber.

9. Arrow points to machine work on Chevy head to reduce shrouding around big valves. When any material is cut from the combustion chamber, higher dome pistons will be necessary to get back compression lost by machining.

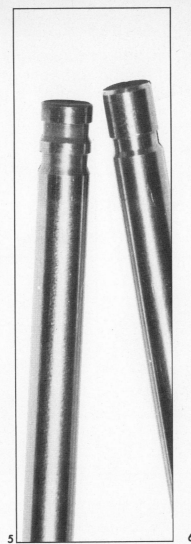

5

6

7

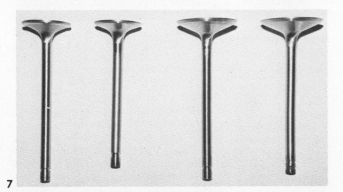

8

9

Porting and Polishing

One of the inner secrets of improved performance is getting air/fuel in and exhaust gases out as quickly as possible. Here's how: open it up, smooth it out.

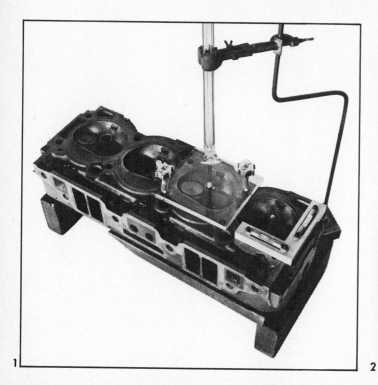

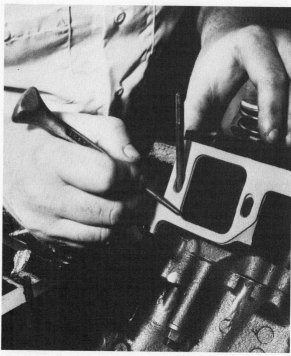

The amount of power that can be extracted from an internal combustion engine is largely dependent upon the rate at which a fuel and air mixture can be introduced into that engine, the rate at which the mixture can be flowed through the engine, the rate at which the mixture can be burned, and the rate at which the resulting waste gases can be extracted. The largest single contributing factor to all those rates is cylinder head port design.

Since few of us are engineers with the financial backing to design our own heads—such as Dan Gurney and Harry Weslake did for the small-block Ford that Gurney used at the Indianapolis 500—the problem becomes one of extracting more power by reworking production heads. A group of special machine shops, including Cylinder Heads America, Valley Head Service, and Mondello's specialize in such work.

Most hot rodders send their heads to such shops for refinement, for to them, porting and related work are black arts to be performed in some secret den. While it does take a professional to do a pro job on a set of heads, anyone can do some of the work inexpensively and get a very noticeable improvement in performance. In this article we will take you step by

step through the things you can do in relative safety to clean up your heads. The improvement in quarter-mile elapsed times will more than justify the time and money spent. For information on how to go about improving a set of heads at home, we contacted Joe Mondello, owner and operator of Mondello's Porting Service, Inc. in Los Angeles, Calif.

Mondello offers a street horsepower porting job which adds 39 hp at a budget price. It consists of porting the exhaust side of the heads, a valve job and larger exhaust valves. Since most American production V-8 engines come stock with fairly decent intake valves, this area is left alone for the budget job. With a little time and less money, you can perform the job yourself. You may not get as much horsepower as Mondello can offer, but the gain will be more than noticeable and well worth the effort.

The first step after you have either purchased a set of heads for the job, or removed the ones already on the car, is to completely strip the head castings. Using a valve spring compressor, remove the spring retainers, springs, seals and valves. If the heads are used, make a close visual inspection for cracks after cleaning the heads in a hot tank. If you don't

have access to a hot tank to "boil" the heads, clean them thoroughly with solvent and dry.

It should be pointed out that heads will rust quickly, so air pressure should be used to dry them immediately after washing. A commercial spray anti-rust compound, such as WD-40, should be used after drying or on freshly exposed virgin metal (such as after cutting or grinding) to prevent any rust from forming.

Mondello stresses that all heads should be milled slightly to true them. Even new heads might be .006 to .014-in. out of level (from end-to-end). A flat surface is a must for optimum performance so a milling cut sufficient to true the heads should be performed by a competent machine shop. Above all, Mondello says not to cut more than .060-in. from the head surface or a "thin head" will result. Such a head can flex under combustion pressures and allow compression leaks, at best, or blown head gaskets, at worst.

Before the milling operation is performed, both heads should be checked for combustion chamber volume. If you don't already have the equipment to do this job, it will be easier and cheaper to let the machine shop do it. This is Mondello's preference since it is advisable to have the check for cubic centimeters done on the milling machine.

If you want to cc your own heads, you will need a graduate marked in cubic centimeters with a petcock on the bottom to release the liquid into the combustion chamber. The liquid can be kerosene, alcohol, cleaning fluid, or just about any petroleum product. A little dye added to it will make it easier to tell if all crevices are filled. Water should not be used because it does not flow readily into small spaces.

Cover the chamber with a piece of clear plastic held firmly against the head surface. With the valves and spark plug inserted, use a level to keep the head surface horizontal, then flow the liquid into the chamber through a small hole drilled in the plastic. When the chamber is full, note how much liquid has been removed from the graduate and you have the volume of the chamber. After the cc check, the head containing the chamber with the largest volume should be milled first, bringing it down to factory volume specs.

With the milling completed, each remaining chamber should be ground to make it equal to the one with the largest volume. Use an abrasive stone on an electric drill or a high speed port grinder to remove the desired material. Be sure to put old valves and spark plugs in the chamber for protection. When grinding metal from the combustion chamber, you should remember that the shape of the combustion chamber is important. Compare the shape of the top of your pistons to the chamber shape and do your grinding in areas where there is the greatest restriction. Follow the basic shape of the chamber rather than trying to change it. Detroit engineers had a reason for the chamber shape. Enlarge it, but don't reshape it unless

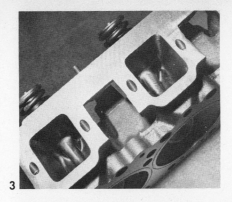
3

4

5

1. Equalizing the combustion chamber volumes should be one of your first steps in performance head work. Here a small diameter glass tube connects the burette of liquid to plastic plate on head. With the fluid system fully contained, no extra liquid drips into chamber when the burette is shut off.

2. Unless you're a professional, it's not a good idea to enlarge ports any bigger than pattern taken from gasket.

3. Finished port has been ground out to size, polished, and makes smooth passage from manifold to valve.

4. If you're grinding your own intake passages, the area around the valve stem boss should be rounded as much as possible, but carefully!

5. Breathing on this 340 Mopar head is considerably improved by porting. Since it is for a street engine, the inside surface is left unpolished.

MONDELLO VALVE SIZES AVAILABLE

Make	Intake	Exhaust
Chevy 265/283	1-3/4, 1-7/8, 1-15/16, 2	1-1/2, 1-5/8, 1-21/32, 1-11/16
Chevy 302/327/350	1-15/16, 2	1-5/8, 1-21/32, 1-11/16
Chevy 6 235/270/292	1-7/8, 1-15/16, 2	1-5/8, 1-21/32, 1-11/16
Chevy II 4 cyl	Same as Chevy 6	Same as Chevy 6
Chevy 396/427 (3/8 stem)	2-3/16, 2-1/4, 2.300	1.720, 1.840
Chrysler Hemi (late)	2-1/4 x 5/16	1-15/16 x 5/16
Chrysler Hemi 331/392 (2-piece 3/8 stem, gas only)	2, 2-1/16, 2-1/8	2, 2-1/16, 2-1/8
Ford 260/289	1-13/16, 1-7/8, 1.900, 1-15/16	1.600, 1-5/8, 1-21/32, 1-11/16
Ford 332 through 428	2.030, 2.100	1-3/4
Pontiac 389/421	1-15/16, 2, 2-1/8	1-5/8, 1-21/32, 1-3/4
Pontiac OHC 6	1-7/8, 1-15/16, 2	1-5/8, 1-21/32, 1-11/16

(Valves are also available from Donovan Engineering and Ansen)

Porting and Polishing

you know that a different shape will definitely increase horsepower.

The entire combustion chamber operation is marginal at best for the amateur. Unless you have a lot of confidence or a set of heads you can write off, have it done by an expert.

GRINDING THE PORTS

Now comes the fun part—grinding out the exhaust ports. While Mondello and other major porting shops use special high-speed grinders, a hand-held drill motor will do the job. In addition to the drill, you will need a couple of rotary files with long shafts (to compensate for the blunt shape of the portable hand drill which won't fit into the ports) and a good selection of abrasive stones, also with long shafts. You will also need a metal scribe to mark the desired cut on your cylinder head.

Using a new exhaust manifold gasket for a template works best and is safest. Lay the gasket on the head and use the scribe to mark the out-line of the gasket port holes on the head. Do this at each exhaust port opening. The lines thus marked will serve as the guide for enlarging the ports. If you have the money, it is advisable to obtain a junk head identical in model to those you plan to port. A machine shop will cut it apart for you so that you can get a better idea of the thickness of the port walls in many areas. The cross-sectioned head, while not necessarily identical to yours because of casting flaws, will still be a very good guide to prevent grinding out too much metal and breaking through into water passages.

In porting, the rotary files should be used only where large amounts of metal are to be removed. The rest of the grinding should be done with the abrasive stones, right down to the final polishing. It takes longer to use the stones but it beats grinding through to the water passages.

The fact that you'll probably never find a square plumbing tube has a bearing on port design. Just as in plumbing, a round shape is best for flowing exhaust gases. While you are enlarging the ports to conform with the exhaust manifold gaskets, try to round the port cross-section shape. Also, try to make the port passages follow as straight a line as possible from the center of the port opening to the center line of the exhaust valve stem. A basic physics law teaches that the shortest distance between two points is a straight line. It's also the fastest.

When you finish grinding the ports, the passages should be smooth, fairly round, and fairly straight. They should also be the same size to equalize exhaust restriction in all cylinders.

One area in the port that requires special attention is the metal that surrounds the valve stem. This hump should be rounded with the grinder to reduce hot spots. Be very careful, however, to stay away from the valve seat. If you plan to add larger exhaust valves, set a pair of calipers to the diameter of the valve head at the bottom of the seat area and grind the port under the valve head to within approximately ⅛-in. of this measurement. Final tapering of the port to the valve seat will be taken care of later in the story.

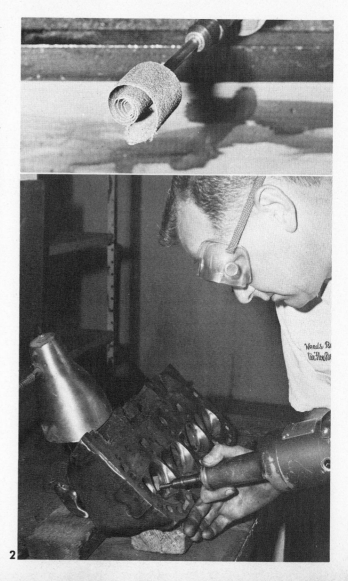

With the exhaust ports finished, use the calipers to transfer the individual intake manifold port measurements to the respective intake ports on the heads. The manifold ports should be larger and you should grind the opening of the head ports to conform to the manifold. Don't go much beyond the surface of the head ports unless you plan to add a high-performance camshaft. The entire procedure discussed thus far assumes that the stock short block (pistons, cam, rods, etc.) will be used, and under those conditions the intake side of the heads should be left alone. Stock intake valves and ports on almost all American engines are sufficient for stock cam timing, carburetion, and engine displacement.

If, however, you plan to add a high-performance cam from any of the many manufacturers, order it and inform the manufacturer that your heads are ported. Just repeat on the intake ports the process already described for the exhaust side and you will retain the balance that is necessary for good engine performance.

Mondello also points out that if you are going to hog out the intake ports and get a better cam, the pistons should also be replaced with higher than stock compression slugs. This also entails having combustion chambers reshaped—a job for a professional only—and pistons should be ordered by giving the chamber volume to assure the correct compression ratio. Pistons advertised for (as an example) 11.5:1 compression ratio will deliver less than that if combustion chambers have been enlarged.

In short, Mondello suggests that unless you plan to go the whole route—pistons, big intake valves, better carburetion, bigger and better combustion chambers, intake porting, and a wilder cam—stick to the exhaust ports and valves, go a bit rich

1. Unless some machinist's blue dye is painted on before scribe marks are made, scribed line will be difficult to see once grinding has started.

2. A strip of abrasive mounted on a drill bit is useful for final polishing on chambers and ports.

3. This is a perfect example of why you need some junk valves and plugs to put in the chamber. They protect the seats from the grinder, but take a beating in the process.

4. The last operation in finishing this racing head is competition valve job. Pilot shafts align seat grinder.

5. The fact that big ports are not necessarily efficient ports is shown by changes in Chrysler Hemi. Factory decreased cross section of ports resulting in improvements in flow and horses. This is reason enough to be careful with a grinder when porting a head.

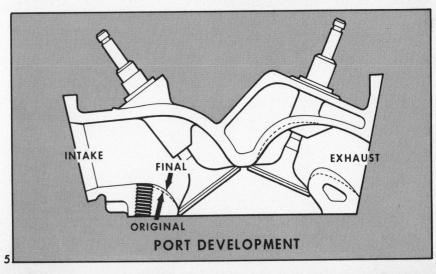

INTAKE   FINAL   EXHAUST

ORIGINAL

PORT DEVELOPMENT

Porting and Polishing

on the carburetion and get a good set of headers to take full advantage of the exhaust work.

Before going on the valve job, some words of caution are in order. First, don't go wild with the port grinding. A little is good, but a lot is likely to ruin the heads. Also, remember that the big gain in combustion chambers comes from shape and that should be left to the experts. Mondello, for example, has spent a lot of time and money testing a multitude of chamber shapes for each type of head on a flow testing bench to find the best possible shape. What looks like common sense may violate every known law of physics concerning the flow of a liquid or gas. Aside from equalizing chamber volumes and grinding off any obvious bumps which can cause hot spots, leave the chambers alone.

CUTTING THE HEADS

Now we're ready to cut the heads for bigger exhaust valves (and intakes if you're going the whole route). First, a commercial metal marking dye available from almost any auto parts store should be brushed onto the area around each valve seat. Mondello has a special tool to scribe the outline of the bigger valve that is to be installed on the chamber surface,

but these aren't usually found in the do-it-yourselfer's tool box. To get the outline scribed, take a valve that is ⅛-in. smaller in diameter than those to be installed, lay it in the valve guide and use a sharp metal scribe to mark its outline on the head. Use enough force to scratch the metal, not just remove the dye.

Set a pair of calipers to the exact diameter of the bigger valve heads. While the seats are being ground with a conventional valve seat grinder, make frequent checks with the calipers until they just fit the seat that is being enlarged.

After the seats have been rough-ground to the caliper measurement, they should be gone over lightly with a topping stone. These usually come in 15- or 30-degree angles but it's advisable to get one that closely conforms with the angle of the combustion chamber floors.

Next, a 75-degree hand reamer is used to make the width of the rough seat uniform. If the seat is wider on one side than the other, the temperatures will vary and this can affect performance. Finally, use a 45-degree stone to grind the finished seat. Valves should be faced at a 44.5-degree angle for an interference fit.

The grinders used to reface valves and recut seats can usually be rented from larger tool rental shops. If you don't have the tools and can't rent them, any good machine shop will

grind them for you to the above instructions.

Above all, be very careful not to grind the seats past the width indicated by the calipers or the valves will sink into the ports. This disrupts combustion chamber volume and produces lower compression.

When installing bigger valves, check piston-to-valve clearance and the size of piston valve relief pockets.

The chart printed with this article gives the size of valves, both intake and exhaust, which can be installed and are available from Mondello. But before you start spending money on valves, check shop manuals and parts interchange books (available at most wrecking yards) to see if a newer set of heads won't provide bigger valves at roughly the same cost. On many engines the basic stock port design will also be better. You will have a lot more to start with and a need to expend less effort. For example, Mondello feels that the only pre-327 Chevy V-8 head worth fooling with is the 283 fuel injection model, identified by a pointer cast on the front.

With valve grinding out of the way, the valve guides need to be restored. Even if the heads are new, knurling is the hot setup for a performance engine. This process actually will decrease the diameter of valve guide bores, making it possible to use heads with worn guides. Knurling

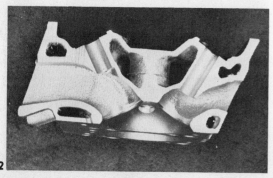

consists of running a special tool through the guide bores with an electric drill. The tool cuts a fine series of grooves in the guide bore that resembles a threaded hole, when finished. This forces material to the center of the bore and reduces the size of the guide. A reamer that corresponds to the diameter of the valve stem being used, plus the factory-recommended guide-to-valve stem clearances, will enlarge the guide after knurling. Stems can also be ground for clearance unless they are hard chromed.

A still better method, one recommended by Mondello for engines that will see a lot of racing duty, is the use of bronze guide inserts. These resemble a brass tube with threaded interior. The guide is drilled to accept the bronze inserts which are locked in with pins. The inserts are then reamed to the valve size plus .001-in. for clearance. This is far less clearance than knurled guides require because the brass inserts aid in lubricating the valve stems, and less clearance for oil passage is required. Hard chrome valve stems must be used with the bronze bushings and should be used with the knurled guides to prevent excessive stem wear. Bronze insert guides are all but immune to wear.

The next item on the agenda is the selection of valve stem seals. Mondello recommends Perfect Circle valve seals. These come in two types: rub-

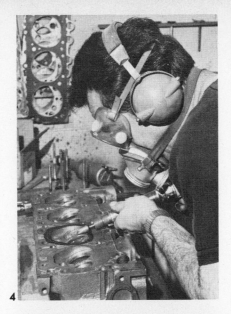

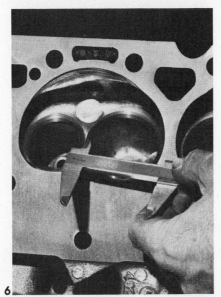

1. This is the other reason you have to be careful. This head will have to be brazed up and ground down.

2. If at all possible, try to get a head similar to the one you're going to port and cut it apart. This Hemi shows clearances to the water jackets.

3. To check for small holes, Mondello uses a special bench to seal all but one water passage opening, pumps air in, then sprays a soap and water mix on the ports and chambers. Bubbles will indicate where any holes are.

4. Using the proper tools includes protective gear. Joe Mondello wears safety goggles, breathing mask and a set of ear guards because of the noise of the other grinders in his shop.

5. A 75° reamer is used to get the valve seat concentric, providing even valve temperature around the seat.

6. Calipers, set to the valve head diameter, are used during rough seat grinding so as not to grind too much.

7. After scribing operation, intake ports on this 340 Mopar head have been roughed out to desired size before porting work is started.

8. This is a finished set of racing heads for a small-block Chevy done by Crane Engineering. The chambers, ports and valves are all polished, rocker studs are pinned, and special valve springs and retainers are used.

Porting and Polishing

ber and teflon for stock engines, and all-teflon for engines that will see frequent racing use. The all-teflon seals require an installation tool which can be purchased where the seals are sold. The operation consists of using the tool to thread the top of the valve guide on the rocker arm side of the head. Instructions that come with the Perfect Circle seals show how easy the installation is.

When installing the PC seals, always use a set of calipers to take a measurement from the bottom of the spring retainer to the top of the valve seal. This measurement should always equal the cam lift plus the height of the valve seal plus .060-in. This ensures against bottoming if the valves float. If there is not enough clearance, the top of the valve guide must be machined down.

Before installing the various parts on the heads, the use of a spotfacer or other suitable tool to flatten the spring seat is advisable. This trick should *not* be used to obtain correct spring height. Make just enough of a cut to expose fresh metal on the entire seat and assure a flat surface for the springs. If you plan to install dual springs on an engine that doesn't have them in stock form, a hole saw may be necessary to reduce the diameter of the valve guide for inner spring clearance. Take care not to disrupt the machining for the valve

seals during this operation. If there is conflict, do the spring machining first.

With all the cutting done, give valve guides a good coat of oil or break-in lubricant and assemble the valves and related pieces. Then use a telescopic gauge, micrometer or other suitable, *accurate* device to measure the spring height. Compare this with factory specifications or those that were supplied with special springs or camshaft if used. Measure from the bottom of the spring retainer to the bottom of the spring at the seat. Don't include any shims. Insufficient height can be corrected by adding shims (Mondello makes a packaged assortment with enough shims for a set of heads) between the springs and the spring seat. Mondello warns that not more than .120-in. of shims should be used on any one spring or that spring bottom will be lifted out of the seat (see drawing of hole saw). It can then "walk" and this causes excessive wear of valve guides due to lateral pressure exerted on the valve stem. Ten hard runs and you'll have enough oil in the combustion chambers to make an engine completely useless.

Later, with the assembled heads on the engine, one final valve spring check should be made. With the engine rotated so that a valve is in the full-open position, take a .015-in. feeler gauge and try to insert it between the spring coils. If your springs are progressively wound (coils closer together at the bottom of the spring

when fully expanded), the bottom coils will probably be touching. You should, however, be able to get the feeler gauge between the wide-spaced coils. If not, you have spring coil bind and high rpm will be impossible to obtain. Replace the springs.

IMPROVING THE VALVE TRAIN

In addition to the major work already outlined, several parts in the valve train can be replaced for better performance and higher maximum rpm. The lighter the valve train parts, the faster they can move so you want special alloy valve spring retainers.

Also, the weakest link in the chain is the valve keeper. These two-piece clips lock the retainers and springs to the valve and should be replaced with high-performance heat-treated keepers for added strength. A broken keeper will let one of those lovely new valves slide gracelessly down into the cylinder to cause the destruction of valve and piston—and can even take the cylinder wall along for the ride.

The 289-cu.-in. Ford standard-performance engine, the 383-cu.-in. Chrysler Corp. wedge, the Chrysler 440-cu.-in. wedge, the 292-cu.-in. Chevy 6 (Nova) and other engines do not have cast-in spring seats. Instead, the springs seat on the head surface itself. On these engines the guides should be narrowed with a hole saw and high-performance chrome-moly spring seats installed. These seats

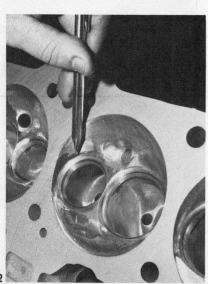

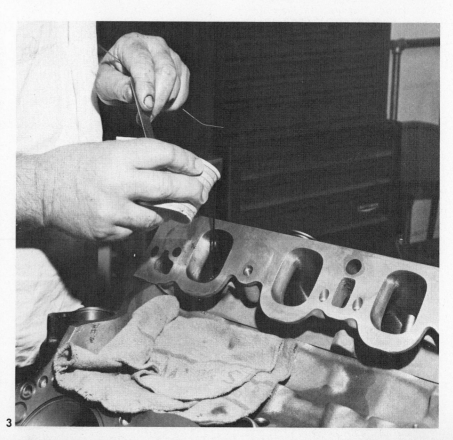

are a snap-fit, removable item and any number of shims can be used. Guide life will be greatly improved.

Before we send you off to the reassembly, a note for owners of 396/427-cu.-in. Chevy engines with removable guides. Like other removable guides, these are a press fit in the heads. However, the guides are larger at one end than the other and *must* be driven out from the combustion chamber side toward the rocker arm side of the heads. Driving them toward the combustion chambers will ruin the heads. If stock guides are to be replaced with stock inside diameter guides, you'll have to get them from Mondello because Chevrolet doesn't make them.

Be sure you lubricate the rocker arm side of the heads thoroughly before you fire up the new engine, and be sure to keep the valve stems coated during assembly of the heads. Take a look at the charts and photos printed with this article and remember the following: Engine performance is the result of a delicate balance between a number of parts which assure that the engine draws in as much fuel as it can burn, burns it efficiently and can then exhaust the waste products. An increase in efficiency in any of these areas except the normally inadequate exhaust system must be accompanied by a corresponding increase in the others.

Don't go too fast and you'll have a winning set of cylinder heads.

4

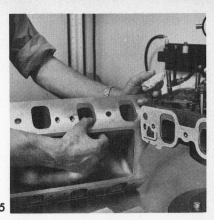

5

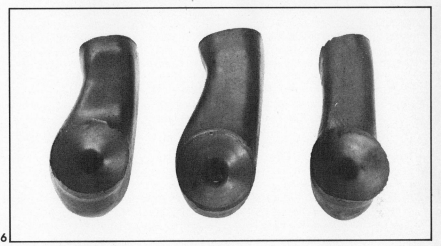

6

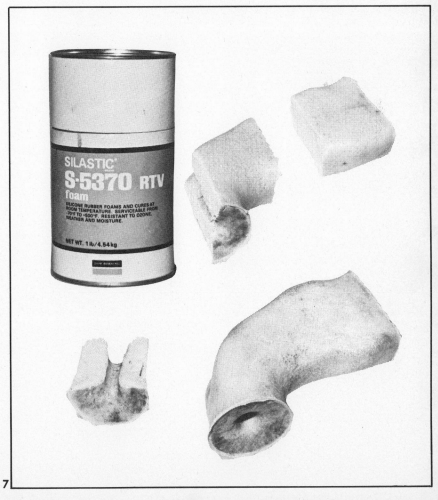

7

1. Exhaust ports on Crane Chevy head have been enlarged and rounded so the port is same shape right from valve.

2. After the chambers are polished, critical areas around valve throats are ground to precision shapes as is determined by airflow testing.

3. Liquid rubber (Black Tuffy) is poured into ports to get a mold to study for port development.

4. The templates are used during both rough and finish machine-work to obtain optimum matching of ports from cylinder to cylinder. Note that a short steel rod has been welded on to act as a handle.

5. With modeling clay tamped into place, the heads and manifold were flow-tested. After a rubber mold of ports had been made, clay was taken out and liquid Devcon poured in to fill up ports around rubber mold.

6. These molds show development of exhaust ports. Final version at right is noticeably straighter.

7. Port Foam is a handy product from A&W Products. A liquid, it is poured into a port where it expands and finally sets to the consistency of foam rubber. It can then be pulled out of port and used to visually compare port shapes. It can be cut apart to compare cross-sectional shapes.

Airflow Testing

The internal aerodynamics of the manifold and head can unlock extra horsepower. Making it easier for air to get into and out of the cylinders is the real key.

Not too many hot rodders are dyed-in-the-wool engineers; most of us rely on the old school of trial and error for our hard-won experience. We make a change here and try it out, then we make another change. While this method of advancement cannot be discounted (it's really the ultimate test of any car performance), there are several ways of finding short-cuts. We're discovering those quick ways home rapidly, and now we've found one in that very controversial area of intake and exhaust porting. Actually, we're talking about the entire realm of airflow, from the carburetor lip to exhaust pipe tip.

A garage door wag once observed, after watching us patiently grind away at a flathead block, that we certainly seemed to have lots of experience grinding big, shiny holes. Unfortunately, the criticism was all too valid, for some time later we learned that our homegrown philosophy of porting was about as erroneous as it could

be. You may fall into the same trap, if you don't know how scientific porting should be done. In other parts of this book we have discussed flow testing and how it is done. Here we have a real treat for you, because one of the top flow-testing experts invited us into his shop to share his secrets. Read on, and you will discover that scientific porting is a lot more than hogging metal out of head ports with a grinder.

How a gas or fluid gets from point A to point B depends upon several things, including density, pressure, friction, etc. Walk down to the river and you'll get a graphic description. Notice that where the river is narrow, the water is shooting along fast, churning white waves, but where the riverbed is wide, the flow is slower. You heave a piece of wood into the middle of the river and it moves along rapidly, but along shore it hardly moves at all. At a bend in the river, the current drives across toward the opposite bank, tearing away the dirt,

while on the side near you the water is shallow and filled with silt. Just past the bend, the near side also has a big whirlpool where the water between you and the current is actually going in the opposite direction. The same kind of thing is taking place inside an engine.

Wherever the intake or exhaust system "riverbed" is straight, the fuel mixture (or exhaust gases) moves with a minimum of restriction. But at the slightest bend, trouble starts to develop. And there are more bends in an engine's airflow pattern than there are in a coiled snake.

Because of the vital importance of airflow (or internal aerodynamics) to the engine operating at or near maximum efficiency, the factory engineers have started leaning more and more toward the airflow box. That is, they've started designing with the physical property, or a prototype. We've heard rumors about airflow experiments for several years, both in

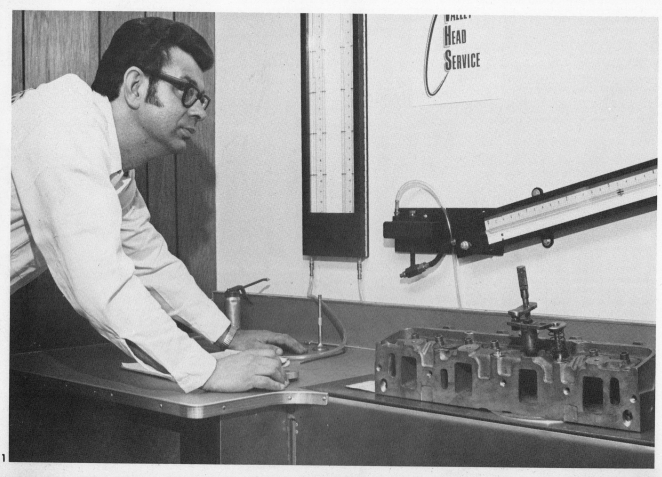

hot rodding and motorcycle racing, but it wasn't until *Hot Rod* Magazine's Jim McFarland visited Ford engineering a couple of years back that we began to realize the value of the procedure.

AIRFLOW TESTING AT FORD

Ford started airflow testing in earnest when performance became a company axiom and body designs were placing tremendous restrictions on intake system designs. To begin with, most manifold design is a matter of making something that will fit the easiest within the available space. Naturally, the car company engineers have an excellent idea of what to start with, so changes aren't likely to be great.

The process begins with a rough pencil sketch developed with allowances for the clearance of hood, fender panels, etc. Based on this drawing, a pair of metal plates are constructed and positioned in such a way that they represent the intake manifold surfaces of the heads to be used. A plaster model is built to depict the runners (passageways) as they will approximately appear in the finished manifold.

The basic premise at this point is concerned with the type and quantity of carburetion (2-bbl., 4-bbl., etc.) and hood clearance. The model then becomes the core of a divided box (upper half and lower half) made when fiberglass is poured into a box-like container and around the plaster model runners. This, then, is a flow box, deriving its name from the fact that the initial plaster mold runners form the passageways later to be involved in the actual flow testing procedure.

And now, enter the flow-bench, a device designed to pass air through a passage (usually via a sucking action) and capable of measuring a quantity of flow. While there are a number of flow machines scattered through the hot rod industry, most of them are of the low-velocity nature and do not really compare with the factory types. This is a pity, because most of the important data is measured at high velocities. More and more high-velocity machines are being introduced, but they usually must be homemade, and getting a perfect read-out seems to be the biggest problem with these systems.

There are differences between pure air and a fuel/air mixture, but both are compressible and can be subjected to dynamic flow studies. As a matter of interest, the combined problems of high-velocity fuel/air separation, and the conversion of small amounts of heat (since the mixture is compressible) generated from mechanical impulses during the course of flow through manifolding and ports, are but two of the gremlins to be considered in developmental stages.

When flow testing a component, the flow box is attached one port at a time to the cylinder head and measurements begin. Note in the intake manifold story that we make mention of flow testing a completed manifold in this manner, by using a typical head and fitting a carburetor to the manifold.

Complementing the flow box/head arrangement is a valve, installed in the proper position and adjustable to lift. By making a series of tests with the valve opened to different settings within its normal range, curves can be plotted to indicate the flow characteristics of a given manifold/head combination throughout the valve operating range.

As the testing progresses, airflow readings can be taken at anywhere along the manifold runner or head port surface by use of a small probe. Thus, the engineer can get a direct readout of airflow past that particular point, and can then make minor passage shape changes with clay. In this

2

3

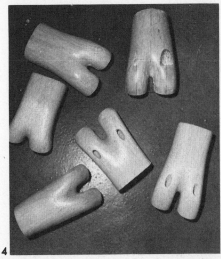

4

1. Larry Ofria, owner of Valley Head Service, Tarzana, Calif., is well known for his racing and street head work. His flow bench is an indispensable part of his business.

2. Mullen and Co., have worked with the Chrysler plant on "A" and Hemi heads. Bob Mullen flow-tests a 340 brazed-port head on flow bench and checks the flow "window" with a probe. Mullen's shop is located in Carson, Calif.

3. With intricate wooden models such as this, almost any workable combination can be sorted out. Valves, valve guides, and seats can be changed. The effects of spark plug location and combustion chamber shape can also be checked with models.

4. These wooden patterns are the internal passages for plaster port molds. Different lengths of runner, different shapes and angles—all are part of program to get best port shape for a given engine.

Airflow Testing

way, the shape and routing of the original passages are refined to produce the most efficient flow. During design stages at the factory, this clay work continues until the best manifold/head port shape is determined. Keep in mind, though, that the engineer does not necessarily want to create a racing engine. Instead, he may want something that will run strong up to around 5000 rpm. Above that, he doesn't care what the heck happens.

Through the establishment of a base flow rate (maximum) for a given manifold runner and head port (as well as valve design), and the method of testing one runner at a time, a finished passage can be designed in which all components are capable of the same volume of flow. Head and manifold units are always flowed together, so that the result is a balanced combination of head and manifold jointly capable of flowing almost 98% of the optimum flow of a head alone.

No pulsations are introduced in the test flow. Engineers justify this deliberate omission by stating that tests are based on comparisons, and although a finished passage may not pass the same volume of air indicated by the near laminar characteristics of the test flow, actual flow of fuel/air mixture will remain at a maximum with the passage working on a "live" engine.

Valve seat and valve pocket design can also be accomplished with a flow box, as can combustion chamber shape and piston head design. Factory attention is frequently directed to the shape of the pocket just below a valve seat. Here is an area where so-called venturi effects can be effectively explored. Along these same lines, some work is being done in which a venturi effect is developed between the valve seat and the valve face. In this vein of exploratory work, such factors as the fluid friction, flow-pressure changes, and effects of friction within the fuel/air mixture itself (viscosity) are considered. Valve seats on both head and valve become a curved surface so that a line of contact exists in the place of normal seat contact. Designs of this type are intended to remove the tendencies for turbulence as a mixture flows past the normally-sharp corners of a valve face or seat, thus introducing more air into the cylinder per stroke.

The friction between manifold runner walls and the high-velocity air comes into play testing, ultimately, has an effect on the shape of the runner floors and cross-sectional patterns

(see chapter on manifolds). Unless mechanical limitations (pushrods, valve positioning, head bolt location, etc.) dictate the shape of port openings, a circular cross section is the shape thought most desirable. This is a fact Winfield pointed out many years ago, at least to the hot rodders who would listen. Rectangular shaped cross sections lose much of their effective area, in terms of flow capability, because of the turbulence created in the corners of a rectangle.

It has also been found that when a maximum flow is achieved, the physical and flow centerlines of a passage do not always coincide. This feature is most noticeable at the junction of head and manifold ports where the manifold runners bend into the head. Small humps in the floor of an intake manifold runner leading up to a head port are built in to adjust the flow centerline at the head/manifold connection. The attack angle at which the flow stream hits the head port is critical (this being the basis for the so-called hi-rise manifolds) and care is taken not to disturb the laminar flow characteristics of the mixture.

It is desirable that the flow pattern be as free from turbulence as possible, since lack of turbulence increases flow velocity and volume at the intake valve and aids in the desired turbulent action of the mix once it finds its way into the cylinder. Due to combustion chamber design, this feature is more effective in wedge-type engines than those with hemispherical combustion chambers.

CRITICAL DESIGN TOLERANCES

When making up a new manifold design, adjustment inside the runners is very critical. Dimensional tolerances must be held almost perfect, since changes as small as .010-in. in runner location or size can radically disrupt the most thoroughly tested design.

It was because of this last bit of caution from the factory that we called on a flow testing expert in the Los Angeles area, Warren Brownfield of Air Flow Research (North Hollywood). Warren is no stranger to hot rodding, having been around it for the past 15 years in one form of racing or another. He has always approached the various phases of engine modification differently than most engineers. That's why he spent 2½ years doing research on airflow char-acteristics before opening a shop specializing in racing engine airflow techhique. That means he makes ports his own special way, as well as unusual injection systems.

Before he could do any serious air-flow work, Brownfield needed some kind of sophisticated high-velocity flow bench. Since most of the units commercially available are custom built and cost well into four figures, he decided to construct his own. Months of labor went into this seemingly simple task, until he finally created just what he wanted—a stable machine with ability to produce small readings. With such a machine, the hot rodder can actually see what is being accomplished anytime he takes a grinder to his engine. Basically, this is what Duntov and Weslake and Cosworth have been doing to get such fantastic horsepower.

An engine runs because of a pres-

1. Engineers use the flow bench to check flow throughout the range of valve opening. Dial indicator measures valve lift. Intake port is being flowed without an intake manifold runner connected to it. A far more accurate measure of actual flow is obtained by placing a radiused opening in front of the port opening to simulate a manifold runner.

2. When a flow box is separated, each port is open for inspection. Note on this model how exhaust valve guide is well to one side of port, but this could change immediately. The entire spectrum of flow testing is only in its beginning stages as far as hot rodding goes, but it promises some good results in the coming years.

3. The strengths and weaknesses of the Boss 351 heads were probed on a flow bench for concrete results. Here Jerry Branch, of Branch Flowmetrics, Long Beach, Calif. checks out a Mondello-ported head.

4. No, that's not a new trick valve spring. Since the valve is not subjected to extremely high forces and cycling rates during airflow testing, only a spring strong enough to hold the valve open is used.

5. Valve throat area, or pocket, is critical to high-performance engines, especially those running without aid of a supercharger. Idea is to get air flowing across valve face with least turbulence, and also with maximum capacity.

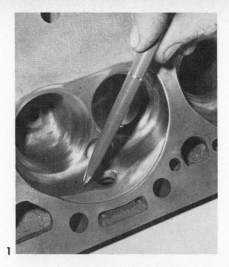

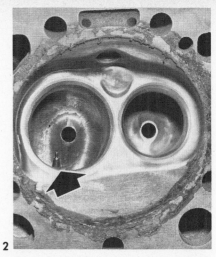

sure differential and temperature change, therefore the weakest link in the induction chain is the valve. A big hole does not necessarily mean airflow will be maximum, if the door (valve) won't let the air pass.

Brownfield has run standard tests on most of the American engines, and has found the 426 Chrysler Hemi to flow the best in stock configuration. The big Chevy and Ford engines are also good, although valve and valve pocket design in the high-performance Ford engine can be improved. Part of the reason the Chrysler engines breathe so well must be attributed to the fact Weslake researched for the company. At the same time, Cosworth should do Ford some good since his little 183-cu.-in. engine is putting out well in excess of 400 horses.

Brownfield feels that high-velocity air is the key to engine performance, and this holds true at any rpm. Because this point of velocity is so critical, the hot rodder cannot afford to be sloppy and should not be messing around with the ports or manifold if he doesn't know what he is doing. The biggest effect of high velocity seems to be on torque, because of the ability to pack the air at intermediate rpm ranges and give better mixture control. In essence, high-velocity air becomes high-pressure air. Even when the cam overlap is up in the radical ranges, high velocity can overcome pulse feedback.

From hundreds of tests, Warren has found that each and every engine is different, so that no set pattern can be evolved as perfect. For this reason, he cannot create a perfect set of production heads, for instance, but he can come extremely close. And here is his big secret— *he does not change the basic port characteristics drastically.* In a nutshell, this is his advice to anyone doing port work. Obviously the factory knew what it was doing, so changes will probably be of the minute nature, although they will often result in considerable performance difference.

Brownfield has found that the most critical spot in a head is ½-inch on either side of the valve seat, where the air is traveling the fastest. A very slight change here—one that would go almost unnoticed—can have a very strong effect on final engine performance. In this respect, a set of racing heads are much like a high-performance camshaft, and for this reason the heads should be treated as more than mere hunks of cast iron.

The valve seat angle is critical, as

mentioned, something Chrysler has pointed out in tune-up tips to MoPar racers. Warren suggests that it is unwise to hog out the port under the intake seat, because this area actually serves to direct the incoming air across the valve face and seat. If the angle is incorrect, it can cram the air into the area at an undesirable angle, cutting airflow.

While engine builders differ on what is the best valve seat angle, Warren has found that 45 degrees will work OK under most conditions, with any change in seat degree di-

rectly related to port shape and flow direction (flow approach).

On the subject of port smoothness, he is adamant in pointing out that a perfectly smooth port can be a hindrance. Try blowing alcohol off a piece of glass with air. The fluid tends to cling to the glass. But try the same thing with sandpaper, and the fluid is blown free immediately. Clay Smith found this out once with a V-8 60 flathead engine. When he used a manifold with perfectly polished runners, the horsepower fell off, but a manifold with rough runners gave a horsepower increase. Anyway, since the runners and ports will likely flow more air than the valve will pass, it is best to leave them slightly rough to help keep the fuel hanging in the air.

Brownfield has found that much can be gained by careful work with the exhaust port. This means continual testing with the flow machine, and it also means that the shape of the port will not be the same anywhere in the 360-degree circumference. The same holds true of the intake pocket, but not to the same degree. It is how the port is shaped that allows Warren to create the customized head. For instance, compare the relative flow values for a stock Chevrolet 327 FI head, and the same head after reworking:

Lift	Stock	Reworked
.100	30	62
.150	60	115
.200	100	182
.250	142	242
.300	190	285
.350	221	310
.400	243	310
.450	250	322
.500	262	332
.550	260	332

It has been found that some ported heads—units reworked without the aid of a flow machine—actually flow less air than a stock unit; that's why it is better to stick with stock configuration.

Some interesting things have come to light during flow testing of the exhaust ports, in that air can form a gate as well as help flow. Again, just the right curves inside the port are necessary to alleviate this unhappy situation.

Another critical area of airflow on some engines is around the valve guides, something that can be shown clearly with the airflow probe. Because of this, Brownfield makes one side of the guide a different shape than the other side, all because tests have shown this work to get maximum flow.

Flow box methods can be used for the design of exhaust manifolds too, but peak efficiency for complete header systems is best determined on an engine dynamometer and at the engine rpm desired. Obviously there is very much to be gained by scientific investigation of "internal aerodynamics." Fortunately, hot rodders learn well. ⚒

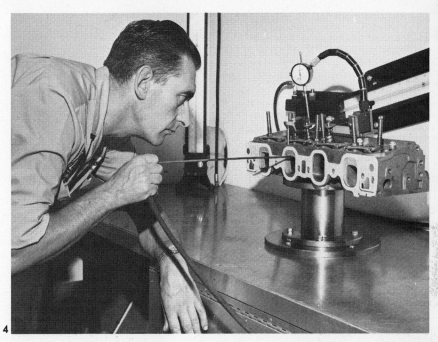

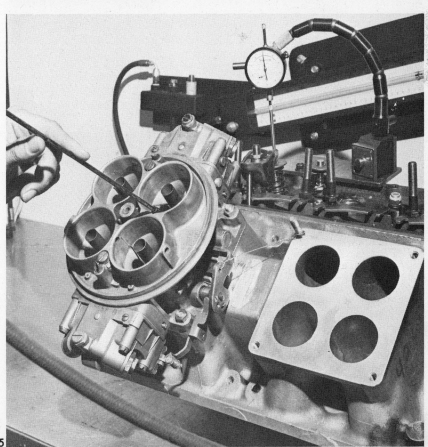

1. The rodder sometimes cuts away portions of the combustion chamber in effort to gain horsepower. This may or may not be beneficial, and in most cases is of little consequence. Only the flow bench tells the truth.

2. Pen inside intake port (arrow) shows how the valve guide is ground to direct the flow of air to best part of throat area. This is critical part of porting and must be followed carefully to get maximum flow.

3. A flow machine sounds like some sort of giant vacuum cleaner when running, but will immediately detect flow problems in critical part of engine. High-velocity flow machines will undoubtedly become part of every specialist's equipment.

4. Noel Stairs, of Falconer and Dunn Racing Engines, Culver City, Calif., checks port velocity with probe on their flow bench. The flow bench is used on heads, manifolds, and carburetors, too.

5. Does it really flow as much as the ads say? It's easy to check on a flow bench. Probe is used to check flow in various areas of the carburetor. Flow distribution between various cylinders can also be measured.

Valve Service Tools

A valve and porting job is only as good as the skill of the operator and the precision quality of his specialized equipment.

There was once a time, and not so very long ago, when life was so much simpler. Picture the hard-working mechanic following FoMoCo's own recommendations of directing a well placed hammer blow to the head of the Model T's valves to insure their proper seating. Try that today and you would stand a very good chance of breaking the whole cotton-pickin' cylinder head. The very fact that common passenger car engine design and execution has come a long way since that bygone era, has brought with it an almost limitless variety of hand and power tools needed to keep the old goat running. Therefore, it stands to reason one needs to exercise a little more caution, both in his selection of tools and how he uses them, before tackling that super-sneaky valve job described in preceding chapters.

So let's look into this wide world of head, valve, and cam tools, see what they do and, quite frankly, how much they cost. Hopefully, you'll then have a better appreciation of why a good port or valve job is not cheap. Follow along with us and we'll play rich mechanic on a drunken sailor's spending spree and buy everything in sight...and bring along your Brink's armored car.

BASIC TOOLS

You will find in preceding chapters that various and sundry references have been made by the authors to this or that specialized hand or power tool. The scope of those specialized valve, head, and cam tools is so wide that we cannot hope to cover them ad infinitum. Therefore what we'll try to do here is to give you some idea of what basic tools are normally used, how they appear in use, a short explanation of what they do, and an approximation of their cost. Furthermore, the tools will be listed in a rather loose sequence of events, such as those we used in disassembly and reassembly, and those used in the actual refurbishing operation. So let's have at it!

We'll begin by assuming that all the power-driven accessories, wires, ignition, water pump, hoses, radiator, intake and exhaust manifolds, etc., have been removed from your trusty mill and are presently residing on your workbench. Your head(s) are ready to be snatched. We hate to say it, but the only economical way to get those miserable things off is to remove those cursedly-tight and crusty head bolts with muscle power. Most of us backyard mechanics will have to settle for a breaker bar, a short extension, and the proper set of sockets. Breaker bars can be bought in a "sky's-the-limit" variety of sizes and prices. But for now, the heck with busting a knuckle and working up a sweat. Remember, we have a fistful of the long green, so it's off to

the local tool supplier we go to find a sweat-saving impact wrench. They come in two basic styles: electric and air. In that most of us don't have ready access to a complete air compressor system, the electric wrench is the way to go. Nonetheless, for the sake of accuracy, we'll bring in tools that are air-operated. Depending upon the features and the amount of accessories in the package, common electric wrench kits can be bought for just under $100. Air wrenches, on the other hand, come a little dearer. In fact, if you want to impress your friends, there is a handy item made by Black & Decker with a one-inch drive that sells for a cool $550, real handy for 20-in. truck wheel lugs. However, don't let that figure scare you. Most quality air wrenches sell in the neighborhood of $150 to $200. Depending on what you have bought, it's either grunt,—phew!, whirrrrrr, ratttttttt or bweeeeepppppp with the head bolts ending up in a handy bucket. Now it's off with your head(s)!

HEAD HOLDERS

The distance from your car to workbench—assuming you use a bench and not the garage floor or the great out-of-doors, and have given the head(s) a nudge with a pry bar (costing about five bucks) to break the seal—will determine the amount of energy you'll expend toting this

mass of iron over to the workbench. After catching your breath, lift the heads onto the holders. Head holders are handy gizmos to have around; they keep that object of your attention rock steady. If you want to save a few pesos, these things are quite simple to make. Just visualize an elongated "U" which acts as its legs, with a vertical tapered metal dowel, bolted to the inverted "U" and offset enough to provide proper balance. Take two of these and place them at the ends of the heads, inserted into any one of the innumerable water

1. If the rocker arms are new, you can set valve lash accurately with a feeler gauge (left). But a feeler gauge bridges across the hollow worn into rocker arms by the valve stem. For super accuracy setting the valves with a P&G valve gapper is the plan.

2. Setting the valves on a 427-cu.-in. Ford cammer is a real hassle. Valves must be set at a specific crank angle and with a specified lift on the cam.

3. A vernier caliper with integral dial indicator is an accurate instrument for taking inside or outside measurements.

4. Valve spring tester is used to measure the converting of required spring pressure into installed height. At an installed height of 1⅞ ins., the desired 240 lbs. of seat pressure is achieved.

5. Valve guides in flathead Ford V-8's can be tough to remove, but that C-clamp will really do the job. The large tool on the right is used with a hammer to remove the horseshoe guide retainer, but it ruins the retainer. If you want to reuse the retainer, one of the two guide drivers will move the guide down far enough so the horseshoe can be slipped out.

jacket passages. The combustion chamber and valves will be facing up, and also, it will make working on the head a much more pleasurable experience. If, however, you're not the fabricatin' type, you can buy this pin-type head holder for under $10.

With the head safely in place, the head gasket will just sort of fall off; if it doesn't, prepare to start scraping. You can use anything from a cold chisel to a razor so long as it has a sharp edge. But for illustrative purposes we went and got ourselves a gasket-stripping tool and paid about $2. With the head surface free from old gasket dregs, we'll move in (again assuming you've got a multi-dollar set of end wrenches) and remove the bolts holding the rocker arms, etc.

VALVE SPRING COMPRESSORS

After completing this simple operation we're ready to pull upon the valves. Here is a world all its own. When it comes to valve spring compressors—be they for that rare antique's 400-cu.-in. 4-banger, a 1-lung industrial wheezer, a standard Detroit-built 8, or an exotic one-of-a-kind racing mill—there seems to be a valve spring compressor especially designed for it.

Valve spring compressors do just what their name implies. They compress the valve springs so you can remove the valve keepers from the stem of the valve. With the keepers out of there it is a simple matter to slide the retainers and springs up and away from the valve. Probably the most common valve spring compressor is the C-type which, according to one manufacturer, is used on 85% of

today's cars. Although these come in many subtle forms, depending on engine type, they can be purchased only as a hand or air-operated tool, not electric.

Another type of valve spring compressor is a scissor-type, designed for hard-to-reach areas found in old flat-head 6- and 4-cyl. Fords, Chryslers, Hudsons, etc. A third type of valve spring compressor is what is known as a bar type, and as the name says, that's what it looks like. The bar type is nothing more than a flat handle at one end and a properly configured shape so as to fit over the valve spring and retainer at the other. It acts strictly as a lever in depressing

2

3

4

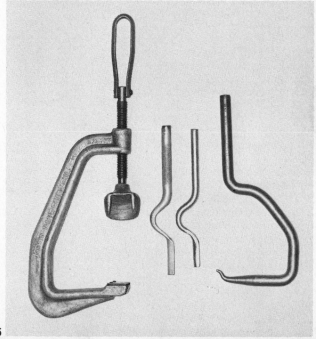

5

Valve Service Tools

the valve spring, and is used most of the time on flathead Ford V-8's. Anyway, you can figure on spending from $8 to $16 for the manual-operated C-type valve spring compressor, $6 to $12 for the scissor-type, and $2 to $5 for the bar type.

Now for a word to the wise. You know what your financial situation is and the car on which this tool is going to be used. So when you drop in on your local friendly tool supplier give him the details and, more than likely, he'll sell you the proper valve spring compressor. None of them is overly expensive, but if we save a little here, we can afford that more expensive jazz we'll be talking about later on.

While we're at it—that is, while we've got the valve spring compressed—out comes the valve keeper inserters. These resemble a narrow pair of pliers and are used to remove or replace the valve keepers. They all look about the same but you can buy ones that have the nose magnetized. Standard valve keeper inserters sell for around $3, while the magnetized ones go for $4. Oh yes, if you have an old Ford V-8, you'll need a bar-type valve spring lifter, in conjunction with a valve guide driver. The spring lifter raises the valve for insertion of the driver, then a big hammer drives the guide down so you can remove the keepers. Together, they cost approximately $8.50. Hopefully, we've now reached a position where your cylinder head or block is completely stripped of its valves and ready for hand-cleaning or hot-tanking.

It's a thing of beauty and cleaner than a whistle. But is your head true, and do all the chambers have the same cc's? For the sake of presenting a point, let's say we've got some warpage and need a little milling action. Milling is important only in that you want the surfaces of the head and block to make good contact, insuring a proper seal, while cc'ing is merely a check to see if the combustion chambers are all the same in size. We suppose you could buy a milling machine, but they take up quite a bit of space and cost by the pound—pounds of dollar bills, that is. Anyway, figure this is one operation best left to a machine shop. We can, though, get into making sure that the combustion chambers are pretty much the same size. Just how one does this is covered elsewhere in this book, but suffice to say, you'll need a calibrated graduate with a spigot, some sort of heavy liquid, a piece of plastic—and about $40 to buy them. Okay, we're through cc'ing the cham-

bers so it's on to some serious cleaning of the head and valve port area— and don't forget that anti-rust compound; you've got some fresh metal just itching to give you trouble.

HIGH SPEED DRILL

First of all, we'll start by refraining from using any elbow grease and steel wool, and in turn whip out our trusty high-speed electric drill. If you don't have one of these, prices start from $15 and end up somewhere in the neighborhood of $75. You can also seek out an air drill which gives you more power, but unless you are privy to an air compressor, forget it. Attached to the drill motor should be one of a series of carbon brushes, each one shaped correspondingly to fit the various surfaces you'll be needing to clean. Brushes come in two forms: one to be used on aluminum, the other on iron. Expect to pay, again depending on style and

form, from $1.50 to $2. Blacky Carbon raises the devil in the combustion chamber so do a thorough job in getting rid of him. While at it, give your valve guides a thrice-over with a two-dollar valve guide brush.

BENCH GRINDER

Let's now switch to the valves, assuming the head itself is free of all carbon and oil deposits and ready for machine work, and set to with our bench grinder equipped with a stiff wire wheel. For ease of keeping track of what valve needs what, it's nice to have a valve holder. You can pick up a yard stick at your friendly local parts house with the proper number and size of holes to hold the valves or you can go out and buy a metal tray-like holder for about $4. However, when you get down to the nitty-gritty and start shelling out for a bench grinder, you're making a lifetime investment, so don't expect to

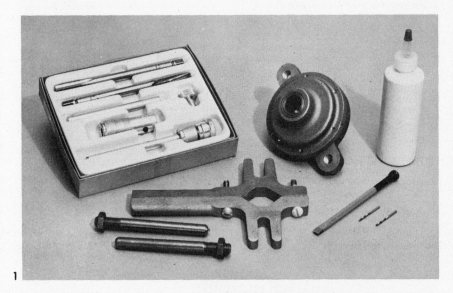

1

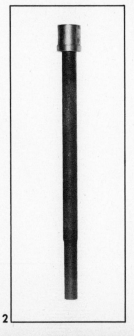

2

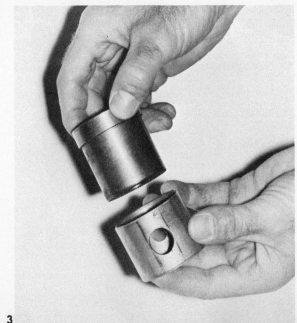

3

pay anything less than $50. If you want to play the Scrooge role, you can go back to your drill, tie it down in the vice, put a brush on and turn your handy-dandy drill motor into a bench grinder.

After all the carbon is removed from the valves and those burned areas and cracks begin to wink you in the eye, your only course of action is to lower the afflicted parts gently in the ash can and cough up some money for some new ones. However, if no knicks or cracks appear, all we have to do is trot over to what is affectionately known as a valve grinding workshop and begin to do our thing. When we say valve workshop that's what we mean. For here is a rather impressive piece of machinery, and we're not trying to sound like a commercial. The valve machine grinds your valves, trues and chamfers your valve stem ends, refaces your rocker arms (unless you use the

1. Manley bushing kit includes all necessary tools to install bronze wall valve guide bushings: speed reducer, drills, chisel, reamer oil.

2. Cam bearing tools are merely long rods with specific diameter heads attached to one end, which either insert or extract the bearings.

3. Collar on the head keeps the bearing from slipping during its removal or replacement.

4. Every serious mechanic should include an assortment of feeler gauges in his tool box. An inside/outside vernier caliper is a luxury, but it's a must for accurate measurements.

5. The head should provide a snug fit around the cam bearing, yet be loose enough so it can be extracted without taking the bearing with it.

6. The prime feature of this particular cam bearing tool is its versatility. With so many diameters found in cam bearings, a mechanic might have to stock 60 different heads, but with this tool he need only have a few.

stampout models popularized by Chevrolet), and squares off your tappets. Any precision machine that can do all of this is far from inexpensive, so any person who doesn't plan to make a living as a mechanic had better forget about buying this costly piece of merchandise. However, if you have a very rich uncle just chomping at the bit to turn you on to a valve grinding workshop as a small birthday present, tell him to expect to shell out a minimum of $500.

KNURLERS

Although we're tempted at this point to get into the tools needed in the refacing of valve seats, we've been reminded that the valve guides should receive a good going over prior to getting into the valve seats themselves. You'll remember we've cleaned the guides with a nylon brush, but it has become apparent that the guides have suffered to the point of needing a little work. When the guides are out of sorts, the valve rocks, causing undue wear on the seat and allowing oil into the combustion chamber. To correct this situation we must turn to a valve guide "knurler." Knurlers don't remove any metal but rather roll a "thread" pattern into the valve guide which brings it back to size. Many valve guide

knurler sets are available from a host of tool suppliers or parts houses and are used in conjunction with a low-speed drill. Low-speed drills can cost around $30 so this might be the place to discuss the economical aspects of purchasing a two-speed drill. A good high-speed drill can run upwards of $50. Buy them separately and you'll be plunking down a quick $80. On the other hand, maybe buying a heavy-duty two-speed drill for $60 is the way to go. Whatever you do, we still need something to drive the valve guide knurler, which is cheap compared to the drill. The knurler kit sells for $20.

In the event your valve guides are in a state of complete anarchy, you can install a set of bronze replacements, which will insure greater longevity in valve life. If you were to do this professionally, you would need a complete set of taps, bits, drills, a motor and speed-reducer, lubricating oil, brushes, carrying case, and hones. This kit can cost up to $225. However, if you want to do it yourself, there are inexpensive drill attachments, including hones, taps, and pilots for less than $20.

For those who are still stroking along with a flathead and want to replace valve guide retainers, you can get a box of one hundred for the bar-

4

5

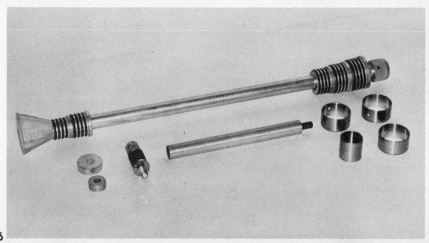

6

Valve Service Tools

gain price of $3. Nonetheless, the guides should have received the full treatment, whatever that is, so we can now get into the fun area of tools for grinding your valve seats.

Approach with gusto the challenge of refacing your valve seats, because we're going to turn ourselves onto a load of tools that can literally reach out of sight. However, we could begin by completely removing the valve seat inserts with a device like a tire iron and a large hammer, which then extracts the hard seat like popping out a man-hole cover. This operation, though, becomes a machine shop specialty because the new valve seats must be frozen in dry ice and then press-fitted into the combustion chamber. We'll allow that this can be done if needed, but for our purpose, we'll suppose the valve seat inserts are not so worn or damaged as to necessitate their removal.

HARD SEAT GRINDING SET

As a start, a rather large metal box full of delightful objects, called a hard seat grinding set, must be bought. This box is filled with things like a heavy-duty driver, a heavy-duty valve stone dressing stand, a ball bearing stone sleeve, heavy-duty carbon removing brushes, a side flair carbon removing brush, valve guide cleaners, various self-centering pilot shafts along with a pilot turning wrench, a load of valve seat grinding stones of 30- and 40-degree angles, a nifty valve seat stone and pilot handbook— and let us not forget a heavy-duty carrying case. By the way, these handbooks are unbelievable. There is a pilot shaft and a stone listed for every conceivable internal combustion engine ever built.

Getting back to reality, these sets can cost you up to $300, but fret not, a volume deal can be had for a trifling $175. But no matter how you look at it, it's down right expensive to make those valves and seats match up correctly. After getting through with the basic grinding operation we can check our work by making a low pass over the valve seats with a $60 valve seat indicator which measures concentricity. That step is usually not necessary, because seat grinders are accurate. If everything seems to be copacetic, we can begin lapping the valves. Valve lapping is controversial, but we won't join the argument here.

If you want to do it, all it takes is a pinch of compound—first medium, then fine, a buck or so a tube—and a funny little dowel-like hand-operated gizmo with a suction cup on one end. The suction cup, like a plumber's friend, grabs hold of the valve head while you spin the other end between your hands. The fun thing about this tool is its cost, a miserly $2.

REASSEMBLY

So there we have it—hopefully the head surface, valves, valve seats, combustion chamber, guides, etc., have received a thorough treatment, and we can now be thinking of bolting the whole shebang back in one piece.

Naturally when we get into a reverse sequence of tool selection and use, things can get a little dull—like we've seen it before—so to keep things moving on an even keel, it stands to reason that the tools we used to disassemble the head are the same ones we'll need to reassemble it. This is true except in one area; that is, first we had better check and recheck all our various operations with a fistful of instruments to make sure ours is an accurate job. Al-

though we've discussed a valve seat indicator at $60, we should also mention calipers, $15; telescoping gauges, $20; dial indicators, $30; valve spring testers, $120; feeler gauges, $2 to $3; *ad infinitum*. Calipers are used in measuring valve seat width, while dial indicators are a must on a whole series of cam setting operations which are covered in detail elsewhere in this book. To proceed further, telescoping gauges are handy for determining proper valve springing, and valve spring testers are necessary for checking the tension of your valve springs. Finally, a set of feeler gauges is vital for setting proper valve lash. Obviously when it comes to mechanic's hand measuring tools and precision instruments, there is no end with which you can walk out the door.

The heads are now assembled to a point where they need only be bolted to the block, pushrods inserted, and rockers attached to their respective stands. However, because this book also deals with cams, we should now turn our attention to the removal and

1

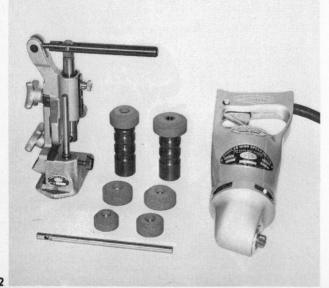

2

3

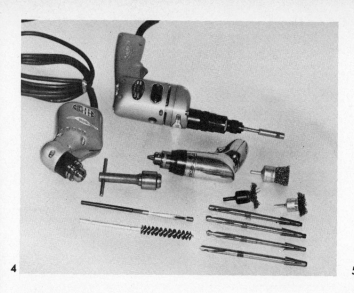

4

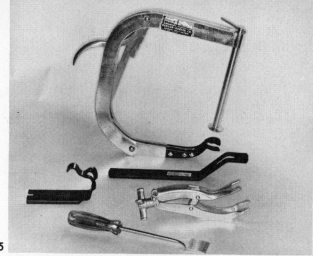

5

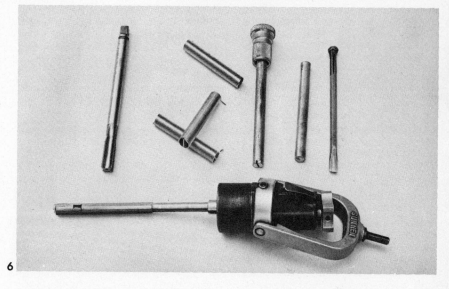

6

reinstallation of what has been termed the heart of the engine. Whether you plan to use a reground camshaft or just replace your worn stick, many of the same tools and just as much care must be used in performing this task.

We assume you have taken off the cam timing chain and timing gear from the front of the cam and crank with whatever tools are necessary for their removal—be it an end-wrench, wheel puller, or socket screw keys. With a bare block staring you in the face and the heads, pushrods, and lifters setting peacefully on the workbench, it is but a simple matter to pull the camshaft gently out of the

1. A closeup of a dressing stand shows how the proper degree is given to the hard seat grinding stone.

2. Found in a typical hard seat grinder kit is a high-speed driver motor, a stone dressing stand, stone sleeves.

3. Truing up the valve stem end is another important duty in the restoration of your valves.

4. High-speed drills and differently shaped carbon removing brushes come in handy for getting rid of Blacky Carbon from the combustion chamber and ports. Pilot shafts in the foreground are of the universal type, which are inserted in the valve guide by that T-handled affair called a pilot turning wrench. The other tools are valve guide cleaners.

5. Spring compressors come in an unending variety to fit various engines. Represented are the three basic types. The scissor type is just behind the gasket stripper, while the bar type is in front of what is known as the C-type.

6. If worn valve guides are giving you grief, this equipment will put your engine back in shape. Shown (left to right) are a reverse pilot tap, bronze guides, ball broach, and chisel. The hone (bottom) is run through the bushings to bring the bores out to the desired clearance.

block and put it in a safe place, to send or deliver to a cam-grinder as a core, or if its condition warrants, to lower it quickly into the round file.

We now attack gently the old and pitted cam bearings with our trusty universal cam bearing tool, priced at a measly $85, that is said to fit most any under- or over-sized cam bearings. If this particular tool is a mite high for your tastes, you can find yourself a bar with a proper head that can do the same job of removing and replacing cam bearings at much less initial expense. The universal feature, though, saves time and expense of having to keep a bunch of different cam bearing heads lying around just itching to be used.

Out with the old and in with the new—bearings, that is—so it's time to install your new cam. Again the proper way to install a camshaft is discussed in length in another chapter, but don't forget to scare up a tube of cam lube, at a cost of less than a dollar, as it will insure against galling your new cam should there be a dry start or if the oil breaks down between the lifter and the cam lobe.

It is strongly recommended that you have at your disposal a good degree wheel. Any of your local speed shops or cam-grinder carries this indispensable item. Plan to spend a few dollars, possibly five, for a good one, but the investment is well worth it. Nothing is sicker than an engine out of time.

Now where were we...? Oh yes, we've got a cam installed and degreed in, lifters cleaned or replaced and nestling next to the cam lobe, and pushrods ready to be inserted just as soon as we're able to put that heavy piece of iron filled with valves and things back on the engine. Don't forget sealing compound or an aerosol can of aluminum paint (maybe $2) to really make the head gasket stick to the head and block. With the head and gasket stuck on the block, the head bolts await the action of a torque wrench. Torque wrenches come in a zillion sizes, styles, and prices. A good one will run $35.

So there it is, ready for action—and you thought that you would never finish—or at least not as quickly. 👑

Engine Breathing

You can't redesign your whole engine, but improving its breathing capabilities can bring you the performance rewards you're seeking.

When the hot rodder decides it's time to pay some attention to cams, valves, and exhaust systems, he sets out to find out something about them. He begins a quest that can become a maze of dead-end streets and unanswerable questions. A visit to the local drag strip will reveal as many theories as there are cars. Some have long intake systems and short pipes; some have short intakes and long exhausts; others will have various combinations of both. In fact, so many exist that one might wonder if anybody really knows what works best. The truth is, they *all* might be best, because all engines, even two of the same make and model, have individual characteristics that must be catered to if they are to perform to their maximum. These characteristics can even vary from cylinder to cylinder, making individual attention a must when considering modifications for improved performance. A V-8 is really nothing more than eight single-cylinder engines with a common crankshaft and, in many cases, common intake and exhaust manifolds. Understanding the characteristics of your particular type of engine, and the theories that make

it so, is the first giant step toward improving performance.

The camshaft, which starts things happening in the first place, has a definite relationship to the tuning of both the intake and exhaust system. The opening of the intake valve allows the air to begin moving in the port, and how long it stays open determines the amount of mixture that can enter the cylinder. There is an overlap period during which the intake valve is opening while the exhaust has not yet fully closed. Burnt gases rushing out of the exhaust port can greatly assist the initial movement of the column of air in the intake port behind the opening valve, and once the column enters the cylinder it reciprocates by sending some of its cool charge past the exhaust valve with the outgoing charge and cooling the valve in the process. The length, shape, and diameter of the exhaust system—as well as the camshaft timing and the rpm of the engine—determine the amount of assist that is given to the incoming charge.

If an engine has an inefficient exhaust system, in that it is too small or shaped in such a way as to restrict

the flow of gases, the best intake system in the world will become useless. The intake system may be capable of excellent cylinder filling, but whatever it delivers to the cylinder must eventually go out the exhaust system. A restricted exhaust will cause the column of air in the intake port to back up to a point where whatever efficiency exists is cancelled out by the inability of the exhaust system to help draw it in. It is just like following a truck and trailer up a steep grade. Your car may be quite capable of passing, but the truck is blocking the whole road and setting the pace for all of those following.

Tests have shown this to be the case with many engines. Once the exhaust system is enlarged to a point where it can both handle large quantities of gas, and provide scavenge enough to draw in the incoming charge, performance increases can be achieved without any attention to the intake side. It is as though the truck and trailer suddenly becomes an Indy car and not only clears the road, but pulls your car along in its slipstream. However, if the speed differential is so great that your car cannot stay in the slipstream, you will revert to the speed that your car, by itself, can achieve.

So it is with engine efficiency. There must be a definite relationship between the capabilities of the exhaust and the intake. If the exhaust is

1

1. The full-race engine breathes so hard it's almost hyperventilating, but the whys and hows of breathing are applicable to any engine.

2. The modern engine is really like a sophisticated air pump. How well the intake side of the pump can fill the combustion chambers, and how the exhaust system empties them, controls how efficient and powerful it is.

3. Increasing valve lift or duration allows an increased flow of gases to feed the combustion chamber, but only up to the point at which your intake system becomes inefficient.

4. The modified exhaust ports (below) have been rounded to keep the shape of the passages the same from valve to exhaust pipe, plus enlarged and smoothed out for better flow.

5. Comparison of the cam timing of a basic 440-in. engine with a high-performance version shows how longer duration and more valve overlap have increased the engine's horsepower.

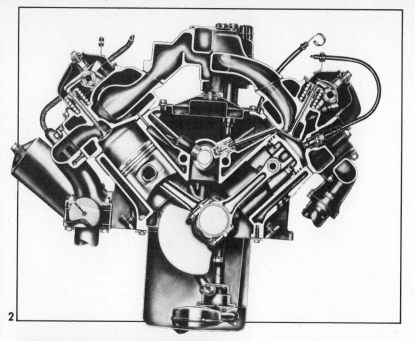

2

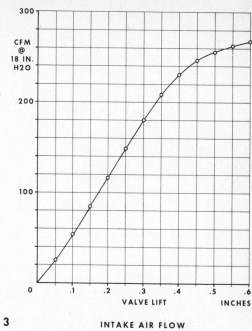

3

INTAKE AIR FLOW

4

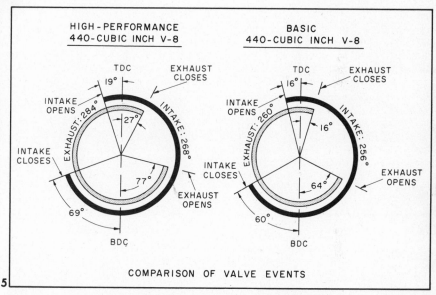

5

COMPARISON OF VALVE EVENTS

brought up to a level that increases the performance, then the intake must be improved until the exhaust again restricts the performance. More work on the exhaust until things get better, and then back to the intake. There are, of course, variables that will have to be considered, but the basic balance of the two systems has a definite effect on performance.

The exhaust will assist the incoming charge only if it is open at the most opportune time and closed as soon as the speed of the incoming charge reaches the point where the exhaust is no longer helping. By that time the cool incoming charge that escapes out the exhaust has done its job in helping to cool the exhaust valve and any delay in closing off the exhaust port will cause a loss of the charge already in the cylinder.

All of us have seen high-performance engines stumble and stutter at low speed and suddenly come alive and run smoothly once a certain rpm is reached. This can be a product of the overlap period due to the fact that all phases of the phenomenon are not in harmony until gas and wave velocities reach their functioning speed in the particular intake/exhaust design. Mechanically, the functions never change in relation to one another—it is just that the particular setting works only when the speeds within the intake and exhaust system reach the pre-determined level.

The opening of the inlet valve before TDC when the exhaust valve is still open actually provides a clear, relatively unobstructed passage from the carburetor intake to the end of the exhaust system. The piston has not yet started to draw in fuel since it is still trying to exhaust the burnt gases of the previous power stroke, so it is quite conceivable that a per-

centage of the charge drawn into the combustion chamber by the escaping exhaust gases is lost out the exhaust port. The advantage of this overlap period is then reduced to its ability to accelerate the column of air in the intake port prior to the major suction period that will occur once the piston passes over TDC and begins the intake stroke. Since the greatest suction will occur during the first half of the intake stroke—due to the greater acceleration of the piston during the first 90 degrees of crankshaft rotation—any assist in getting the column started will help fill the cylinder.

Once the piston passes the halfway mark on the downstroke it begins to slow down with a resultant reduction in suction. Providing that the column of air has been accelerated quickly enough by the exhaust depression, and then by the downward stroke of the piston, its inertia

Engine Breathing

and any ramming effect built into the intake system should keep it going in spite of the reduced effectiveness of the piston. Were it not for the assist of this inertia and varying degrees of ram, the intake valve could be closed shortly before the piston reaches BDC with no appreciable effect on performance. In fact, the reverse of this is shown by the long cam timings (time the valve is off the seat) that are common to racing engines taking full advantage of the free assist available.

Since all horsepower is developed above the piston, the shape and location of the many components in the cylinder head become very important. It is impractical to think that any major design changes can be made by the individual, but improvements to the design, dictated as much by manufacturing convenience as by performance potential, can and are being done every day.

The intake port, and the exhaust too, must share the available space within the cylinder head with other essential components. It must often wind around cast-in bosses that are necessary to support rocker shafts; there will be cavities incorporated for the pushrods, unless of course the engine is of the overhead cam type; water jackets occupy as much space as possible; and in addition, the location of the intake end of the intake and the exhaust end of the exhaust must be situated in such a way that the manifolds locate conveniently and keep underhood dimension within reason.

Once the location of the port is decided upon, there will still be additional restrictions incorporated within the port itself. There must be a valve and a guide for the valve that will invariably be long enough that it hangs down in the port. Some valve guides can be shortened to favor the flow of the column of air, but others would sacrifice control of the valve on the seat and lose by valve leakage what was gained by reducing the port restriction. In addition to this, valve timing limitations exist in all types of engines, with the possible exception of the Flathead's side valve, which is all but obsolete in any case.

Cylinder heads with hemispherical combustion chambers have the valve opening and closing limited by the fact that both the intake and exhaust must be open at the same time during the overlap period, and both share a common area when open. Therefore, the timing must be set at a point that provides clearance between the two valves and the piston, if mechanical reliability is to be retained.

Inline-valve cylinder heads avoid the problem of valves colliding since in most types the valves are parallel and remain the same distance apart whether open or closed. However, they are limited in both lift and duration if they are to stay clear of the head of the piston as it reaches TDC. In both types the cam design is dictated by the need for mechanical reliability, at the expense of the ideal.

Side valves have none of the limitations of overheads when it comes to optimum cam design, although other

VALVE COOLING

CONVENTIONAL DESIGN　　　**NEW 351-4V DESIGN**

1

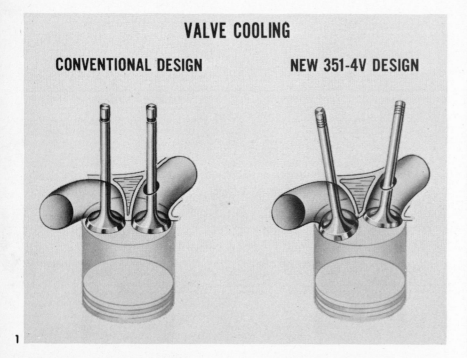

2

3

factors offset this advantage. The valves, being off to the side of the combustion chamber and in no way conflicting with piston travel, are not in any danger of striking each other or the piston and therefore can be opened and closed at any time, and remain open as long as deemed necessary.

INTAKE PORTS

The intake port of any engine is nothing more than a tube, closed on one end by the intake valve, necked down to a venturi at the approximate center of the carburetor, and open to atmosphere at the carburetor intake. There is some form of adjustable throttle valve obstructing this tube in order to supply varying amounts of air, but for our purpose we will consider this valve to be fully open, as at full throttle, so that the port has a minimum of obstruction to the airflow.

Within the port there is air of identical volume to the port itself. This air has weight and is therefore subject to the law of inertia which states that, "a body at rest will tend to remain at rest, and a body in motion will tend to remain in motion unless acted upon by an outside force." This inertia must be overcome by an "outside force" in order to get the column of air into the cylinder, and once overcome, can be used to assure that adequate velocity continues filling the cylinder once the cause of the initial movement has ceased.

In very early internal combustion engines an automatic intake valve was used, and its function gives an indication of the suction pressures present within the cylinder. The valve was held on the valve seat by a very light spring and had no actuating mechanism whatsoever. As the piston passed over TDC and started down on the intake stroke, the suction it

1. Inclined valves allow a smoother gas routing, and run cooler because of more combustion chamber wall and head material between them. However, there is more chance of the valves colliding during the overlap phase if the cam timing is not just right.

2. Exhaust ports have their built-in restrictions, such as the valve stem and the angle of the port.

3. Some flow restrictions in heads can't be eliminated, merely improved. On the intake side, the valve stem and head boss get in the way.

4. Increases in both carburetion and valve lift can boost power and torque and extend the engine's rpm range.

5. A separate tube for each cylinder is a must for high performance. A set of steel tubing headers such as these can add horsepower, increase mileage, and reduce weight over stock by 30 lbs.

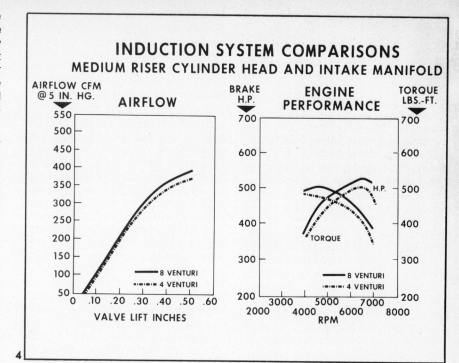

INDUCTION SYSTEM COMPARISONS
MEDIUM RISER CYLINDER HEAD AND INTAKE MANIFOLD

AIRFLOW CFM @ 5 IN. HG.

AIRFLOW

VALVE LIFT INCHES

8 VENTURI
4 VENTURI

BRAKE H.P.

ENGINE PERFORMANCE

TORQUE LBS.-FT.

H.P.

TORQUE

RPM

8 VENTURI
4 VENTURI

4

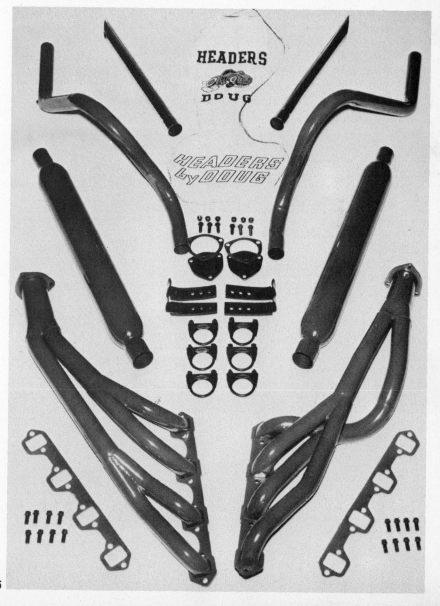

5

Engine Breathing

created opened the valve and allowed the charge to enter the cylinder. How soon after TDC the valve opened was controlled by the strength of the spring and the speed at which the engine was turning. At low speed there is a difference in suction and consequently the valve would not open at the same time as it would when engine speed was increased. It was actually a variable valve timing that would provide desirable duration for both low and high speed but, unfortunately, the time of the intake opening for both ends of the scale was too late for good performance. Valve closing was taken care of by the change in pressure created as the piston came up on the compression stroke, and was again dependent upon the strength of the spring and the speed of the engine.

When it became obvious that improved performance would require positive control of the opening and closing of the valve, the lessons learned by use of an automatic valve were put to good use. The intake opening was given enough of a lead over the suction of the piston to assure that the valve would be open far enough to supply the maximum amount of charge when the piston suction began. From these early findings the present day intake systems incorporate even more assists in the form of the earlier opening intake and the later closing exhaust.

The "outside force" that starts the column in motion is the low pressure area in the port that is caused by opening the intake valve and connecting the port to the cylinder. Quite often, the term suction will be used; however, the charge is actually being pushed into the cylinder by atmospheric pressure, which is higher than the pressure within the cylinder. At the actual time of opening, the lower pressure within the cylinder is caused by the rush of exhaust gases still going out of the open exhaust valve. The piston is still coming up on the exhaust stroke and is only assisting the pressure drop because the exhaust valve is open. Were it to be closed, the piston would increase the pressure in the intake port to something more than atmospheric, and the mixture in the port would be forced back out the intake system, through the carburetor intake, and into the atmosphere.

At the time the piston passes over TDC, the exhaust valve is getting closer to its seat with a resultant decrease in the exhaust column pressure. Fortunately, the piston now takes over and as it moves down toward BDC, decreases the pressure even more. This continues to increase the relative pressure of the atmosphere outside the cylinder and the flow of incoming gases continues. The exhaust valve must close at this time to minimize the loss of the incoming charge out the exhaust port.

FLOW TESTING

Unless you are loaded with enough dough to be able to sacrifice many sets of heads to the trial and error method, a flow tester is the only way the ports themselves can be changed for the better. It too, can get expensive, but it will tell you much that you want to know when it comes to getting more air on the combustion chamber side of the intake valve.

Flow testing devices have been around for a long time. Although complex looking, they are relatively simple. By means of a suction device, not unlike the household vacuum cleaner, they create vacuum in a tube that is then attached to the combustion chamber of a cylinder head.

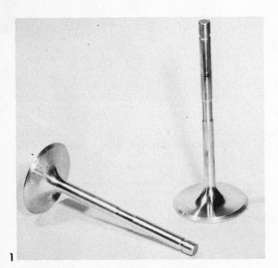

1

2

3

The vacuum in the tube simulates the vacuum created by the pressure drop in the cylinder during the intake stroke of the piston, and draws air through the intake port. By controlling the amount of vacuum, and then measuring the amount of air drawn through the intake port, an arbitrary factor can be established. Modifications to the port that allow it to pass more air are increasing the flow. Not surprisingly, improvements on the flow tester usually show up as horsepower improvements on the dynamometer.

Before we tackle the job of designing or redesigning an intake port, it will be helpful to look at some of the known behavior patterns of air. Examples of its behavior are all around us, and although they may not be directly applicable to automobile use, they do show a consistency that can be expected to continue when the same air is used in a different situation.

Aircraft designers rely on the consistent behavior of air to get aircraft off the ground and then control them once they are airborne. By the use of airfoils they control the location and amount of high and low pressure areas in order to get the air to do work. As the air passes over the airfoil, or wings, the shape causes a decrease in pressure over the top, and an increase in pressure on the bottom. This difference in pressure then lifts the wing, and hence the aircraft.

In an intake port of an engine the ideal is the elimination of the opposing pressure areas in order that the whole area of the port is guiding the column of air into the cylinder. The pressures involved in the aircraft application are relatively low compared to the intake port but nevertheless air travelling at approximately 175 mph will lift a 125-ton Boeing 707. Actually, the air is not travelling—the aircraft is—but the speed over the wing that is creating the pressure variable is

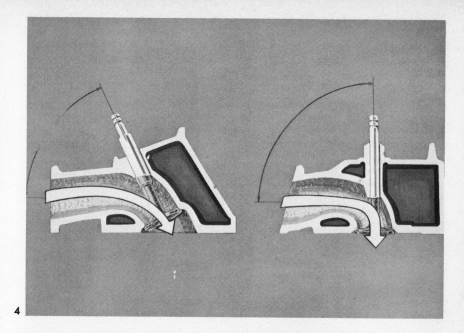

4

1. These valves, reworked for racing, have been highly polished and reshaped to reduce friction with the columns of gases.

2. Using longer duration and higher lift cams may necessitate installing special pistons, with depressions or "eyebrows" cut in to clear the valves.

3. Larger valves can increase flow, but the shape of the valves can also have an effect on the amount of air that can be inducted into the cylinder.

4. More and more engines today are using inclined valves to reduce bends and restrictions in the ports.

5. The supercharger is nicknamed the "lung" because it provides one of the most dramatic increases in an engine's breathing and power output.

5

Engine Breathing

still approximately 175 mph. What about this same air, travelling at four times the speed, when it must change direction to go around valve guides, valve stems, and the valve head itself? Not to mention any curvatures in the port that could very likely take a similar shape to the wing of an aircraft with similar pressure changing results. In aircraft use it is a known fact that by doubling the speed of the air (or wing through the air), the pressure-created lift is four times as great.

When these pressures exert lift on the wing, the aircraft moves in the direction that the pressure dictates and the flow continues. In the port of an engine the air cannot move the port and therefore the flow is disturbed and turbulence is created. Elimination of this turbulence with a port that controls the air without creating either high or low pressure areas will invariably show improvements in horsepower. With these known facts about the behavior of air, the flow tester then becomes a device for improving internal aerodynamics.

The cylinder head being tested is first evaluated in standard form and the amount of flow measured with the intake valve at various lifts of the standard camshaft. This is accomplished by installing both the intake and exhaust valves with very light springs and a calibrated screw adjuster to open the intake valve. The flow can be checked at any amount of lift from zero through maximum.

Once the port has been checked through—and even beyond—maximum lift, the valve should be inserted upside down in the guide so that only the stem protrudes into the port. Another test can then be made to determine how much restriction is caused by the valve head itself. Quite often an improved valve shape can be responsible for a 20% increase in flow with no attention to the port. Other valve shapes sometimes flow very well at cam lifts beyond the maximum lift of the particular grind, and in this case either a valve to suit the lift or a lift to suit the valve must be considered before further testing.

The required horsepower range of the particular engine must also be considered so that the flow is not confined to a lift range that would make it unusable. Extensive testing and modifications can provide the best flow only if cam lift rates and maximum lift are known prior to testing. Substitution of another camshaft after the port has been modified can very easily cancel out any horsepower gains that were made with the original camshaft. In many, many cases the valve can be shaped to offer no more restriction than the port without a valve. In these cases all attention can then be focused on the port itself.

One of the controversial features of a flow tester is the fact that it is not simulating the vibrations and heat that are present in a running engine. However, the port can, in many cases, be reshaped with clay and tested without the permanency of filling and grinding. Then too, it can be done to only one of the ports, where a running test would require that all ports be modified. The amount of time saved in man-hours is tremendous when you consider the number of different shapes that can be tried, then accepted or rejected.

Before reshaping, the points at which any pressure areas exist can be determined by the use of a pitot tube. This is a device that is used on aircraft to measure the speed of the air passing over the wings, and can be adapted to the port since it measures high and low pressure areas and where they exist. It is hand-held and moved around in the port as the air is drawn through the intake valve. Pressure differences that are found can be eliminated by reshaping the clay

1

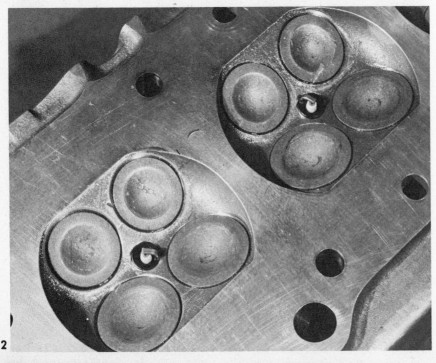

2

and retesting. Often this will develop another area, and the clay is again used to eliminate it.

Obviously, the clay is filling areas to improve things, so some permanent filling will be needed when the port is working as well as it can. In some cases, the clay only indicates a desired shape, and removal of material to conform to that shape will improve things. This removal of material may even be from the other side of the port. In all cases, thorough testing of many shapes will be necessary since it is quite possible that only a small amount of work will be required to accomplish what at first seemed to be a job that would require the removal or addition of a lot of material.

When a series of flow tests show a particular shape to pass a larger quantity of air, it is wise to reconsider what has been tested. The flow tester has only shown the shape and diameter of the port, and the cam opening rate and maximum lift that work on the particular head. It has not given any indication of the total length of the intake system. The passage of the air (which is, after all, a fluid) is directly affected by the shape and volume of the port. The length of the entire system will only determine the assist given by the pressure waves travelling back and forth to the intake valve.

Once the column of air has passed the intake valve and is in the cylinder, there are additional factors that must be considered since, in intake testing, the flow tester measures air through the restriction of the port and intake valve only; it does not include the physical presence of an exhaust valve that is opening and closing or a piston that is going up and down.

In many engines with hemispherical combustion chambers, the head of the piston can actually block the flow as it reaches TDC. We have seen how the late-closing exhaust assists the incoming column of air by using the low pressure that the escaping

gases create to draw in the new charge. If the valves are inclined in the head at steep angles, the top of the piston can cut off this flow and stop the assist. In addition, steeply inclined valves limit the effective area of the intake since when the exhaust closes, and the intake opens further, it will get very close to the exhaust valve head which will restrict the opening. Factors such as these are difficult to determine on a flow tester, and cannot, for structural reasons, be changed in the engine. Fortunately, most modern engines are constructed

with this in mind, and the valves' inclination and combustion chamber shape are designed accordingly.

It was stated earlier that at certain times there is an unobstructed path from the intake of the carburetor to end of the tailpipe. Further, it was pointed out that a restricted exhaust can offset any advantage gained by a free-flowing intake system. With this in mind, the flow tester can be used to improve the efficiency of the exhaust port. Successful improvements will help the breathing of the intake as well as make it easier to get rid of

3

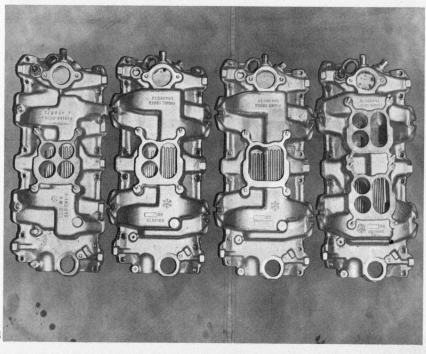
4

1. Using multiple valves offers some advantages such as more valve area and reduced valve train weight, but there are problems in port routing, and cost is high in manufacturing and design.

2. The valves of the 4-valve Cosworth Vega head are canted 20° from the vertical for a straighter flow of gases.

3. 2 hp per cubic inch results from Weslake 4-valve conversion for Chevy small-block. Timed fuel injection, headers and magneto prepare the engine for Formula A competition.

4. The problem with street manifolds is that of distributing intake from one or two carburetors to all eight ports, and there are a host of stock and aftermarket design approaches.

Engine Breathing

the burnt gases on the exhaust stroke.

The same flow tester can be used, but an adapter must be employed so that the vacuum draws air out of the exhaust port rather than into the simulated cylinder. Again, the absence of a piston and the changing pressures that exist within a working cylinder will limit the improvement to one of free flow at a constant vacuum. Procedures will be the same, with the full valve being tested first at its proper cam lift, and then the stem alone in the port.

Current design of exhaust valve shapes seems to overlook the fact that the exhaust port has the exact opposite function of the intake. Since one column (the intake) is coming downstream—in that it passes first the stem of the valve, then the increasing diameter up to the maximum at the valve head—and the other column (exhaust) is going upstream against the valve head first, and the less restricting stem on the other side of the head last, it seems likely that a different shape for the different function could assist the initial filling of the exhaust port. Granted, the initial pressure trying to empty the cylinder is much greater than that trying to fill it, but the easier it is for the gases to get by the head of the valve, the less effort the piston must exert on the upstroke. As with the intake, it may not exhaust more volume, but it will take less horsepower to do it. And more horsepower is what we are after anyway.

Unfortunately, many of those wishing to improve the performance of their particular engine by means of more efficient intake systems do not have access to flow testers or dynamometers. When that is the case, the application of common sense—with the understanding that air is a fluid that has weight—can eliminate the more obvious causes of restriction that exist in many production cylinder heads. The ultimate will probably not be reached, but the mere fact of getting all the intake ports of approximately the same volume will be a step in the right direction.

Air has weight, and therefore will act just like any other matter that has weight. If a port makes a very sharp bend, the column of air cannot be expected to follow the inside of the curvature. It will have a tendency to keep going in the direction it was going, and the result will be a low-pressure area just around the sharp bend. If the port makes a sudden change in cross-sectional area, the air will not flow smoothly from a large hole to a smaller one. From a small one to a larger, perhaps—but not without the creation of a low pressure area just inside the larger diameter.

In order to make their way from the manifold to the intake valves, some ports must take the form of an "S" bend. The air will then have to change direction twice, with pressure changes occurring each time. Much of the air will go straight, just as a racing car does when going through "S" bends. However, if three cars approach the bend side-by-side, someone will have to give way if they all with to get around the corners at close to maximum speed. If none gives way, then it is very likely that one or more of them will wind up off the road. The air is confined within the port, but gives way in the form of turbulence when the curve of the "S"

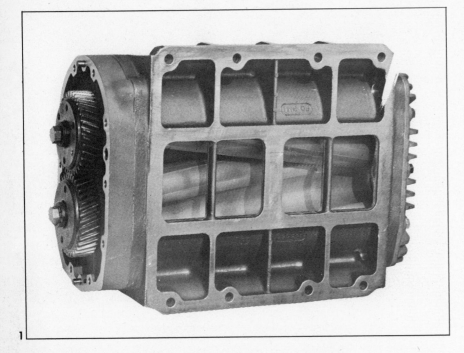

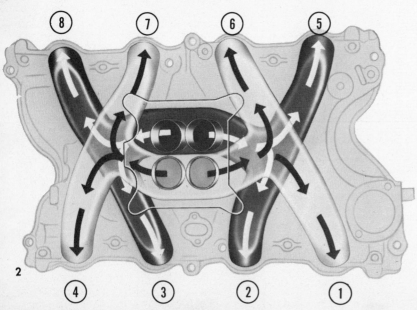

1. Shown from the bottom or manifold side, this GMC blower has interlocking rotors which, when turned by a belt driven off the crankshaft, literally suck air and fuel in and force-feed the mixture into the cylinder heads.

2. With a single-carburetor manifold the intake must make sharp bends to reach all of the intake ports.

3. Longer and straighter manifold passages produce a "ram" effect, and this design is a logical extension of the high-riser type manifold. These ram manifolds have become extremely popular for racing applications.

4. The optimum design, but one which is usually reserved for racing uses, is a single carb throat and manifold passage for each cylinder.

5. The cross-ram type manifold has long passages but still retains a low silhouette for hood clearance.

3

4

5

bend leaves it without room.

Smooth, polished ports can offer something to any engine. Most production engines are quite smooth to begin with, and it is doubtful that polishing will actually improve the flow of air. However, roughness of any kind can be a resting place for fuel that either fails to mix properly with the air, or becomes separated after the intake valve closes. Smoothness and attention to gradual changes of direction will do more good than harm, but are by no means a substitute for the flow tester method.

BLOWN ENGINES

If head work is being carried out prior to installing a supercharger, the methods are a lot simpler. No longer is the port trying to induce the column of air; it now has to guide it to the valve under considerable pres-

sure. Turbulence may exist, but it will have little effect on the incoming charge due to the tremendous velocities involved. It will be pushed into the cylinder whether it is flowing smoothly or in a turbulent state. Smooth flow will not hurt, of course, but it is not nearly as important as having necessary area through which the air can pass.

The flow characteristics of a large port can be improved easily enough by boosting the blower pressure. This is a lot quicker, and easier, than spending a great deal of time on the shape. The force drawing in the column of air is no longer coming from within the cylinder. It is now really being pushed in by pressure at considerably more than atmospheric.

MULTIPLE VALVES

With all of the restrictions that are

imposed on the intake and exhaust systems, one method of increasing their efficiency is the 4-valve head. By incorporating more valves of smaller diameter, the total valve and port area at a given opening is increased, particularly at the beginning of the lift. Notable examples of this practice are the Meyer Drake Offy, the Indianapolis Ford engines and now, the Cosworth Vega and Weslake's 4-valve head for Chevy Smallblocks.

Logical reasoning will reveal the several advantages that this design offers. In addition to increasing the valve and port area, the valves will be lighter in weight and therefore require less spring poundage to control them. Due to the smaller diameter of the valve head, the included angle of the intake and exhaust can be greater, and one of the disadvantages of the

Engine Breathing

combustion chambers with valves set at an angle to each other can be eliminated. The problem of valve masking is minimized, if almost completly not eliminated.

There does remain a problem of splitting the column of air somewhere within the intake port, since the valves must have support for their seats in the form of a wall between them. This fork in the port must channel the column of air in two different directions with as little disturbance as possible to the flow. This can become a problem since the velocity is increased once the original larger-diameter port becomes two smaller ones. Another possible advantage to this type of valve layout is the fact that the flow past each valve can be pointed in opposite directions once it is in the combustion chamber. This may create a favorable swirl within the cylinder and accomplish both better breathing and more complete burning during the power stroke; however, it could well be a disadvantage if the column is incorrectly aimed.

On the exhaust side, the increase in area gives the gases a better chance of escaping and provides more room on the other side of the valve heads. This additional room can

then be shaped as the designer wishes, with little concern for a vast reduction in total area. Production costs for a 4-valve engine are naturally higher than the 2-valve but, as the Cosworth has proven, this design is far more efficient. The results are better gas mileage, lower emissions with fewer smog devices and higher performance too. A few years ago, these considerations weren't too important and the success of such an engine would be doubtful but suddenly, everything has changed and the future looks brighter for the American 4-valve. However, some still think the day of production engines with more than two valves per cylinder is a long way off due to the manufacturing costs involved, and the limited advantages of such a system in a passenger car.

INTAKE MANIFOLDING

Once the ports in the cylinder head have been modified, and hopefully improved, the majority of engines will require an intake manifold to connect the ports to the actual air intake. The ideal is a separate intake system for each cylinder, a practice that is standard procedure on racing engines. Each intake can then be the exact same length and will only be subject to the pressure changes within its particular cylinder.

Unfortunately, most cases will in-

volve manifolding of some kind, and even if the path to the port is separated from the rest, the sharing of common air intakes can have harmful results. The plenum type of induction is best if the number of carburetors is limited, but more than likely it is not as efficient as completely isolated intakes for each cylinder, when each intake has its own carburetor.

The manifolds on production engines are subject to the same design problems of the cylinder head. They must be easy to cast, and easy to machine, since many thousands of each type will be produced. There are so many special-purpose manifolds available from independent supplies that it would be difficult to evaluate all of them. However, the use of any of them is probably an improvement over the standard one since they are designed with ease of manufacture as a secondary consideration. Therefore, if they have only a few desirable features, this is possibly an improvement over the original stock equipment.

There are some exceptions to this and they should be noted. The auto manufacturers make the inefficient manifolds on purpose, for one or many reasons. They can, however, also make very efficient ones on purpose, and in many cases they do. The original intention for your particular car is the key. If it was designed

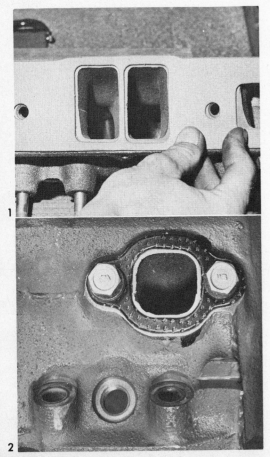

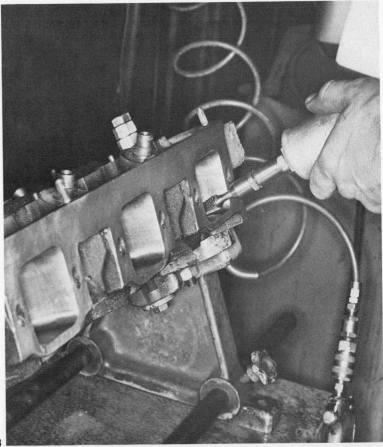

for use in a taxi or for a little old lady, it can probably use a different manifold. If it is for the high-performance enthusiast the factory manifold could well be as good as, or better than, any after-sale bolt-on.

In either case, the manifold to be used must be treated as an extention of the port itself. The air passing through it will not know whether it is in the port or the manifold, so the mating surfaces and any changes in section should be smooth transitions that will not disturb the flow. Remember the three racing cars that tried to go around a corner side-by-side?

When the carburetor, or carburetors, are attached to the other end of the manifold, the same attention should be given to matching the size of the openings. The carburetor itself is more easily replaced than modified, so consideration should be given to the former first. If the existing unit is retained, the flow can possibly be improved by careful smoothing of the casting. As little as possible should be removed from the bore since a change in the venturi can destroy any other performance gains.

Installation of velocity stacks, in place of air cleaners, on the openings of the carburetor has become a popular modification with hot rodders and can be of some benefit if the proper one is chosen. Its effect on the power range can be proven on the dynamometer but the selection of the right one is difficult. It gets back to that matter of positive and negative waves back and forth between the intake valve and the intake opening, a phenomenon that has yet to be fully resolved when applied to the internal combustion engine. Logic tells us that the air will be more easily persuaded to enter the intake system if it makes a gradual turn over a large area, but how much of a bell shape the stack should have seems to still be a matter of controversy.

People and engines being what they are, the controversy is bound to continue.

1,2. A basic rule for street use as well as racing is matching the port size to the gaskets by grinding. When everything is the same size, the flow can enter and exit the head freely.

3. Short of trial and error, testing on a flow machine is the only way to tell how much to remove from where when modifying cylinder head passages. Wanton grinding sometimes results in a loss of air velocity, cuts horsepower.

4. Velocity stacks have been popular accessories for years, but determining the best size and shape is difficult. This one fails to take advantage of the air, should be aimed to the front.

5. Intake and exhaust manifolds also have to be brought out to match the gaskets and cylinder heads.

6. Air entry into the carburetion system can be made easier by the use of velocity stacks, which bell out and make the transition a gradual one.

4

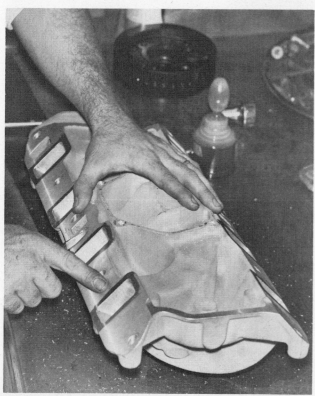

5

6

Picking an Intake Manifold

A scientifically designed manifold can be the key to a power-packed induction system.

After more than a decade in the doldrums of a hot rodding siesta, the induction system is again in the spotlight of horsepower and economy hunters. Time was, in the dim days past of finned heads and relieved blocks, that proper intake manifolding was considered one of the most important approaches to extra performance. Then along came the glamor days of super blooper cams and way-out superchargers and long-arm cranks, and the manifold began to gather cobwebs. The factories didn't help, what with quads, and dual quads, and three-two's, and all that stock car option stuff. But glory be, things are a'changing.

Speed equipment manufacturers, particularly those in the induction system business, have been searching out the mysteries of manifolding, uncovering a bundle of hidden horsepower. Coupled with some excellent improvements in carburetor design, manifolds have returned significant performance gains to the bolt-on agenda. Interestingly enough, most of the manifold improvements are a direct result of improvements in the basic secions of engine design *i.e.*, cams, valves, and ignition. You don't start looking for something unless you need it and it isn't there.

Some rather strong claims have been made concerning the value of recent intake manifold designs; a few such claims are obviously "happy," but most have been valid. There is considerable performance to be gained when the intake manifold and carburetion system are teamed with the mechanical portions of an engine in just the right manner. Getting the *n*th degree of performance through perfect manifolding might be termed induction blueprinting. In any case, the average automobile engine is in dire need of better induction if extra performance is desired.

Contemporary manifold design—indeed induction design from the very beginning—is little better than an acceptable compromise. Anytime an engine must perform the herculean tasks associated with everyday driving, it should not be expected to offer the optimum in performance, either in gasoline mileage or in power.

Because of the many and varied demands made upon an engine in passenger car use, engineers have traditionally turned to the simplest possible design. This usually means a single carburetor for several cylinders, with carburetor location dictated somewhat by body design. During recent years, lower and lower hood lines have restricted induction practices considerably, leading V-8 engines to very low profile carburetors and inline engines toward side-draft configurations. As far as the American engineer is concerned, any way you slice the body design cake, the induction system is likely to suffer.

Before the lower profile carburetors came along—allowing an extra inch or so in hood lowness—most of the engine height reduction had to be consumed by the intake manifold. This had a number of disadvantages, especially to the performance-conscious. In the first place, it restricted the cross section size of the ports. It also placed more unwanted curves in the port length, and fuel charge cooling or heating (whichever the case may be) suffered adversely.

In cases where body styling is secondary to raw performance, such as at Daytona or the National drags, the factories could utilize intake systems designed to give top horsepower and torque. This meant bubbles in the hood, but who cares when a win is at stake? The highrise and various ram manifolds have been the result, with the factory interest in induction serving to encourage the hot rod industry into a renewed look at one of its original mainstays.

About this same time, roughly in the late 1950's, the carburetor builders began quietly looking at the high-performance field, not so much because of the hot rodder, but because of the increasing demands from Detroit. Performance had become a byword, so the staid old carburetor people decided to do their part. Where the Stromberg 97 and Carter AFB had been the big thing. Holley hung up a strong one with the new 3-port design. Increased attention to diverse carburetor needs further emphasized the possibility of tailoring the induction to an engine, rather than taking second best.

Even so, the speed merchants rush to admonish caution when carbureting an engine. It has been true since the first Rajo or Hal banged a note at the dry lakes that hot rodders tend to live by the dictum that "if a little's good, lots is gooder!" This may hold reasonably true with displacement, but with induction it is seldom entirely

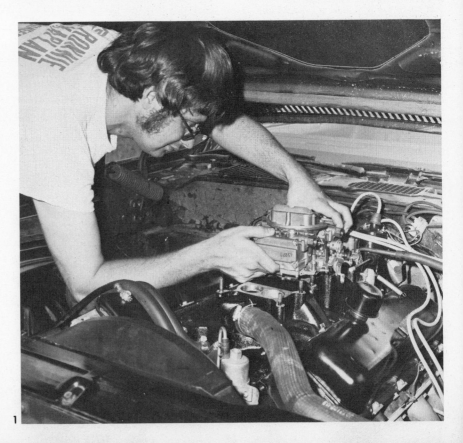

1

valid. It is highly possible that the stock carburetion system of a modern engine is ideally suited to that same engine hopped up. The Z-28 Chevrolet aluminum manifold is an excellent example of this.

Reams of material have been written on the subject of carburetion recently, certainly enough to make most rodders cognizant of dangers in overcarburetion. Suffice it here to reiterate the simple virtue of selecting a carburetor(s) with a flow rate in cfm (cubic feet per minute) that is compatible with the engine at maximum desirable power range. There are several sources from which to determine the facts. The speed equipment manufacturer who builds manifolds is an ideal fountain of information. If he says a 950 cfm carburetor is enough, it's enough!

Like the custom wheel, the modern intake manifold is enjoying quite a lasting popularity binge with hot rodders, both street and racing types. And like the wheel, such a system is not inexpensive. Counting all the accoutrements, such as throttle linkage and special fuel line and carburetor(s), a special manifold may set the

bank account back as much as $200. In unusual cases where something exotic like Webers are involved, the National Debt can be enriched by upwards of $1000. Still, a good intake manifold and carburetor combination can do as much for horsepower versatility as headers or camshafts. The combination has the added advantage that at least a portion of the partnership may be applicable to other engines—*i.e.*, the carburetor.

In current induction circles, the big names are High Rise, Cross Ram, Vertical Ram and now, Torker and Streetmaster. In essence, the High

Rise is a takeoff from the Daytona-type factory manifolds, and the Cross Ram is a modification of the Chrysler long and short ram ideas. The new Vertical Ram, which is known by serveral trade names so far (including Tunnel Port, D-Port, Channel Port, etc.) seems to be nothing more than a combination of the two, with a little injection engineering thrown in for good measure. The Torker and Streetmaster are Edelbrock's latest contribution to fighting the gas shortage. The Torker, designed for street and track, can be used where engine speeds don't exceed 7000 rpm. It im-

1. Just as with a camshaft, the most important thing to keep in mind when picking an intake manifold is: Don't overdo it. Over-carb and you will wind up with less performance than you had with your stock engine!

2. Many performance designs used to come right from Detroit, back when the factories were interested in performance. This '60's Chrysler ram had a better high rpm performance than any previous inline dual-4's, because of the long runners.

3. Unusual new manifolds from Offenhauser employ dual-port design. Result is an increase in low speed driveability and low end torque.

4. This is a manifold setup made specifically for big Holley carbs. Note the large mixing chambers below carb throat, small clearance cut in runner between port chambers.

5. Small-block Ford 2-bbl. manifold. The arrows show direction of the flow to each cylinder.

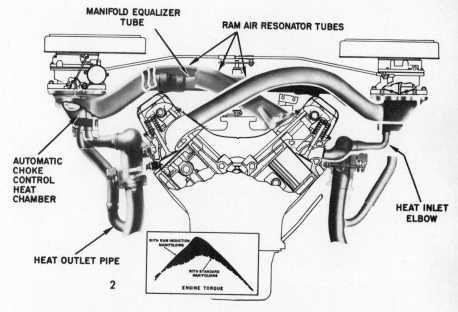

MANIFOLD EQUALIZER TUBE

RAM AIR RESONATOR TUBES

AUTOMATIC CHOKE CONTROL HEAT CHAMBER

HEAT OUTLET PIPE

HEAT INLET ELBOW

WITH RAM INDUCTION MANIFOLDING

WITH STANDARD MANIFOLDING

ENGINE TORQUE

2

3

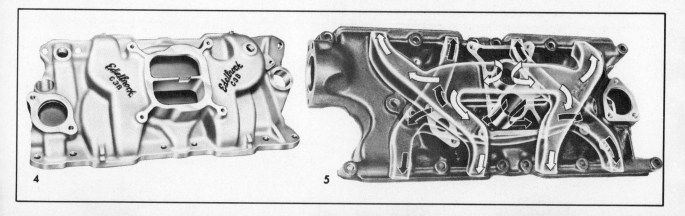

4

5

Intake Manifold

proves mid-range torque and gas mileage. The Streetmaster, offers the highest air/fuel velocity of any of Edelbrock's street manifolds. It improves volumetric efficiency through a new "step wall" design and this results in lower emissions and mileage increases of five mpg have been reported. Like the Torker, the Streetmaster connects to factory smog equipment making it street legal.

To recap the issue, it can safely be said that the heyday of the 2-throat carburetor is over, if only because of superior carburetor design advancements in the 4-throat field. In the beginning, there were flatheads—4's, 6's, and V-8's—all of which needed additional carburetion when performance was upped even the slightest. It is standard practice, even today, for engineers to design an engine with a high-performance potential, then achieve popular economy figures by restricting the induction system. The lowly Volkswagen is a prime example of this. No wonder then that prehistoric hot rodders had to look for increased carburetion at the very beginning of any hop-up session.

With some of the old 4-bangers, it was possible to get all the extra carburetion needed by merely adding a carburetor from a larger displacement engine. But with the V-8's, the only answer was another carburetor, or perhaps two additions. While a couple of "store-bought" dual-manifold designs were available commercially before WW II, they didn't really come on strong until after the war. By 1950, dual carburetors automatically meant power.

As displacement of the old reliable (?) flathead Ford V-8 engines was increased, through either boring or stroking or both, more carburetors were added, usually Stromberg 97's. Finally, the epitome came when four of these units were sardined atop the flathead. Overcarburetion became even more commonplace. If two are good, obviously four are better; so ran the argument of the neophyte. It was a long time before the faithful old 97 gave way, mostly because early 4-throat carburetor designs left much to be desired. It wasn't until the small Chevrolet engine began to run so well on factory quads that the 4-throat idea really took solid root.

Two 4-throats were found to work very well with an average manifold, although manifold design itself consisted primarily of how to get the carburetors in place. As Detroit engine sizes grew, so did carburetor capacity and capability. Finally, attention turned to the manifold itself.

We remember a very significant and practically unknown meeting that also helped current manifold development. Several years ago members of the NHRA technical committee met to discuss what was and what wasn't legal in the stock car classes. Manifolds were subjected to much of the controversy, but it was determined at the time that any manifold could be used as long as it were of factory *type,* and carburetion was not altered. This was a wise decision, obviously, since so much of the speed equipment industry depends upon

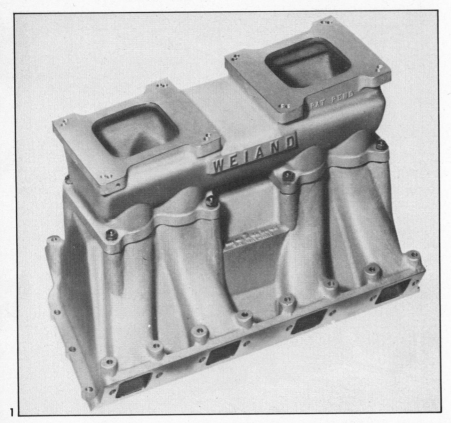

1

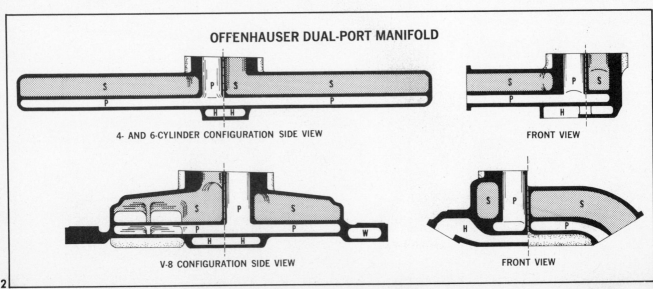

OFFENHAUSER DUAL-PORT MANIFOLD

4- AND 6-CYLINDER CONFIGURATION SIDE VIEW

FRONT VIEW

V-8 CONFIGURATION SIDE VIEW

FRONT VIEW

2

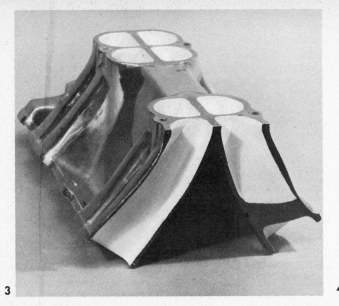

3

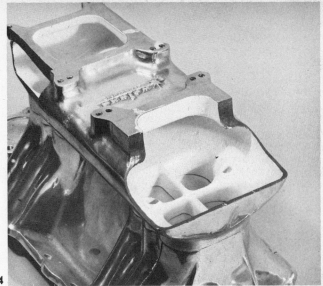

4

drag racing experimentation, and it left the door open for this industry to pace Detroit. The speed manufacturers didn't wait to start looking for that hidden horsepower.

While so much attention was being focused on supercharging and fuel injection, the old carburetion pioneers were designing and building and testing all kinds of combinations. Pacing the crowd was Edelbrock. Vic Edelbrock, senior, had been designing high-performance manifolds since before WW II, so it was natural for Vic Edelbrook, junior, to follow suit. Since manifolds have been an integral part of the Edelbrock establishment for so long, the company has endeavored to lead the way in advanced developments. They utilize dynamometers and exhaustive testing to evaluate each design's potential.

In 1961, the firm introduced the

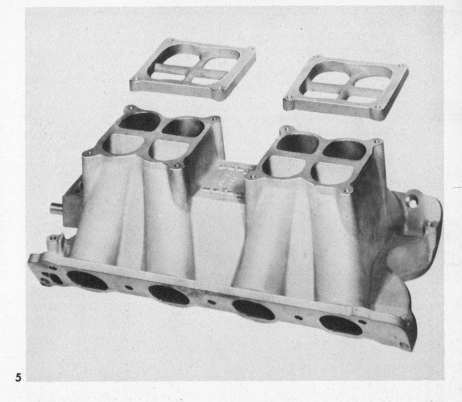

5

1. Weiand High Ram manifold with plenum chamber is designed for the Chrysler 426 Hemi. It's available with provision for mounting either a single or dual-quad carbs.

2. At idle and low speed operation, only the smaller portions of each port flow mixture. As engine demand increases, the secondaries open and feed the larger section of each port.

3. Cutaway of Weiand High Ram manifold illustrates direct path of mixture into each cylinder. Manifold has been dubbed an IR (individual runner) manifold design.

4. Cutaway of plenum chamber of Weiand High Ram manifold shows smooth surfaces cast into plenum for improved distribution.

5. This is a Weiand High Ram individual runner manifold with adapter plates for use on a Boss 429 engine.

6. A typical high-rise manifold. Cutaway illustrates the path the air/gas mixture travels to reach the different cylinders.

6

Intake Manifold

Ram Log (cross ram) manifold, a unit suited to an engine requiring a power bracket between 4000-7000 rpm. At that time, although it seems only yesterday, few engines were honestly capable of sustained operation in excess of the top mark, with the exception of the small-block Chevy which was being spun over 8000 at times. Port, combustion chamber, and piston design in this engine was such that response to the long intake runner manifolding was measurable, just as it was with the special versions of Chrysler B-series engines. These manifolds were originally intended for the race car, but it was inevitable they would find their way into street machines.

Interestingly enough, this important advancement in speed equipment is now considered "old," in that something even better is now available. Not because the ram log design is obsolete—not by a long shot—but because a number of modern V-8 engines are capable of power above 7000 rpm. Trying to fill this apparent power gap, Vic Edelbrock, junior, has come up with the "Tunnel Ram," or vertical ram pattern. In the area of competition-type manifolding, it is an admitted horsepower advantage.

Essentially, the port runners and plenum (box) atop the new manifold have been patterned after the Rochester fuel injection system of pre-1960. However, inclusion of a removable top provides ready latitude for an assortment of manifold/ carburetor combinations (including everything possible from Webers to the steady old 2-throats).

The location of the port runners directly beneath the holes in a set of dual quads makes the design well suited for their use, obviously, but the plenum chamber is designed so that all ports will get their fair share of fuel mixture. Unlike the Ram Log, this manifold is for racing only, and hasn't yet been proven entirely adaptable to street conditions. With the long port runners, it is a "tuned" system, set for the upper power ranges.

Edelbrock continues to run tests on this amazing manifold, primarily in the carburetion department. He started with two 4-barrel Holleys equipped with 4160 end bowls and .097-in. needle and seat valves. Fuel flow has proven so vital to this unit that needle size has been increased to .120-in. (number 79 primaries with power plug and .081 secondary plates). Subsequent tests have introduced some prototype carburetors which are really a combination of two past Holley designs, the 4160 and the R-3977.

Because this manifold can allow the engine to circulate in the rather heady atmosphere of around 9000 rpm (an area restricted to injectors in the past), it takes lots of fuel. To get this fuel, pressure must be at least 7 psi at engine idle, accomplished by a couple of good electric pumps placed in parallel, drawing through at least ⅜-in. tank-to-pump line.

Alterations to the port runners is to be avoided, to the Edelbrock as well as the new Offenhauser and Weiand vertical ram manifolds. Of course, some slight changes in engine response can be achieved by port modification, but this can only really be determined on a flow bench and is well beyond the scope of the average rodder. Air scoop placement is very

important, incidentally, so always check with the manifold builder on this subject.

While performance increases for all engines using the vertical ram type induction are not available, Edelbrock was able to get 21 extra horsepower at 7000 rpm, and a whopping 62 additional horses at 8000! Obviously, the vertical ram idea works, and we can expect some really significant results from these manifolds within the coming year, especially with valve timing and piston designs compatible with the discovery.

All this furor over the new vertical rams, as well as some real excitement in cross rams equipped with Webers, does not mean to say that the standard manifold is dead. Far from it, judging from the sales figures quoted by the big three in induction— Edelbrock, Offenhauser and Weiand.

The similarity between a manifold so sophisticated as a vertical ram and one necessary for the everyday car is really very little. Where the performance manifold is designed for power ranges normally well above the stock engine's rpm limit, the stock manifold must deliver a well mixed fuel charge to the cylinder at low rpm and under all kinds of operating and ambient temperatures. To this end, the stock manifold may actually be designed with apparent restrictions— restrictions found necessary to keep the fuel mixture usable although they can (and do) restrict total airflow. It is for this basic reason that a stock manifold can seldom be modified enough to compete.

A big word of caution for all performance manifolds—don't get happy with the grinder and waste the port configuration. It's true you do have to

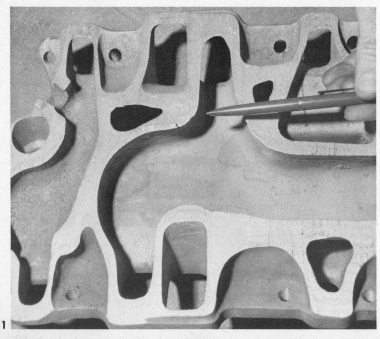

3

4

1. Sharp edges can be made to work for designer as well as against, but only airflow check of final design will tell what shapes are best to use.

2. Edelbrock's Tarantula design has the high efficiency required by a racing engine at above 6500 rpm.

3. Ollie Morris (left) and Fred Offenhauser designed Offy's new Dual-Port manifolds.

4. Clifford dual-quad manifolds for Chevy-Pontiac (5) and Ford 6-cylinder engines are designed for maximum performance use. Manifolds are recommended for engine sizes of 250 cu. ins. or more.

5. Many, Many hours of research and dyno time go into the development of a good manifold. Then it takes many machining operations to bring it from a prototype, to a casting, to a finished piece of bolt-on power.

5

match each port to the head port size and shape, but this should be very close to begin with. Honk around with manifold ports and you may find yourself fresh out of horsepower.

The intake manifold has undergone some impressive changes in the last few years, but even better things are in the wings, dependent upon improvements in carburetors, and enthusiasm of the hot rodder. We'll lay our money on the rodders.

HOW TO SAVE AN OLD MANIFOLD

Because there have been so many special performance manifolds produced by the speed industry, especially since 1949, it is possible to find exactly what you need for under $10.

Intake Manifold

Of course, this only applies to the older engines, usually those over 4 years of age, and in some cases like the Studebaker, a used manifold is about all that's available. In any case, just because the manifold is cracked, or a piece is broken from an edge, or there is corrosion, the unit is not necessarily beyond salvage.

These older manifolds are every-where—from big city speed shops to small village gas stations. When one is found, first thoroughly check the manifold to make sure there is no core shift during the casting procedure. A shifted core rarely gets pas the inspectors, but it could happen a few years ago. Here the internal portions of the manifold are not equally spaced from the outside walls. If a core shift has taken place, the manifold can be used only if any resultant holes are welded up.

If there are any cracks, or more commonly, if a piece is broken off (this is a very common malady), it can be repaired by any good aluminum welder. There is usually someone around who can weld aluminum—the blacksmith, aircraft mechanic, etc. A common problem is one or more of the bolt flanges broken from the mounting face by overtorqued bolts. If the piece is missing, and it usually is, any kind of sheet or plate can be substituted.

After the manifold is welded, whether on the outside or inside, grind down the weld area with small stones or rotary files. The rotary file is the best to use, as it will not fill up with aluminum particles so readily. You can get them at most auto parts houses, hardware stores, and welding supply shops.

All of the mating surfaces must be cleaned up, since they will surely be pitted or warped. Any machine shop can do this, but don't take off more material than is absolutely necessary. If too much is shaved from a V-8 manifold, for instance, it will no longer line up with the head ports. Remove all the studs and run the proper size tap into each threaded hole. If you've got some threaded holes that have been ruined by cross-threading, too large a bolt, etc., install Heli-Coil thread inserts.

Any area where water has eroded the aluminum should be cleaned with a stone or rotary file, especially around the mating surface edges where prolonged erosion can eat through to the outside of the manifold. If excessive erosion has eaten the manifold, it can be filled by weld and then machined.

If later model carburetors are going

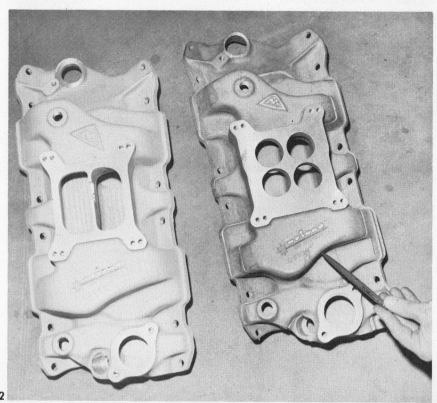

to be used, chances are the throat bores will be bigger than the manifold's. The bolt patterns may be different also. The machine shop can drill and tap new holes, as well as cut larger throttle bores. Because the basic port patterns are usually acceptable, working on the carb mounting area for better carburetion seldom has an adverse effect on the system.

PHIL WEIAND TELLS WHY—AND . . .

It wouldn't really be fair to the reader if we went about a manifold discussion without showing how the speed equipment industry creates such a unit. To this end, we made a special call on Phil Weiand, sum and substance of Weiand Power and Racing Equipment. *"Let's start at the beginning, Phil. How long have you been making manifolds?"*

"You mean commercially? That would go back to 1940, before the war, although I made my first homegrown intake for a 'T' when I was still in high school. Had a Winfield carb and went very well." *"That means you're really among the pioneers in this sport."* "I suppose so. At that time there were a couple of manifold designs on the market, namely Meyers and Thickstun. Incidentally, Vic Edelbrock, senior, worked for Thickstun before he went on his own." *"What was the first manifold you designed for sale?"* "Oh, that would be the old Hi-Weiand. We called it that because the carburetors were up high enough to clear the Ford generator. I didn't intend to make a ram manifold then, nor did anyone else—it just worked out that way. A fellow named Nick DeFaberty (I think that's how he spelled his name) used to use my manifold, and he held the lakes record for years at 121 mph. He must have understood something about ramming then, though, because he kept working with spacers between the manifold and the carburetor." *"Give us a little briefing on manifold development in the speed industry."*

1. If an old manifold is used with a new and larger carb, be sure to match the manifold openings to the size of the carb's throttle plates.

2. The Weiand manifold at right had restriction (pointer) that cut flow to a particular point. Note the new design at left with smoother angles.

3. The runners were changed to more direct routing on the newer design, at bottom, compared to the original.

4. In order to fit big Holleys on some dual setups, the carbs must be mounted sideways and special linkage used to change throttle direction.

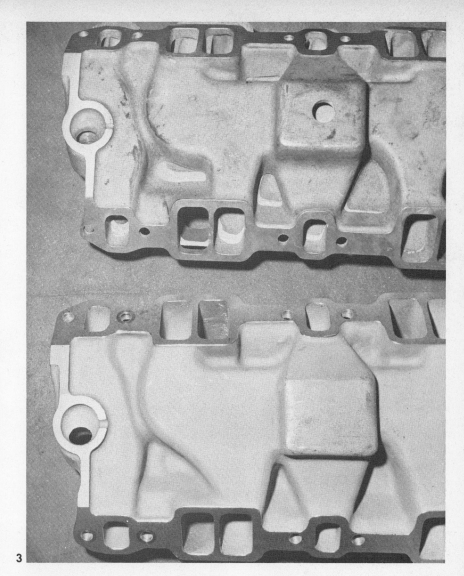

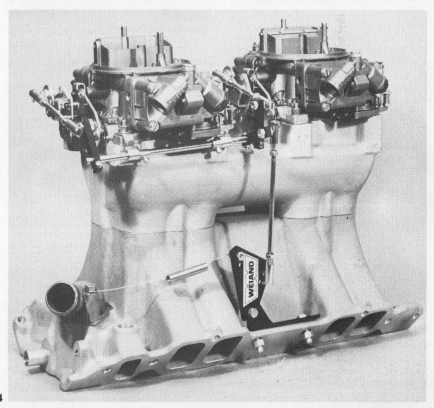

Intake Manifold

"Well, frankly, there isn't anything really new. It's just that the particular application is always changing as engine design changes are made. The plenum chamber that we now use so effectively was common to many really old stock manifolds, and so were the 180-degree and 360-degree designs. But in our end of the business, the first significant change in the old flathead manifolds came after WW II when we went to the low carburetor mountings. This happened when we started moving the generator off to one side.

"The log manifolds for the early overhead valve engines were next, with the first units made from steel tubing and water hose. Superchargers got into the act about that time, so we jumped on that quick and remained there until we started getting some really good carburetors (Carter AFB's). The highrise manifold design followed and finally the vertical ram. We call ours the Channel D-port, or High Ram." *"You mentioned earlier something about flow testing the High Ram. We've seen limited flow testing of manifolds—what do you do?"*

"We've taken a little different tack, in that we felt the manifold is a part of the overall engine package, and should be designed along those lines. So we contacted Warren Brownfield at Air Flow Research at the very beginning. He has a high-velocity flow machine that operates in the area we're interested in, and we have designed the manifold around those early tests. Some of the things we found out were amazing, to say the least. That's one of the reasons for our unique port shape, so that we can get maximum window." *"What's a window?"*

"You look down the port, and the size and shape of the opening you see straight through at the other end is a window. It has a bearing on airflow, and consequently, on performance." *"What are some of the other things you found by airflow testing?"*

"Well, for one, we knew that the trouble in porting usually comes in going from a round manifold port to a square head port. At the same time, the shape of the port—shrouding, diameter, curvature, etc.—is vital to getting maximum fuel transfer.

"Before we made any flow tests on the manifolds, we flowed heads to get the optimum flow possible in any particular head—that's Warren's specialty. Then we designed the manifold to equal those requirements. Since this is far greater than what the valves will actually allow into the combustion

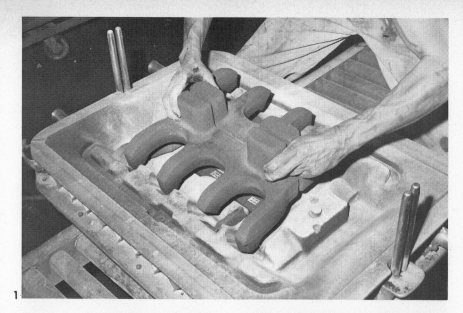

2

1

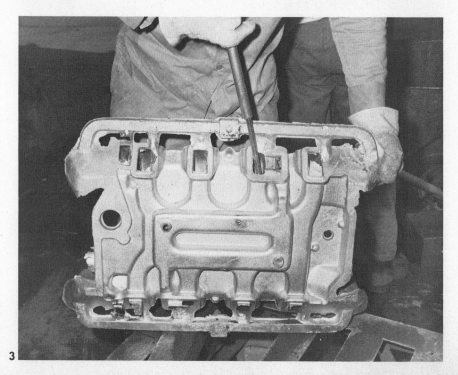

3

4

chamber, we end up with a giant plus factor.

"Of course, you can't just whittle a manifold out of aluminum or something. We worked with port facsimiles at first, then went to plaster prototypes. At the same time, we flowed street manifolds and found a variance at each port as great as 100 cfm. This couldn't mean much on the stock car maybe, but for performance it can rob you. For us, the beauty of flowing a preliminary design is that we could begin to see any future trouble spots and correct them long before they would crop up. Sure wasn't that way in the old days of cut-and-try." *"Is the manifold all you flowed?"*

"Oh no—you set it up the way it will be used, with carburetor and all.

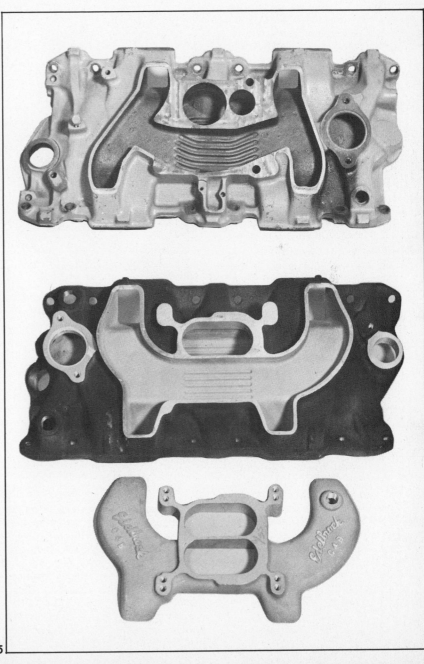

1. The internal runners (cores) are placed in bottom part of permanent mold and positioned very carefully to insure against core shifting.

2. After a manifold mold has been put together, it is packed around with casting sand; then the molten aluminum is poured through holes in the sand into the mold. When aluminum has cooled, the sand is brushed off.

3. The sand used to make internal cores must be knocked free before the machining process starts, and is usually more than a casual job to remove. Here worker uses prybar.

4. Restricted breathing is the bane of all VW's. Aftermarket intake manifolds such as this one from Superior Industries will boost the performance considerably.

5. Comparing a stock, dual-plane hi-rise manifold with an aftermarket design, you can see how the sharp corners inside the stock design have been smoothed out in the Edelbrock unit. Note also the distribution cuts or "fixes" on the manifold floors.

5

Intake Manifold

That means a lot of painstaking work to get the very best combination. At the same time, you still want to have a design that has a wide range of applications, something you can do if you keep trying." *"We understand you own a foundry, which means you make your product from conception to production. Just how is a manifold born?"*

"Oh boy, through lots of patience. We start out with a fairly good idea of what is needed, then we put this on paper. In the case of flow checks, changes are made to the design until it is right, then the blueprints are sent along to a pattern maker.

"The pattern shop will make up a master from hardwood, and this will in turn be used to make a permanent metal pattern. There will be several patterns, the one for the outside shapes (top and bottom), and the inner cores (ports, water jackets, heat runners, etc.).

"It's expensive to make up an entirely new manifold—over $10,000 usually—but we do make changes we find necessary. In fact, we have such a change on one of the regular manifolds now.

"Ever notice how smooth the interior port walls are on some manifolds? That's because we use the shell casting technique. With this, a special formula of sand and resin is baked to form a hollow shell for the internal parts, and we can hold much closer internal tolerances.

"When the manifold is being laid up, the sand cores are inserted inside the external molds and then the outside molds are clamped tight. They are packed around with special cooling sand inside a large tray and poured full of 319 alloy aluminum, which has been heated to around 1400°F. We blend a special additive into the aluminum while it is being heated to drive off gaseous impurities that tend to make aluminum castings pitted.

"The molten aluminum is poured through tubes into the mold and is allowed to cool slowly. After it is down to a reasonable temperature (still hot enough to burn the hands), the raw manifold is removed from the mold and the internal sand cores knocked loose. They're hard, too, so this means an air chisel.

"Next the casting is trimmed, carefully inspected, small flashings ground off, and sand blasted. That's when the machine shop first sees a raw casting." *"No wonder some of the more complex manifold designs are expensive."*

"Sure, it takes a lot of steps before the finished product can be shipped. At the machine shop we surface all the mating edges to factory tolerances, and drill and tap all the necessary holes. Incidentally, we drill the head mounting holes slightly oversize because we found we were holding closer tolerances than the factory. We were using factory engineering drawings to work from and sometimes the slightest deviation in an engine would cause mounting problems. The oversize holes take care of this and everybody does it now." *"It sounds simple, but there must be more to it."*

"There is, but this is a thumbnail sketch. As an example, we don't want to release a design until we've backed up the predictions with actual dynamometer tests, and that can take a little time." *"Do you have any suggestions for hot rodders contemplating use of a special intake manifold?"*

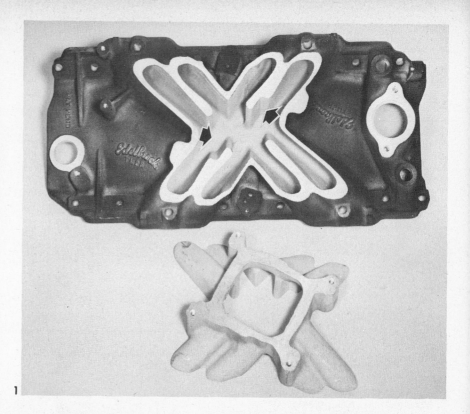

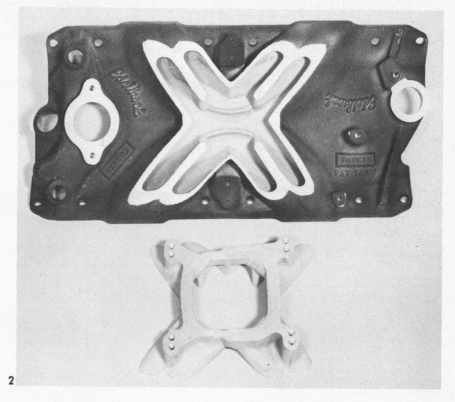

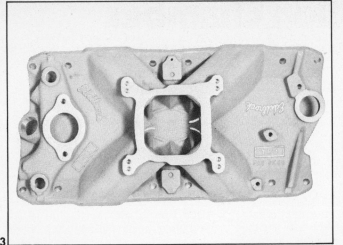

3

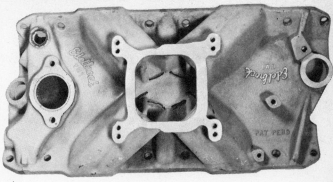

4

1. This Edelbrock manifold for a big-block Chevy is cut apart to show two internal notches (arrows) which effectively give similar length to the runners as far as the mixture is concerned. Because of the cylinder head offset of the Rat, the carb is mounted at an angle for more equal cylinder-to-cylinder distribution.

2. Since the small-block Chevy has less head offset, the carb doesn't have to be turned, and there isn't such a problem with the 1,3,6, and 8 group of cylinders. One of the new breed of street manifolds, Torker features a smaller plenum with two distribution fixes to balance flow out to the longer runners.

3. Edelbrock's latest Tarantula has three "troughs" (white lines) on the plenum floor, as well as four ridges in front of the shorter runners to even out the mixture distribution.

4. You can update any Tarantula to the latest configuration by welding some aluminum rod in place for fixes and grinding the troughs yourself.

5. Detroit's problem in designing a NASCAR manifold was to get long "ram" tubes with only a single carburetor and still have hood clearance. This is Ford's version of the "bathtub" manifold. The sharp angles inside required channels to direct the flow.

6. Remember Chevy's dual-quad setup for the Trans-Am 302's? It kicked off many of the ram designs to come. The dividers and distribution fixes here (arrows) prevent wet fuel travel.

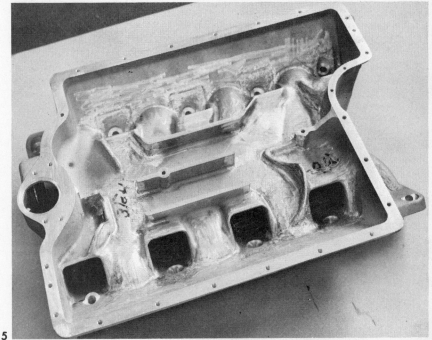

5

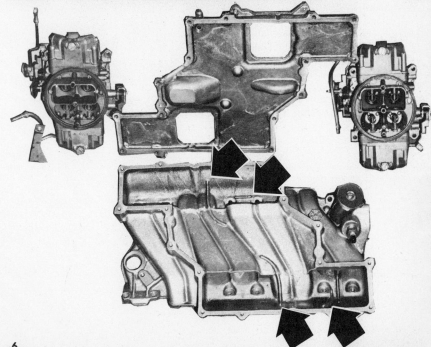

6

"Several. In the first place, don't put on more carburetion than the engine can take. (Editor's note: *See, we told you so!*) Always match the manifold and head ports exactly, match the carburetor to the engine, and remember that no two engines are exactly alike. Both may be Chevys, with identical equipment, but they will still be different engines. Don't over-torque any of the mounting bolts, and do keep the manifold clean."

So there you have—the inside story on how a manifold is designed and produced. ♔

The Combustion Chamber

The valve and spark plug location, the piston top and the chamber shape are all related to engine efficiency, and that's what determines horsepower.

When you get down to the nitty gritty bits and pieces, there are really only two basic ways of increasing the power output of any internal combustion engine—increase the volumetric efficiency, and increase the efficiency of the combustion cycle. Hot rodders are most familiar with methods of increasing the volumetric efficiency—that is, the degree to which cylinders are charged, exhausted, and recharged during each engine cycle.

Volumetric efficiency is the reason for boring and stroking, putting in larger valves, polishing and shaping ports, changing valve timing, using multiple carburetion and supercharging, and tuning the intake and exhaust cycles. All of these things have a direct effect upon engine performance, with the hot rodder concentrating on getting a bigger gulp of fuel and air packed into the combustion chamber.

Advancements in the field of metallurgy have kept a fairly close pace with those in the automotive racing arena so the modern hot rodder can take a stock, production engine and double, triple, and even quadruple the power output with a reasonable degree of reliability.

Once the big charge is shoved into the cylinders, it has to be ignited at the precise time, burned at the correct rate, and consumed as completely as possible. This is the efficiency of the combustion cycle, and if it isn't right, all other modifications will be wasted effort. Combustion cycle efficiency is where the results from all the typical hot rod modifications meet for the big payoff. Unfortunately, the highly critical combustion chamber and its related engineering seem to be the one area of engine design that hot rodders know the least about. Of course, much of this cobwebbing is being swept aside as all aspects of American automobile racing converge on common principles, with the hot rodders learning from Indianapolis, Daytona taking a cue from the sports cars, and vice versa.

SIR HARRY RICARDO

Back in the dim, dark, early days of automotive engine experimentation and development, a real pioneer Englishman named Harry Ricardo (later Sir Harry when he was knighted in recognition of his very important experiments and discoveries in the automotive field) came to a conclusion that remains the most important factor influencing any internal combustion engine design. His conclusion stated that of all the many design features which control and limit the power output and efficiency of the internal combustion engine, the most important by far is the shape of the combustion chamber. This is the true heart of the engine, upon which depends not only the efficiency with which fuel is burned—and therefore the engine's power output—but also the liability to detonation, which limits the highest usable compression ratio practical.

For the hot rodder, then, the combustion chamber is even more critical than for the normal passenger car engineer. The designer works from scratch. He takes a set of specifications and a clean sheet of paper and designs a combustion chamber to do a specific job. The foundry casts up a few experimental heads, the shop assembles an engine, and test engineers set the whole affair on a test dynamometer. If the chamber design doesn't work out exactly right, the whole process starts over again.

Whatever the final production combustion chamber shape happens to be is the one hot rodders are going to be stuck with, the same old chamber that's going to be called on to do four times what it was originally designed to do. The mere fact that the chambers have been doing these jobs is a tribute to engineering. At the same time, the wise engineers have been leaning over backwards to incorporate racing experience in further designs.

CHANGING CHAMBER SHAPE

Generally speaking, there is very little the rodder can do to change either the basic combustion chamber shape or its performance characteristics. In some cases slight improvement is possible with grinding and polishing, and there is the possibility of changing the piston head shape, which will greatly alter the shape of

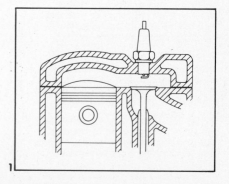

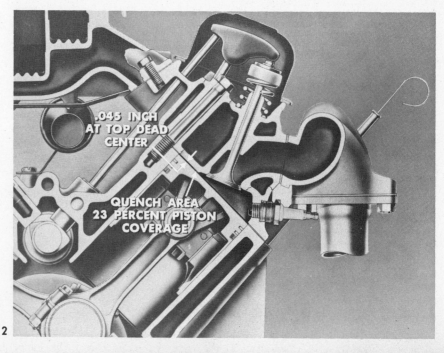

.045 INCH AT TOP DEAD CENTER

QUENCH AREA 23 PERCENT PISTON COVERAGE

2

the chamber (the piston top is an integral part of the chamber shape).

Working with piston shapes can be a tricky business, and the results are not always desirable. It has only been recently that accessory piston manufacturers have taken a really serious look at the piston top as a means of improving the shape and characteristics of a production combustion chamber. Some of the experiments on the small-block Chevrolet engine

are a fine example of this. While several basic piston shapes have been settled on as optimum for the small Chevy, minute changes for little performance increases are still possible.

Since the hot rodder cannot dictate exactly what the combustion chamber shape will be on a production engine, the next best thing is to choose an engine that has a good design to begin with. After all, the only real difference between engines of the same

cubic-inch displacement, but from different builders, is in the design of the combustion chambers. An Oldsmobile and a Chrysler are good examples. The chamber potential, then, should be a major consideration when choosing any engine for modification. Unconsciously many rodders do this simply by emulating others who have had success with this or that particular engine.

Since the chamber shapes have already been prescribed, it becomes necessary for the serious rodder to then learn all that is possible about the combustion process and how his particular engine utilizes combustion to create power. It all starts with a simple definition of the combustion chamber itself.

WHAT IS THE COMBUSTION CHAMBER

The combustion chamber is that area in which combustion takes place, and is comprised of any surface within that area exposed to the actual combustion. This would include the surfaces of both intake and exhaust valve heads, the cylinder head, the top of the piston, a portion of the upper cylinder wall, the edges of the head gasket, and even the portion of the spark plug that extends into the chamber Each of these areas will have a definite effect on the efficiency of the chamber shape, and in turn, on how the chamber affects overall combustion characteristics. For all practical purposes we can say that even though the engine may be turning at a very high rpm, the basic shape and volume of the combustion chamber remains nearly constant during the short time it takes for actual combustion. This is because even though the crankshaft speed remains constant, the piston

3

4

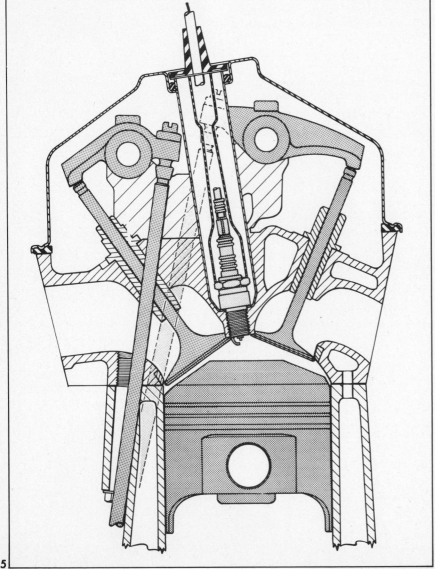

5

1. The old sidevalve flathead engine had little squish area and end gases were too far from the spark plug. It was a detonation-prone design.

2. By contrast, the modern engine's combustion chamber is wedge-shaped, offering squish and quench. And with overhead valves the chamber is more compact for shorter flame travel.

3. Due to its shape, the hemi chamber can be machined instead of cast, so it's smoother than the wedge. You'll notice that it's so smooth most racers don't even bother polishing it, but the chamber shown has been polished.

4. Another hemi chamber, this one's from a motorcycle. It offers really large canted valves and has the plug near the intake for plug-end cooling.

5. Combustion chamber of the famous Chrysler Hemi. It allows huge valves, central spark plug, and gets quench and squish from domed pistons.

Combustion

near top dead center has to slow down, stop, and reverse direction.

THREE BASIC STEPS

The combustion process can be divided into three distinct, basic steps: final compression of the air/fuel mixture, ignition of the mixture, and the spreading of the flame through the mixture. In a modern engine this process occurs during the time it takes for the crankshaft to move through approximately 60° of travel. If the engine were turning 3000 rpm this time would be slightly more than three thousandths of one second, and only half that time at 6000 rpm. Not much room for error, so let's consider each of the three combustion steps in detail.

FINAL COMPRESSION

As the piston comes up on the compression stroke, squeezing the air/fuel mixture, the resultant pressure rise causes a rapid temperature increase. This happens so quickly that almost none of the heat is lost to the surrounding metal, but is retained in the mixture. The process is called adiabatic compression by engineers and it sets up what is known as a preflame condition, or the first obstacle that has to be overcome. If the temperature gets too high, the air/fuel mixture will ignite spontaneously. This is called preignition and in this case would be the result of three major things: too high a compression ratio, too low a grade (octane rating) of fuel, and an overheating engine which is transferring too much heat to the incoming mixture. The auto-ignition point is above 1600° F.

Preignition can also be caused by several other factors, the most common being hot spots in the combustion chamber and/or incorrect ignition timing. The hot spots could be a glowing piece of carbon, the edge of an exhaust valve or head gasket, or most common of all, an overheated spark plug. Most hot spots would show up as a result of insufficient engine cooling.

Preignition isn't too common, but it does occur from time to time. When it does, it can quickly destroy an engine if not corrected. Typical failures are holes melted in piston heads, seized pistons, and burned exhaust valves. Preignition causes excessive cylinder pressures, which occur before the piston reaches top dead center and cause a large amount of negative work and a direct fall-off in power.

Preignition is almost always accompanied by a harsh, metallic sound (knock) which can easily be confused

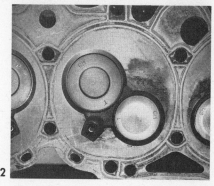

1

with the knock more commonly caused by detonation. Sometimes an engine will "run on" after the ignition is switched off (common to many foreign cars). This is primarily due to hot spots in the combustion chamber igniting fuel-air drawn through a throttle plate not fully closed.

To prevent preignition, the combustion chamber must first be designed to have sufficient clearance volume to provide a compression ratio compatible with available fuels.

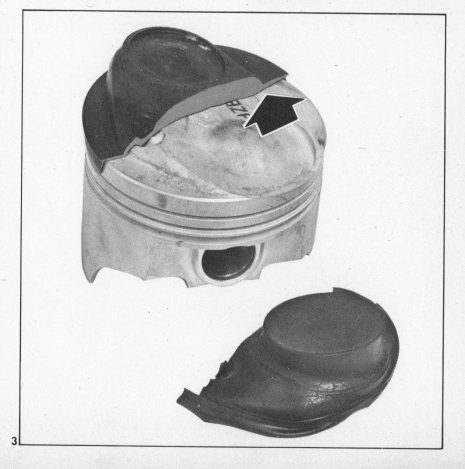

2

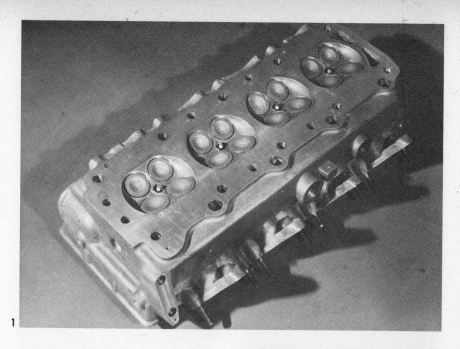

3

4

5

6

That is, not over about 12.5:1 with pump gasoline and about 14.5:1 with alcohol-based fuels. To prevent hot spots, the chamber should have a mirror-smooth surface which will discourage the buildup of carbon formations, and it should have no sharp edges which will tend to localize heat and cause a hot spot. Most important, because it is the most common fault, the spark plug must be of the correct heat range so that the tip will cool adequately.

IGNITION

The next step in the combustion process is that point at which the air/fuel mixture is exposed to the ignition spark and the actual burning begins. Theoretically, it would appear that the best time would be right when the piston reaches TDC and the mixture is fully compressed. This might be true if a spontaneous ignition or explosion were involved. But the engine can't stand an explosion; instead it needs a controlled *burning* of the mixture, necessary because of the sharp rise in cylinder pressure which

accompanies the burning. An explosion would also create undesirable piston and bearing overloads.

The high pressure has to be applied to the working parts of the engine as smoothly as possible or the engine will be harsh, rough, and noisy. To accomplish this smooth power transition, the spark is introduced to the mixture before the piston reaches TDC. Just how long before TDC depends on the rate which the mixture burns, which in turn is determined by compression ratio, the turbulence present in the mixture, and the chemical composition of the fuel itself. At any rate, it should be at the point which will allow the peak combustion pressure to be reached just after the piston passes TDC. If timing is early or late, there will be a decrease in power output.

FLAME FRONT

At the instant the spark ignites the mixture, the combustion process is in its third and final stage. The actual burning process moves out from the spark plug and through the mixture

1. Four valves per cylinder create the pentroof combustion chambers of Cosworth Vega head. The central plug location makes for more complete burning. And valves—exhaust on one side, intakes on other—are angled toward their ports for smooth, efficient flow of intake and exhaust gases.

2. Sharp edges in the chamber lead to hot spots that can cause preignition. Also, with the plug "pocketed" as in this design, gases can stagnate there and the plug won't get the cooling, cleaning benefit of swirling gases.

3. With piston at TDC on a ZL1, some liquid rubber is poured through the plug hole, making a perfect mold of the combustion chamber. Cutaway shows precise clearances for head machining.

4. This is what the chamber of the Chevy aluminum ZL1 heads looks like. The chamber is open more than stock iron version to clear the ZL1 pistons.

5. This steel head has been modified by Manley Competition Machine Service, Bloomfield, N.J., to work like a ZL1.

6. Dick Landy and Dodge developed a set of these twin-plug heads for his racer. Now used by top hemis, the new design provides improved burning.

Combustion

much in the same way ripples move out from a stone dropped in still water. This movement is called the flame front.

As the flame front travels through the mixture, an area of high pressure is pushed along in front of it. If the pressure becomes great enough, the resultant heat will raise the temperature of the remaining air/fuel mixture to the point of auto-ignition and spontaneous ignition will take place. This is called detonation and is undesirable because of the extremely high pressures and temperatures that are created.

If unchecked, detonation can burn exhaust valves and plugs, and will literally chew its way right down the side of a piston. When things get this hot in the combustion chamber, preignition will also take place. Complete engine destruction is right around the corner. As detonation occurs, the resulting shock wave bounces back and forth in the cylinder causing an audible knock (ping). In some cases borderline detonation won't produce enough noise to be heard—not at first anyway. The smart hot rodder must therefore learn to look for other danger signs. A spark plug that has been exposed to detonation will show pinpoint-size black specks on the porcelain around the center electrode. If the exhaust stacks are short enough, the flame color might be a tipoff. Normal combustion will show up as a blue-colored flame while yellow, or traces of yellow, flame shows that the engine is in the detonation range. If the exhaust stacks are too long for the flame to be seen, detonation will be signaled by quick puffs of black

smoke. Don't confuse this with the clouds of steady black smoke from an over-rich mixture. Detonation is the biggest enemy any engine has, especially a highly modified engine.

RESISTING DETONATION

The modern engineer controls detonation in the same basic way discovered so long ago by Sir Harry Ricardo. With the exception of the octane rating of the fuel, which determines its resistance to detonation, all the methods hinge on the shape of the combustion chamber. Ricardo's experiments showed that an engine's resistance to detonation depended on four main factors: spark plug location, degree of turbulence of the air/fuel mixture, temperature and disposition of the end gases, and proper compression ratio-fuel rating compatibility.

The spark plug has to be located at a point that will allow the flame front the shortest path through the combustion chamber. This keeps to a minimum the time available for the buildup of the pressure wave ahead of the flame front. It also keeps the time that end gases will be exposed to the flame front temperature as short as possible. The spark should also be exposed to the hottest part of the mixture first, so this means locating the spark plug as close to the exhaust valve as physically possible. Other considerations include placing the plug so it gets the cooling benefit of the incoming charge and the cleansing action provided by the rapidly swirling, burning gases. In other words, the plug shouldn't be pocketed, nor should it provide a pocket where residual exhaust gases are liable to collect, which would dilute the fresh charge.

Some engines, such as the Offy

and certain motorcycles, deliberately place the plug in a separate pocket, actually out of the combustion chamber, and get excellent results. It's called cartridge fire, and is usually done because of space limitations in the combustion chamber.

Turbulence is important for several reasons. The first is that it greatly speeds up the burning process and allows more complete, efficient combustion. Speeding up the process also cuts down on the time end gases will be exposed to heat and pressure. In any internal combustion engine there will be a boundary layer of working fluid that tends to cling to the relatively cool cylinder walls. This layer, by its very proximity to the cool surfaces, gets rid of heat so rapidly that it escapes complete combustion. Turbulence is relied on to scour this layer from the surfaces and distribute it evenly through the mixture. It is virtually impossible to completely clear the cylinder of all exhaust gases after combustion. Turbulence insures that whatever residual gases do remain after the exhaust valve closes will be more evenly distributed through the incoming mixture.

To promote turbulence in the mixture, Ricardo designed his chamber so that in one area there was very little clearance between it and the top of the piston. He called this the squish chamber because that's precisely what it does. As the piston comes up on the compression stroke, the mixture in this area is forcibly squished out into the main combustion chamber, setting up turbulence. The degree of turbulence is dependent on the size of this part of the chamber. Engineers also refer to this as the Ricardo chamber in honor of the discoverer. In some engine de-

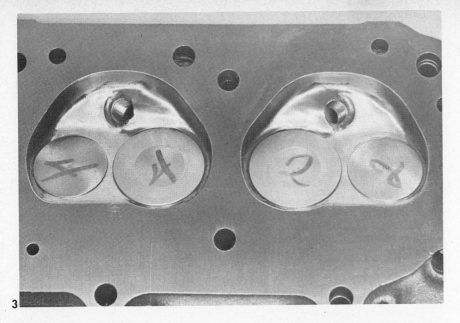

quenched out of the end gases, helping them withstand the temperature rise caused by the flame front-driven pressure wave.

In the prior discussion on preignition, the importance of providing the combustion chamber with enough clearance volume was considered. This is for a compression ratio that will be compatible with available fuels. In the end result, no matter how efficient the shape of the combustion chamber, the engine's liability to detonation will still depend on the fuel. In Ricardo's day, a 6:1 compression ratio was considered high and not too long ago, production engines had the optimum 12.5:1 c.r.—thanks to advancements in both engine and fuel design. However, with the recent reductions of fuel octane (low-lead and no-lead) and tougher emissions laws, it's doubtful that compression ratios that high will return.

CHAMBER DESIGN

The good combustion chamber design, in addition to providing the above features (adequate squish and quench area for turbulence and cooling of end gases; low clearance volume for high compression ratio; short flame travel for rapid efficient combustion), must also provide the following: a low ratio of overall chamber surface to volume so that a minimum of combustion heat will be lost to the surrounding surfaces (heat is the energy that does the work); and enough room to allow the use of adequate-size valves for high volumetric efficiency.

There have been many chamber designs used in passenger and racing cars through the years, but the hot rodder is still limited to what Detroit offers—simple economics being what they are.

This makes the choices fairly simple because all the engines now in production use the wedge-type combustion chamber, with the exception of the Chrysler and Ford Hemi-head versions and the Cosworth Vega pent-roof design. There are two reasons

1. These chambers have been furnace-welded, and the one at right has been sandblasted. Later, grinding the welds smooth makes finished chamber, which company claims is stronger than heads that are just ground out to size.

2. Most headwork should be left to experts, but simple polishing can be done by anyone who is careful. This head has had a rough cleanup grinding.

3. This Trans-Am Javelin head has had final shaping and polishing, and all chambers are trued to the proper cc's.

4. Tech-Alloy of Long Island takes a different approach to same problem. They grind away most of the wall, and furnace-weld a new wall to dimensions.

signs, a degree of turbulence is set up in the incoming charge by the shape of the intake port and by angling the port slightly in the approach to the cylinder. This is where considerable hot rod innovation can be applied, but where working without some visible means of experiment verification can lead to serious trouble.

Obviously, the tests made on airflow benches will be of great aid here, and some of the more advanced speed merchants are working in this direction now. Where the hot rodder has relied so heavily on "no substitute for cubic inches," the emphasis is now being directed to getting the last ounce of available power. To this end, piston top shapes are being carefully scrutinized as companions to camshaft profile and

port shape. If the piston shape is wrong—and tests have shown the common "eyebrow" piston is not at all the most desirable—the entire problem of better airflow is often too big to solve. The shape of the combustion chamber must also pass a good airflow.

The temperature of the end gases has to be kept low enough to keep them from exploding and setting up the detonation shock wave. Ricardo found that by exposing the end gases to a large, relatively cool area of the chamber, temperature could be kept low. This area is actually the squish area, but at this stage of the game it is referred to as the quench area. Because this part of the combustion chamber is fairly large in surface area and low in volume, the heat is rapidly

Combustion

the wedge-type chamber enjoys such wide acceptance. First of all, it's a simple design that is easy to produce and offers low production costs. The second reason is that all the desirable features mentioned can be applied simply and efficiently.

This doesn't mean that all Detroit engines will have the same combustion characteristics. Not by a long shot. There are several ways of designing the basic wedge chamber to get desired results. Two engines of the same bore and stroke might have a wedge chamber of similar design, but one could produce more horsepower than the other (we're concerned with chamber design only, now). This might be because in one design the valves are shrouded slightly by the chamber walls while in the other the valves are open. Or perhaps one engine has more squish and quench area than the other and can stand a higher compression ratio without detonation. These are the things to look for when choosing an engine for modification.

The most common method Detroit uses in building the wedge is to use a flat-top piston and cast the desired wedge shape into the head. As in any wedge design, the intake and exhaust valves will be side by side and the spark plug will be located as centrally as possible. This is the chamber type common to the 283-327 Chevys, as well as most other cars. In this design, the valves are usually inclined slightly off the cylinder bore axis with the main part of the combustion chamber located over the lower side (on a V-8) of the piston, and the squish and quench areas over the higher side.

A slightly different method of obtaining a wedge is used on the 348, 409 Chevy, and 430 Lincoln. Here the block and head join at an angle other than 90° to the cylinder bore axis. The resulting wedge is formed by the piston head, cylinder wall, and flat surface of the head bottom. In other words, the combustion chamber is mainly located in the cylinder block. Control of the shape is provided by the piston. Chevrolet used a gabled roof piston while Lincoln used a step roof piston. Since none of the chamber shape has to be cast into the head, this design gives the effect of a fully machined chamber. Another big advantage of this method is that from the valve point of view, the cylinder has an oval shape instead of being circular. This provides more free room for larger valves than the normal wedge design. Central location of the spark plug is no problem. Buick uses a slightly different ap-

proach to the wedge. They locate the main chamber toward the higher side of the cylinder with the squish and quench areas toward the lower side. A pent roof piston is used and the spark plug is located almost dead center. This chamber has good combustion characteristics, but has a major drawback in that the exhaust gases follow a rather torturous route through the head. This is partly compensated for in the stock engine by valve timing, but becomes a greater disadvantage when a modified camshaft is utilized.

Some engines have dished pistons which enables them to offer several different compression ratios with the

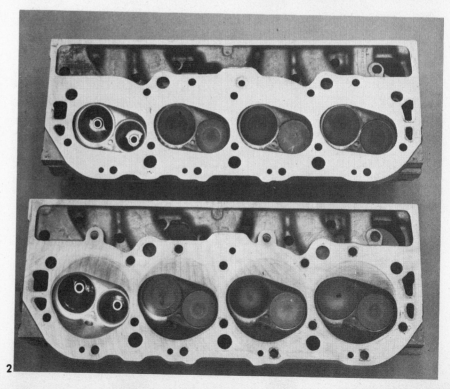

same bore, stroke, and head. This has worked well for Detroit where such cost savings pay off big. Some rodders, in trying to follow this lead, have run into problems. In changing the piston head shape to obtain a lower compression—which may be common with a supercharged or big stroker—the rodder has inadvertently defeated the purpose of the original squish and quench areas! Detroit engineers can make such a change, because they always keep the squish and quench areas effective. The hot rodder who neglects this point is going to lose several "mechanical octanes" in his engine. Any piston used to lower compression should be de-

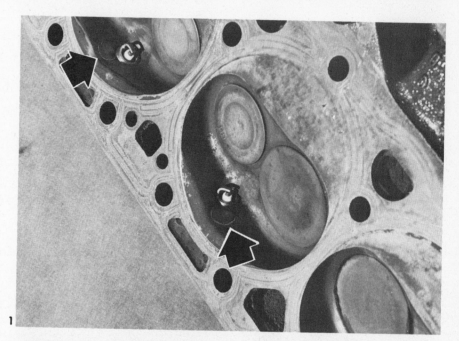

signed to keep the squish and quench areas as large as possible. These designs are more commonly known as "step" pistons because of the head shape.

THE HEMI

Perhaps the most famous combustion chamber is the hemispherical, introduced to the hot rodder in mass production by Chrysler from 1951-1958. The new Chrysler Hemi and the Ford Hemi engines retain this "half dome" chamber.

The shape gets its name from the fact that when viewed in section, it does form half of a sphere, at least when a flat top piston is used. There are many advantages to this chamber, as well as disadvantages.

The chief advantage offered by the Hemi is valve layout. With the intake valve located on the higher side of the chamber and the exhaust valve on the lower side—with both inclined away from the cylinder bore axis—the volumetric efficiency is far greater than can be obtained with the wedge chamber. This is especially true at

high rpm. The Hemi also allows a centrally located spark plug to keep the flame as short as possible.

The biggest disadvantages of this design are high production costs and lower combustion efficiency. The complicated valve layout, with twin rocker shafts and tricky rocker arms, runs the costs way up. The lower combustion efficiency, as compared to the wedge, results because the Hemi doesn't offer either squish or quench areas and because the lack of turbulence makes it more prone to detonation at comparable compression ratios. Higher octane fuels will cure this problem, however.

A small amount of turbulence is induced by the intake port and this can become a major factor at high rpm. Still, the wedge with the same compression ratio will run a lower octane gas without detonating. Domed pistons have been tried to give some squish and quench area where the top is near the valves, but the Hemi is still inferior to the wedge here. Detonation is not a major problem when alcohol-based fuels are used. This is the reason the Hemi has become the

undisputed, horsepower-producing champ of the big fuel burners.

One other type of combustion chamber is worth mentioning: the polysphere. Most famous in the 318 Dodge and Plymouth engines, it borrows a few features from the Hemi and a few from the wedge. The intake valves are located on the higher side of the chamber, inclined almost as much as those in a Hemi, while the exhausts are in the center of the chamber almost on the cylinder bore axis. The spark plug is near central location. A flat top piston is used and some squish and quench area is provided where the piston comes up close to the intake valve area. For power output from a given engine size, this shape seems to have a slight edge on a wedge, although it requires higher octane fuel for a given compression ratio. If you're looking for a place to get some unusual ponies, the polysphere chamber would bear investigation.

A word of caution: Hot rodders have a reputation of rushing in where fools fear to tread (or is that wise men?) Anyway, indiscriminate reshaping of a combustion chamber has become stock in trade of the "trick" head artists. But what they don't tell is the number of failures before a workable design was found. If you're not sure what is being done, stick with the stock head chamber shape and limit changes to piston top. And when the piston is being changed, keep squish and quench area considerations foremost, along with the critical problem of airflow across the chamber from intake to exhaust valve. Otherwise, the chamber is free to exploration for an extra hot horsepower or two. ♛

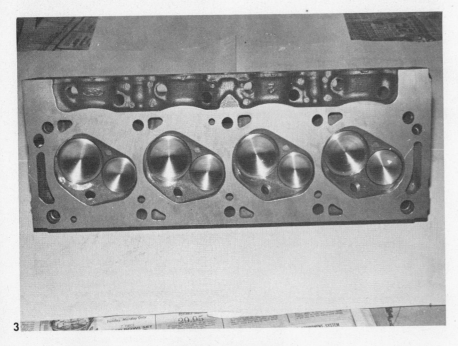

3

4

1. No backyard operation, arrows are pointing to iron plugs that have been epoxied into old spark plug holes on small-block Chevy. New plug holes are drilled, changing plug angle to take advantage of cooling intake gases and direct the flame over the piston dome for more power. The factory now makes a canted-plug head for small-blocks.

2. Chevy's '68 L-88 (427) head (top) had a closed chamber design. In '69, (bottom), chambers were opened up (ZL-1 head shown) for improved breathing and greater efficiency.

3. BOSS 302 head has been modified with 427 valves. The stems were cut down and regrooved to fit. Not much room left in those chambers.

4. Looking just a bit different from the L-88 is this Riley 2-port head. It was an early aftermarket conversion for the Model A. It replaced the stock head shown to the rear. Many were milled for even more compression but this particular one wasn't, for it still retains the lip around the chambers.

Headers and Mufflers

Headers are designed to play the sweet tune of improved performance—not to be merely an exercise in exotic plumbing.

As a piece of specialized high-performance equipment, the header is a Johnny-come-lately to hot rodding. Sure, we had some isolated exhaust experiments in the early days, but the real value of a custom exhaust system didn't become apparent until after WW II. Even then, most of the attention was paid to smooth-flowing bends in thin-wall steel tubing. Things like tuned length or collector boxes weren't common knowledge. The ohv engine and concentrated efforts for the last possible ounce of horsepower have changed all that.

The high-performance exhaust header (actually, the entire exhaust system) has undergone some strange and wonderful transitions during the past decade, and still the ultimate answer has not been found. The questions are as strong as ever: equal-length tube versus common collector; 3-tube versus 4-tube; cross-fire versus common collector. On and on it goes.

But no matter what end result may be desired, there are some basic aspects to headers that each rodder must understand. In the first place, a major percentage of any internal combustion engine's energy is passed out the exhaust system in the form of heat. Engineers have long since given up any hope of utilizing this spent energy effectively, except through turbosupercharging. It is possible, however, to use this mass of moving gas to advantage on the induction cycle. This, then, becomes a principal function of the header (other than relieving undue exhaust restrictions).

Since the exhaust system has the job of dissipating heat and gases, the factories have found that no tubing unit can compare with the cast iron exhaust manifolds for sheer brute service. The tubing header is constantly undergoing strong expansion and contractions due to uneven temperature changes, and this flexing will eventually cause small cracks to appear around the welds. While this will not be of major concern to the hot rodder, it cannot be tolerated by Detroit. The cast iron exhaust manifolds have nevertheless been improved through the years, when made possible by new innovations.

We continue to be amazed by the tremendous volume of high-performance headers being turned out by the speed industry, a volume surpassed only by custom wheels. Furthermore, anyone with a good design and production schedule can get into the header business with a reasonable expectation of success.

There are differences among headers, the distinction being in the intended use. The competition header may or may not include a collector box (and the collector block-off plate), while the street header must meet all the vehicle codes relative to cut-outs, smog equipment, etc. Natu-

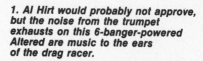

1. Al Hirt would probably not approve, but the noise from the trumpet exhausts on this 6-banger-powered Altered are music to the ears of the drag racer.

2. The new domestic mini-cars don't have to be mini-performers. This header system for the 2000cc Pinto is one quick way that you can improve performance.

3. Casler is one of the smaller header manufacturers but they have a header to fit almost any car/engine combination that you can imagine.

4. Header manufacturers make careful checks of clearances on mockup models before putting a new header into production.

5. Zinc plating gives shiny appearance to these Hooker small-block Chevy II and Camaro headers. Designed for all-round street and strip use, these headers provide low and mid-range torque needed by stockers.

6. Snowmobile craze has opened up new avenue for performance equipment manufacturers. This exhaust tuner is from Hooker.

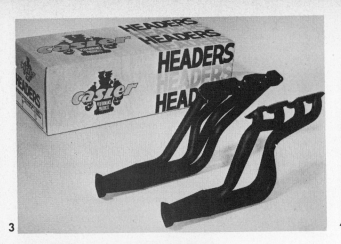

3

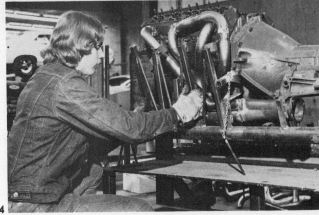

4

5

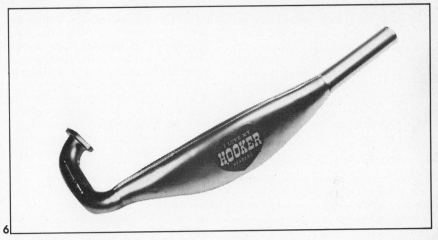

6

rally, the latter type accounts for the greatest percentage of sales, and because of the production problems involved, such a set cannot be called a "tuned" header in the strictest sense. Which brings up a major problem in header use.

A performance header is not an instant route to gobs of extra horsepower. While it is acknowledged that a good set of headers will increase the engine power up to 40%, such an increase is only possible if the engine is in the best possible state of tune *compatible with the headers!* This requirement for having the engine in tune cannot be overemphasized.

Quite often, the enthusiast will bolt on his shiny new tubing headers and expect great things, only to find the car actually goes slower. He immediately places the blame on the header. He fails to realize that the header is doing nothing more than pointing out a fault within the engine itself, For instance, if the car is equipped with a smog device in good working order, chances are the carburetor is adjusted until the engine is operating on a very fine edge, almost too lean. If the stock exhaust system, which has inherent restrictions, is removed, the engine can then breathe better. The mixture is then much too lean. In fact, dynamometer tests have shown this incorrect mixture condition

caused significant horsepower decreases when headers were installed without changing the air/fuel mixture of the engine.

The solution, then, is to install the headers recommended for the car (tell the manufacturer if the engine has been hopped up, what kind of equipment has been installed, etc.) and thoroughly retune the engine. Unless the carburetor has been running slightly rich, there will usually be little performance increase without retuning.

Interestingly enough, there is considerably more to the production of a set of headers than bending pipe. At the same time, the experiments necessary to produce a maximum design are staggering.

Construction of headers starts with selection of the right gauge pipe. To facilitate production, each bend is catalogued on a mandrel bender (such a bender does not neck-down the pipe diameter in the curved area). After the bends are made, the individual pipe sections are trimmed to length, if necessary, and positioned in a heavy-duty jig. All mating ends are tack-welded, then the header flange is arc-welded in place. Final welding of the tubing is by acetylene torch. An extra header flange is bolted to the original to minimize heat distortion.

After welding, the header flange is

ground smooth and checked for flatness. Of course, when the header is bolted to the engine and heated to running condition, the stresses created by welding will tend to normalize. Any cracks that show up in the system after prolonged use are the result of vibration and can usually be repaired quickly without removing the headers from the car.

To make sure that production headers will fit the average car, the original pattern is built around a typical car and checked many times for clearance. Whenever possible, a single design is created that will fit a wide variety of vehicle models, including those with power steering. This is not always the rule, however, and while it is possible to modify a set of headers to clear some particular obstacle, a custom header would be better.

While the competition header is aimed only at extracting the exhaust, the street header must channel the exhaust gas through a legal muffler system. To this end, the average street header will use a collector of about 3 ins. in diameter, with a block-off plate flange at the rear. To this flange may then be bolted a tapered secondary collector which cuts pipe size down from 3 to about 1¾ ins., or roughly the same diameter as the vehicle's head pipe. A big advantage of

Headers and Mufflers

this system, other than being perfectly legal, is that the muffler and tailpipe are usually suspended in rubber. By unbolting the head pipe from the header at the flange, the head pipe can be moved to one side and held in place by a bolt through each flange. This allows for occasional trips to the drags.

As delivered, most headers are painted. Some are sprayed with high-temperature paint, others with ordinary lacquer or enamel. Therefore that strong odor after starting the engine (following header installation) can be ignored. What can't be overlooked is the obvious increase in engine compartment noise level. Tubing headers are like organ pipes, in that they do not soak up the noises like cast iron headers. The engine will seem to ping noticeably with tubing headers, but this is mostly imagination. The trained ear can detect a car with headers, though, without ever lifting a hood.

HEADER TUNING

If you've read the chapter on intake and exhaust breathing, you're already familiar with the importance of header tuning, especially when maximum performance is desired. As a recap, remember that in the simplest terms we are confronted with both acoustical and inertia tuning, and each has a definite place in hot rodding.

Acoustical headers are the ones common to competition, where individual lengths of pipe are used, one for each cylinder. Because most engines develop maximum torque between 2000 and 5000 rpm, the tubes are between 25 and 68 ins. long. The tube diameters are not extremely critical, except to the exacting racer, as long as diameter is close to port size.

In the acoustical approach, hot gases rushing from a cylinder are under a compression of from 50 to 100 lbs., with a pressure wave that travels at about 1700 ft. per second. When this pressure wave leaves the open end of the tube, a suction wave is generated back up the tube. When the tube length is correct, the suction wave reaches the port near the end of the exhaust stroke and actually helps to suck residual gases from the combustion chamber. Obviously, if the timing of the suction wave is not correct, it will work as a hindrance.

While acoustical tuning is good for a very limited rpm range, it is not too hot for street use. So we turn to inertia tuning, where the weight of gases in motion is effective. Here pipe the same diameter as the port is used, and there are several approaches to the design. Long individual pipes of equal length can lead to a collector; two cylinders can be paired off (usually 90° to 130° apart), with the tubes joined in smooth fashion before reaching the collector. Or individual pipes of equal length can be set up 180° apart from bank to bank, following the firing order. The latter approach is the most sophisticated and is usually restricted to race cars because of the exotic design and construction problems involved in their formation.

The principle of inertia tuning is that exhaust gases have weight, which means they also have inertia. Since exhaust gas is expelled from the cylinder at high velocity—between 200 and 300 ft. per second—the mass will continue to move down the exhaust pipe even though the exhaust valve is closed. These loads will pulse in the exhaust pipe, with a resultant suction area between each pulse which can be used to scavenge the cylinders.

TYPES OF HEADER DESIGNS

It is in the individual header designs available commercially that the average enthusiast finds the confusion. Claims by this or that manufacturer do little to clear the picture. The unvarnished truth is that almost all headers will get the job done. Again, the crucial point is how well the header design is mated to the engine components. Individual pipes for each exhaust port may seem most effective, but a system taking advantage of maximum exhaust tuning effect may require a collector box, an expansion chamber, etc. Generally speaking, the collector box will add horsepower over individual pipes; most header manufacturers with lots of experience are adamant in their claims that collectors are absolutely necessary. Maybe even on supercharged rails.

The general feeling is that a collector takes maximum advantage of tuning; that is, by using a collector some

1. Small-block Chevy Corvettes will really turn on with headers. Set shown here is from Jardine.

2. Competition headers from Douglass are designed for 1968 Chevy II's and '67-'68 Camaros.

3. Beginning of any header or exhaust system starts with tube bending machine. Mercury Tubing machine is automatic. Various bends for a particular shape are programmed directly into the machine.

4. You can add style as well as performance with a set of Trend Setter side pipes for a Corvette.

5. Well designed exhaust extractor makes a big difference in the performance of a VW.

6. Corvair owners can replace the stock restricted exhaust system (bottom right) with either a dual exhaust system (upper right) or a header system (lower left).

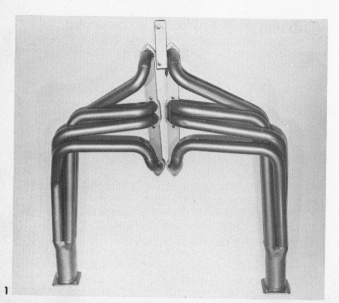

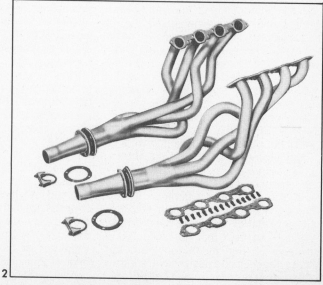

additional low-end power can be picked up for automatics. Or the rpm limit can be extended several hundred revs. The entire power curve can be reshaped simply by experimenting with the collector tube, so it must be important. In the complex combination of weight, traction, gearing, tire size, transmission type, shift points, etc., the collector can (and does) make the difference between winning and just being there.

There are two basic types of headers for competition: the individual pipes and the collectors, or boxes. In the collector design, the most common is the 4-tube unit. Ports thus breathe through separate pipes, each pipe free to make its own way rearward but with a minimum of bend restrictions. The collector tubes or boxes may be short or long, but almost always are tipped with a flange for either the block-off plate or the exhaust head pipe.

It is always interesting to see what this or that particular piece of equipment shows on the dynamometer, and in this case we can quote some figures Iskenderian has found. While working on camshaft development, Isky set up the dyno with a 350-cu.-in. Camaro with 12:1 pistons, reworked 375-hp fuel injection heads, dual 600-cfm Holley carbs, a Mallory distributor and an Isky RR-550 gear

3

4

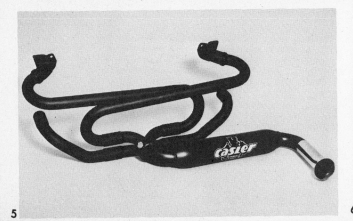

5

6

Headers and Mufflers

drive cam and kit.

Jerry Jardine assisted in the project, starting with a set of production 327 headers. After the first comparison tests between the open headers and the ordinary dynamometer mufflers, it was found that the headers actually registered 35 hp less, even though the fuel flow had been adjusted. Hmmmmm!

So referral to basic airflow was necessary. According to theory, the exhaust valve closes as the piston reaches the top of the exhaust stroke; the intake valve then opens on the piston downward travel. Trouble with this is that a quantity of burned gases would be left in the cylinder as the intake stroke began, which would dilute the incoming charge. To prevent this, the exhaust valve is held open after piston top dead center and the intake valve opens sooner. This overlap of the intake and exhaust valves can then be used to advantage, as the escaping exhaust gases can be used to scavenge the last of the burned gases and actually help the incoming charge enter the cylinder. This is apparent to a very great degree in all-out racing engines, where some incoming mixture may actually be drawn out the exhaust system in an unburned state.

An important thing to note here is that an exhaust system could actually overscavenge—that is, draw out too much of the unburned fuel mixture. Isky figured the Jardine header was, in fact, doing exactly that.

To check their theory, they bolted an extra 18-in. collector onto the short stock collector. This would create a slight back pressure which would result from the drop in exhaust gas velocity. The dyno showed a return of the lost 35 horses, with a couple extra to boot. At the same time, the power curve was much smoother, especially at the lower rpm range where the street machine can use it.

Using the information thus gained, Jardine made up several sets of special headers to find out what the perfect diameter and length should be. Different sizes and shapes of collectors were tried, as well as various engine tuning methods. After three months and 600 runs on the dynamometer, it was proven that the right header/engine tuning combination depended largely upon the collector shape and length, and that the results could not be duplicated by engine tuning alone. That's a pretty strong argument in favor of collectors in particular and headers in general.

As it turned out, the best header for this engine (which could be termed a typical hot rod powerplant), used 32-in. primary pipes with 1¾-in. diameter. Each header had a 3-in. grouping area where the pipes terminated in a 3-in. diameter collector which was 23 ins. long.

During the experiments, a small pyramid-shaped airfoil was placed between the ends of the four pipes in the grouping area, thus forming a small spike that extended into the collector. This hot rod gimmick showed an immediate 7-hp gain throughout the power range. This device is not new, but it works. It serves to streamline the exhaust flow into the collector and to prevent too rapid a drop in velocity. Incidentally, there are some other minor factors that enter the picture, so while it may work with one header, it will not necessarily work with another.

After installing the 600 Magnum cam and four Weber carbs, this engine pulled a whopping 533 hp. On a 427 Chevy scheduled for Bonneville, individual pipes produced 44 horses less than the same headers with a slip-on collector.

Jere Stahl feels that collector length is critical, since camshaft design is being upgraded so rapidly. He has found that the collector should be a minimum of 15 ins. long, measured from the tip of the four individual pipes. Maximum length should be 22 ins. For more low end, Jere believes a long collector the best, teamed with a leaned mixture. As for header design itself, he feels the Tri-Y design is best for general use, although the proper independent header tuned with the engine can't be beat by the Tri-Y.

Gary Hooker (the one with heart) insists that no one exhaust combination is right for every application. Tests have to be run on the car to find out what is exactly right for the existing conditions. Gary has found that Chrysler wedges and Hemis are best with a 12-in. (by 3-in.-diameter) collector behind a 6-in. transition. This is for an engine over 340 cu. ins. Under that displacement, a 2½-in. collector is best, 12 ins. long. As to Tri-Y versus 4-tube, he feels the 4-tube is best for a sharp engine, the Tri-Y best for anything in less than perfect tune.

1. Thanks to good design, the installation of Thrush Outsiders is a simple backyard operation.

2. Hooker adjustable headers incorporate removable collector. Hot rodder can install special inserts to lengthen the primary pipes for more torque and low-rpm power on tracks with good traction.

3. Collector portion of header is first tack welded to individual pipes. Afterwards a bead will be run around entire collector to seal leaks.

4. Cyclone header-equipped Boss 302 Mustang turned 13.8's first time out.

5. Stock exhaust pipes have to be cut for header installation. Flanges will be welded to ends of cut pipes.

6. Zoomie headers sweep back and upward. They are most common to rails and funny cars.

7. This header system exits outside the body to take maximum advantage of equal length design with minimum number of bends.

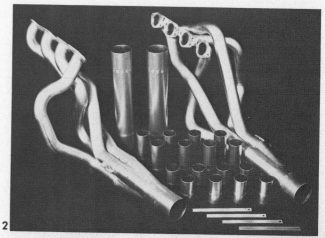

Jerry Belanger uses a different type of collector on his headers, called a reverse tapered cone. It starts at 4½ ins. O.D. at the grouping area and tapers to 2½ ins. O.D. within 12 ins. of length. Although his collectors show a definite advantage in street use, he doesn't feel collectors per se are necessary for the supercharged car. The Tri-Y headers are strong up to 2500 rpm; above that the individual pipes are stronger.

Don King of Cyclone believes firmly in collectors for all engines. Standard Cyclone collectors are about 8 ins. long, with new extensions bringing them out to 28 ins. total.

From the foregoing it is possible to see that the trend is to a collector somewhere between 12 and 30 ins. long (the average seems to be around 18 ins.), with a diameter of 3 ins. for the big engines and 2½ ins. for the smaller displacements. In all cases, because of the trial and error involved, it is best to start with something too long and cut the pipe off in 4½- or 5-in. lengths until the performance starts to fall off, then add a couple of inches. As to the type of header, the Tri-Y is best for the average street machine; the 4-tube is better for competition.

Recently Mickey Thompson has come up with some more facts about headers and collectors. While setting up a header design for a Detroit marque, Mickey found that the perfect pipe length might show one horsepower reading with straight pipe, quite another reading when curves were involved. Intricate bends in tubing rob power, caused by back pressure. To demonstrate, Thompson used two pieces of equal length exhaust tubing, one straight, the other bent with a few mild-angle bends. At 1 in. of vacuum on the flow bench, the curved pipe moved 26 cfm of air, while the straight pipe showed 38 cfm.

Based on these experiments, Mickey has developed what he calls the

Super Scavenger. The header design uses as few bends as possible, although each pipe is equal length. The difference in length is taken up by extending each pipe into a long, tapered collector.

Howard Douglass, an oldster who has literally grown up with the hot rod sport, has as much experience with headers as anyone. His firm, Douglass Muffler, is perhaps the largest exhaust system specialist in the country and annually ships over 200,000 mufflers. When we talked

with him about headers, he "dropped everything" to show us the real nitty-gritty about construction.

Howard has found that any time an equal-length header design is involved, it becomes an experience in clearances. Most modern cars hardly have enough room for a cast iron header, let alone a snake's den of tubing. Therefore, pipes that are wandering around hither and yon must practically touch each other. That's *practically* touch—they shouldn't actually come into contact.

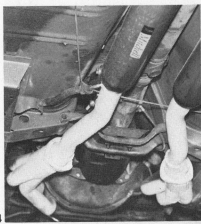

Headers and Mufflers

This is why he has installed three very special (and costly) programmed mandrel tubing benders that can create compound curves of extremely short radius. At the same time, he has come up with a unique device for shaping the ends of each pipe until they fit perfectly with the flange port.

In keeping with the precision production approach, the flange-mounting holes are punched (these are often drilled) to insure perfect accuracy, and if a particular pipe does not fit exactly during the jig welding process, it is discarded. The average Douglass header is made up of four single pieces of pipe, with no welds between header flange and collector.

It is obvious that the well-designed header is bound to encourage engine response, but the key to this axiom is the phrase ''well-designed.'' Header manufacturers have not arrived at their particular designs simply by cutting and welding. Indeed, it is possible to send power plummeting should the design and construction be crude. This does not, however, preclude your successfully building a set of homegrowns.

In fact there are several header kits on the market that contain everything you need to produce a good set. They have been cut and trimmed and in general set up so all you need do is weld. This alone will save a big buck. At the same time, there are simple header flange kits available, as well as 180°-bend tubing. The cutting has not been done here, but that is accomplished by either a hacksaw or tin snips, and you're on your own as to design. The best approach with this basic kit is to duplicate a production header as nearly as possible.

You'll find working with an exhaust system quite pleasant, but don't expect it to be an afternoon affair. Lots of hard work is required when you don't have all the jigs that go into production header welding, but it's worth it.

A FINAL WORD—ON NOISE

Pardon us while we get a little technical, because the subject of automobile noise is something that just can't be handled by a flat statement—although you're most likely to get a very flat statement from the law if your car's noise is too great.

You see, it has been proven that the aggravating aspects of noise cause fatigue and sometimes illness.

A very loud or grating noise may get on the nerves instantly, but the lower noise may do more damage over the long run. The body unconsciously uses energy to fight noise—that is, to shut it out.

Sound is caused by a series of alternating pressure vibrations in the atmosphere, with the audible range between 16 and 16,000 variations per second for the average person. The rate of variation is the frequency and number of complete cycles of change per second, with a continuous series of such variation of a single frequency setting up a pure tone. It is possible for different frequencies or modes of vibration to be superimposed on an existing vibration, like a stack of pancakes. If the superimposed frequencies are simple multiples of the original, a harmonics series results in a musical sound. But if the frequency range extends throughout and beyond the audible range, you end up with ''noise''—that is, a roar or rattle or hiss (the scientific name is *aperiodic* sound).

The car emits five typical noises: exhaust, intake, body, aerodynamic and mechanical. Careful design can eliminate or drastically reduce the last three, but the first two can only be suppressed. It is possible to silence a car engine in one of three ways: by baffles, with absorption by the phenomenon of resonant absorption or by absorption through acoustic-absorbing materials. As far as we're concerned, the baffle method is out, having been tried in the past to the definite disadvantage of engine performance. The resonance absorption

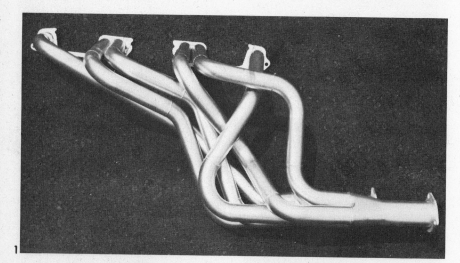

1. Clifford put out these Vipar tuned headers for all Firebird and Tempest ohc Pontiacs with 230 to 250-cu.-in. engines in the 1967-70 series.

2. Header manufacturers often go to great lengths (no pun intended) to achieve equal length tubes working within the confines of a given body configuration.

3. If you fabricate your own headers, don't forget the tubes have to be matched to head size and shape.

4. Jardine design for new low compression engines incorporates a tapered collector which results in better extraction.

5. For the do-it-yourselfer, Douglass manufactures precision formed exhaust header flange kits.

6. There is limited space under most cars but specialized headers are available for practically all makes. Buying a set that has been tested on your type of engine is so much easier, and usually less expensive, than trying to build your own.

7. Mercury Tube bending machine is fully automatic. Just install a tube, push the button, and zap, instant exhaust pipe!

4

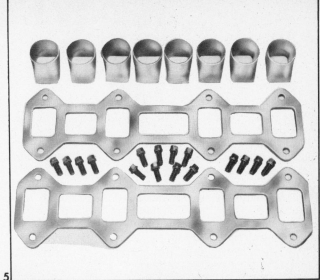

5

method has some tricky mechanical engineering problems, so that leaves the acoustic-absorption method—which is exactly what we have in the typical straight-through muffler.

We checked into the muffler situation with Howard Douglass, who has been around long enough to know far more than we do about high-performance ''silencing.'' It turns out that experience has shown the simple steel-pack muffler to be superior to the more popular glass-pack (although the steel-pack was all we had in the hot rod sport for several years). The reason is that fiberglass has a tendency to trap and hold moisture—which is natural to the engine—leading to an early corrosion factor, while the steel will heat up throughout and evaporate the water. Of course, the steel-pack is slightly heavier.

In the straight-through muffler design which Douglass helped to pioneer, the sound is frictionally dampened, especially effective in the higher frequency waves (that's why some mufflers on strong engines give a pleasant, almost musical sound). In such a muffler design, the absorbent material must be at least one inch thick to be effective at all, and special attention must be given the core pipe design.

Sound waves pass through holes far more readily than does the gas flow. Still, it has been found that if the core is stabbed full of holes with the lips facing the packing, the noise level is reduced well below that in a core with drilled holes. To this end, Douglass has created a unique ''core machine'' that can instantly turn a 6-in. piece of steel strip into a very efficient core. We were appalled to learn, however, that only the better speed shops have understood this principle, with a great percentage of

6

7

the buying public still sticking with the ''sliced'' or ''sawed'' core pipe.

As to the difference in core or center pipe size—if there is a difference in the size of inlet or outlet pipe, then the muffler is no longer a true straight-through design. That is why some of the performance mufflers use a slightly smaller outlet (exhaust pipe end) diameter, which tends to reduce the noise level even more while slightly raising back pressure.

Construction of the muffler itself is a great variable, but Douglass prefers to stick with an 18-gauge core and 16-gauge steel for the outer case. The heavier case will obviously last much longer, and the round configuration eliminates drumming, a sound that is common with the flattened or oval automotive muffler.

As for the life of a muffler, it really doesn't seem to make a significant difference whether construction is by crimping or welding. A perfectly stock Detroit muffler, which has the unenviable reputation of lasting only long enough for the car to get out of the showroom, is usually of the crimped type. Here the failures are usually from corrosion and internal construction breakdown rather than from the end caps coming off.

The amount of sound absorption that any particular straight-through muffler will register is a variable of design, but as an example, a glass-pack 18 ins. long will normally lop off around 25% of the high-frequency waves, while two of these mufflers in series will take care of 65%. Certainly back pressure will be slightly higher with the series application, but this is a graphic explanation of why a long straight-through muffler is so much more effective in cutting abrasive noise.

Unfortunately, you can't have your cake and eat it too when it comes to mufflers and headers. A good muffler and minimum-bend exhaust pipe will certainly cut exhaust flow restriction to a minimum, but maximum performance is still going to be obtained with a muffler disconnected from the collector box. About the only way you'll ever get to check this out is on a chassis dynamometer, and even then the horsepower differential is not great. Suffice it for us to say that mufflers from a reputable firm have been tested for the car. The sound is something else, something only you can determine—and that depends on whether you want a low, low rumble or a throaty growl.

Handy Header Hints

How to get maximum performance on a minimum budget and a few hours of time.

Headers, mufflers, collectors, U-bends, flanges or kits—you name it, and it's available. Whether you're driving a little 4-cyl. Pinto or a 454-cu.-in. Chevy V-8, there's something out there waiting for you. While most manufacturers offer only completely welded headers, there are still a few providing complete kits—all the bends, flanges, collectors, what have you—so you can build your own headers without having to worry about bending and cutting your own tubes, etc. Of course, if you really dig working things out, don't mind the extra work involved and want to save a few bucks, you can buy U-bends in different sizes along with flange plates and collectors from many specialty firms or your nearest speed shop.

But right here and now, we're going to show you what's involved in header installations on three popular small cars—a 1973 Pinto, a 1974 Vega and a Mustang II V-6—courtesy of Doug Thorley Headers, 7403 Telegraph Road, Los Angeles, Calif. Basically a breeze to install, the Pinto's headers shouldn't be beyond the capability of any Saturday afternoon mechanic. The Vega is a slightly different story, as its intake manifold sits

HOW-TO: Pinto Headers

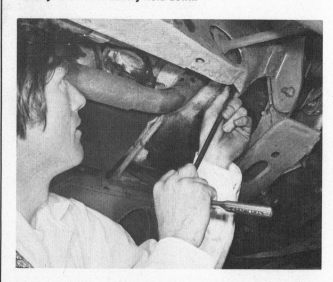

1. Pinto 2000cc installation should take you between 1½ and 2 hours, providing you have all the necessary tools and work steadily. Start with battery hold-down.

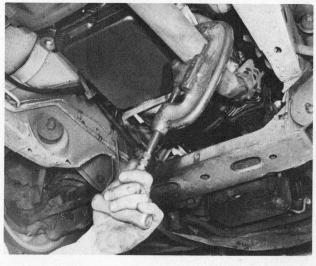

2. Lift battery out carefully and place it out of the way, then remove the four bolts holding the battery box on fender panel. This is slow work on the bottom two bolts.

3. You will notice that Brad uses a long extension and socket from underneath to disconnect the muffler inlet pipe from the exhaust manifold flange.

4. Make a rough cut of the inlet pipe about here. To speed things along, we used a pipe cutter, but a hacksaw will do the job just as effectively.

directly over the exhaust manifold, presenting somewhat more of a challenge, especially on 1974 versions equipped with the EGR system. And all we can say for the Mustang II V-6 is that it presents a real headache, even to the experienced installer. Frankly, the header people aren't happy with the prospects for this one, but the race is on and they'll all be selling kits despite their dismay.

You see, the Mustang II is a special case. Ford's better idea for 1974 has turned out to be a repairman's nightmare, with everything packed tightly in place—just take a look at where they put the starter motor and you'll see what we mean. If you own a Mustang II V-6 and just can't wait to slap on a set of headers, consider the following first. The Ford shop manual lightly passes off exhaust manifold removal by simply stating, ''Remove the manifold attaching nuts.'' Well, friends, that's the understatement of the year.

What they neglect to mention is that removing the manifold attaching nuts is an almost impossible task, especially for those working with hand tools. Unless you work slowly, apply even pressure and swear a lot, the chances are excellent that you'll break at least two of the 12 nuts off, which means pulling the heads, leading to all kinds of problems that we'd rather not even think about. So if you're not really cool with a wrench in hand, we suggest that you let a pro install the header kit on this baby.

With the help of Doug Thorley Headers' two R&D experts, we've installed a Thorley kit on each of the three cars mentioned, and on the following pages, we pass along to you their wisdom, accumulated during 13 combined years of experience with designing and installing headers on all kinds of vehicles. The Mustang II V-6 installation was done with prototype headers which will be in production by the time that you read this, accounting for the many visible welds in the set that we used. So if you're ready, let's follow Brad Anderson and Omer Clautier as they show us how it's done—the right way.

5. As you can see, there's a considerable length of the inlet pipe to be disposed of when installing a header kit like the one we have.

6. A little cussing and much fussing will let you remove the heat stove. As this Pinto is equipped with a Weiand manifold and Holley carb, it's not used and will not be replaced.

7. Once all these goodies are out of the way, you can unbolt and remove the stock exhaust manifold unit. Take off the old gasket and throw it away.

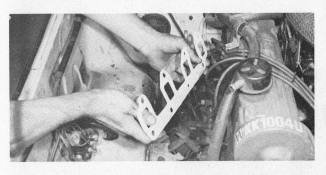

8. There's no difficulty in telling how the new gasket furnished with the header kit should go. Just slip it in place over the studs.

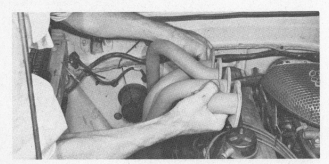

9. You'll find it necessary to loosen the alternator. Homer used a pry bar from underneath to move the motor over slightly while Brad slipped the header in from topside.

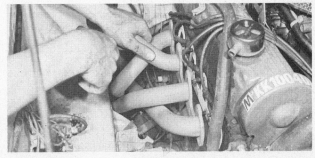

10. Once the header is positioned between the engine and frame, hang it in place on the studs and make sure the gasket doesn't slip off.

11. As the studs are much longer than necessary when installing headers, kit includes a set of pre-cut spacers to be used before replacing the nuts.

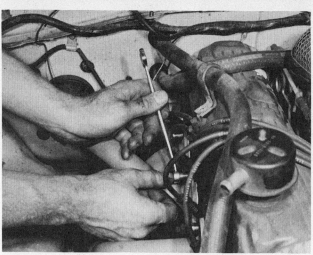

12. Fit nuts onto the studs and tighten with a wrench. There's no torque requirement here, but you should tighten them all snugly.

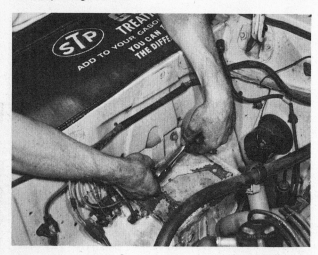

13. When replacing the battery box, the top two bolts go in easily, but as space is limited to reinstall the lower W, try slotting the holes to make the job easier.

14. Replace whatever fixtures you had to remove to gain access to the exhaust manifold. On this particular Pinto, it was just this hose clamp.

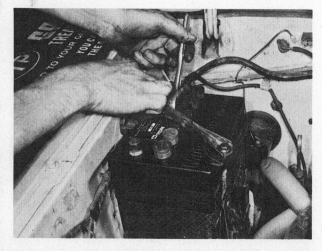

15. Set the battery back in place and reposition the holddown, then tighten. Don't forget to tighten the alternator bracket before putting your tools away.

16. This finishes the topside part of the Pinto installation and here's how your completed work under the hood should look. Now we go back under the car.

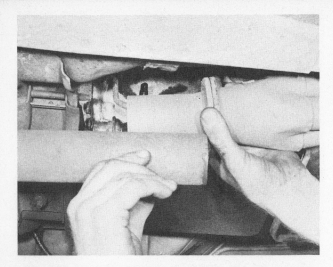

17. Holding the header adapter in place, Brad brings the muffler inlet pipe alongside it to mark for a finish cut. Set the adapter down and cut the pipe.

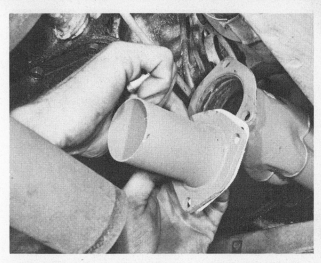

18. Don't forget to install the gasket provided with the adapter. Once the adapter is bolted in place, the inlet pipe should butt against it.

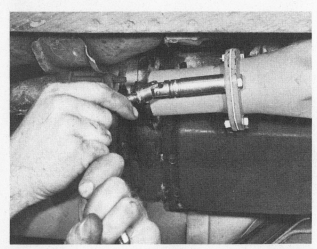

19. Now tighten the adapter bolts in 1-2-3 rotation. There's a lot of vibration inherent in the 2000cc engine, so you'll need to recheck these after a brief run-in period.

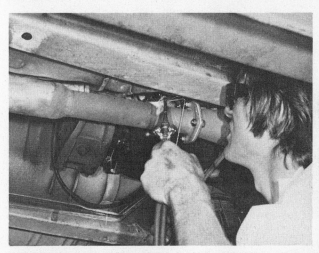

20. You will notice here that the muffler inlet pipe and adapter are welded together. Resonator unit shown on this particular car is not a stock installation.

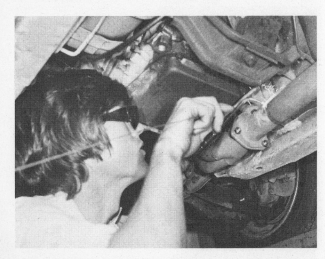

21. Because of that excessive vibration we mentioned, be sure and take pains to make this welded joint as strong as possible or unwanted problems can develop.

22. As a final precaution, Thorley recommends and Brad installs a ⅛- x 1-in. support strap connected to a trans hold-down bolt and welded to the inlet pipe to complete the job.

HOW-TO: Vega Headers

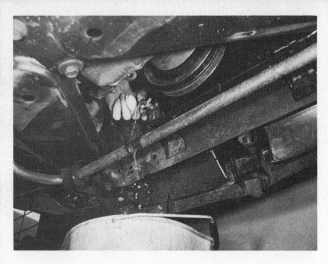

1. First step in installing Vega headers is to drain the radiator. This might sound strange, but L-11 engine circulates coolant through intake manifold passages.

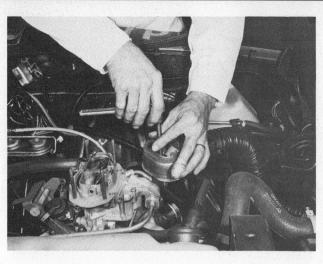

2. Disconnect and remove air cleaner from the carburetor, then unbolt the hot air duct and take it off. Disconnect all linkage, vacuum and fuel lines, plugging the latter.

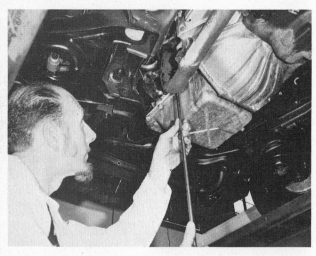

3. From underneath the car, Omer unbolts the attaching nuts that hold the inlet pipe to the exhaust manifold. A long extension is a blessing in disguise here.

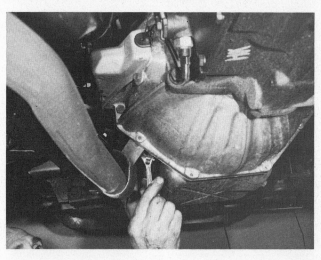

4. The bellhousing clamp that holds the inlet pipe has to come off first in order to drop the pipe free of the exhaust manifold flange.

5. Back on top again, Omer removes the alternator. This is necessary to provide access to the bolts at that end of the intake manifold.

6. A slip-fit metal tube connects the EGR valve on the intake manifold with an outlet on the exhaust manifold. This one was frozen and required a touch of heat.

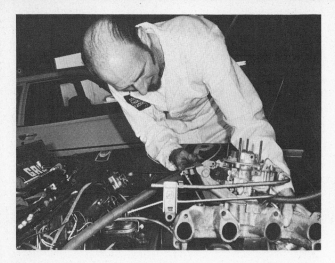

7. After unbolting the intake manifold, it can be lifted up and out of position. Set it out of the way carefully to prevent accidental damage.

8. Here's that pipe that gave us so much trouble. This must be adapted before being replaced, so you'll have to remove it from the EGR housing. Vegas before '74 don't have it.

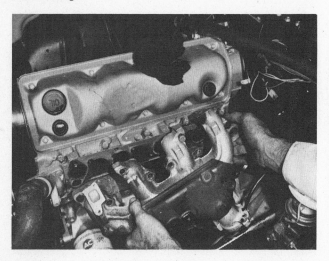

9. Removing the exhaust manifold is a breeze now that the hard work has been done. Unbolt and lift the manifold off. Set it to one side, as you'll need it again.

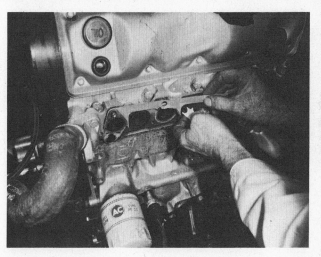

10. With most Vegas, you can simply peel off the old gasket and throw it away. A single gasket serves for both the intake and exhaust units.

11. Unfortunately, the 1974 Vegas use a sort of epoxy to hold the gasket in place. This necessitates cleaning the gasket area with a scraper to get the old one all off.

12. Once the surface is clean, position the new gasket furnished. New gasket is slightly different in shape, so be sure you have it on correctly to prevent blocking water tube.

13. Next, you have to unbolt and remove the motor mount and its bracket on the driver's side. Header cannot be installed without this step. We know—we tried.

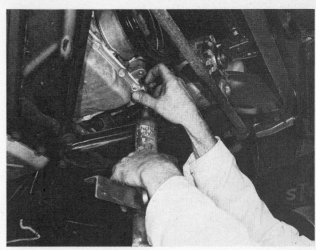

14. With the motor mount/bracket removed, Omer used a hydraulic jack to lift the engine up about 1½-in. to give sufficient room between frame and engine for installation.

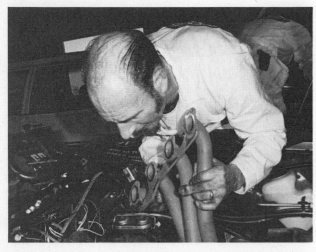

15. At last! Omer is now able to slide the header down from the top between engine and frame, positioning it by screwing in two bolts to hold it in place.

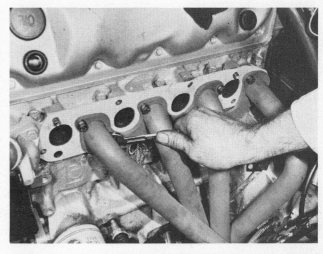

16. New bolts furnished with the kit are installed by hand and then tightened down snugly with a wrench—no torque requirements here.

17. Hot air takeoff is removed from exhaust manifold. While many don't bother with reinstalling this, we went the route. You'll have to trim it slightly with tin snips.

18. Here's what the adapted heat stove looks like. We used two clamps to hold it in place. Don't tighten clamps until intake manifold is replaced.

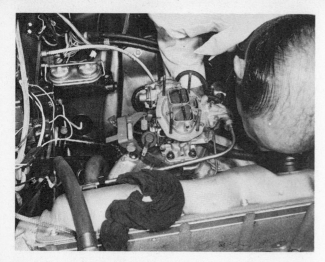

19. After reinstalling the intake manifold and tightening it in place, the hot air takeoff is brought up against manifold bottom and the clamps tightened.

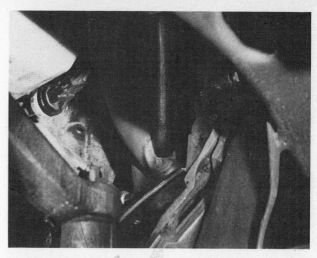

20. Here's that pesky EGR tube, adapted and arc welded in place against header inlet. Position the tube and mark it carefully before cutting it.

21. Reconnect all linkage, vacuum and fuel lines, then replace hot air duct. Topside work is now done except for reinstalling the air cleaner.

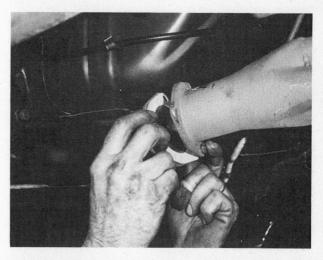

22. Reducer unit and gasket are installed on header. Bring muffler inlet pipe alongside reducer, then mark and cut it for the correct length.

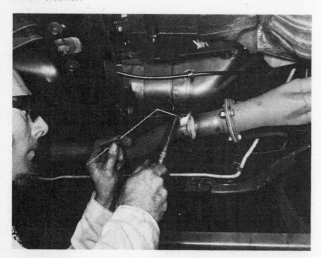

23. Inlet pipe is positioned with reducer and the two are welded together. Be sure to reinstall the bellhousing clamp around the inlet pipe.

24. Don't forget to refill the radiator as your final step, then start and idle motor until it reaches normal operating temperature. Recheck water level and bolts and you're done.

HOW-TO: Mustang II Headers

1. Mustang II with V-6 engine is a real bear to work on. Brad begins installation by disconnecting the dual exhaust inlet pipes from the manifold flanges.

2. A rough cut of the inlet pipes is made and the excess pipe discarded. A pipe cutter like this really speeds the job along, borrow one if you can.

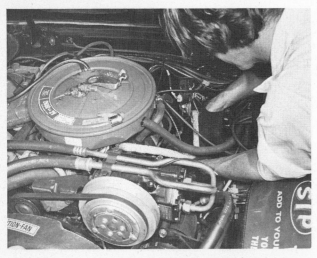

3. You'll have to work pretty much by touch when removing the manifold bolts. Work slowly as bolt pitch differs from that in manifold; too much pressure will twist bolt head off.

4. If that happens, you're in real trouble, so go easy and take your time. With luck, you'll be able to lift out this side in about 20 minutes.

5. The other side is even worse because the heat stove, an alternator bracket and other goodies interfere. Remove the upper bolts from topside.

6. You may find lower bolt removal easier from underneath, but again, you'll need a long extension and socket, as well as lots of patience.

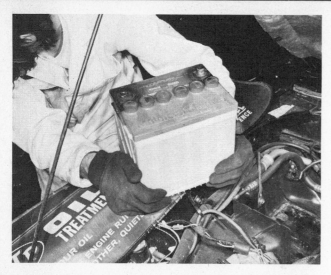

7. Battery removal, as on the Pinto 2000cc installation, is a necessity here to make enough room in which to work. Gloves are a good bet to prevent burns from a hot engine.

8. The air injection manifold connects to the rear of each exhaust manifold and must be disconnected before attempting to remove either manifold.

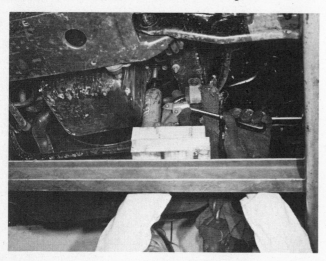

9. Unbolt the motor mount on the passenger side and jack up the engine about 2 ins. It's the only way to remove the heat stove.

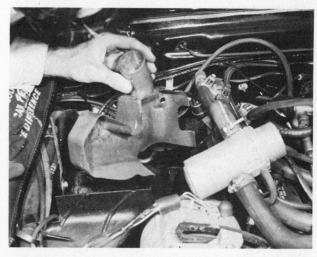

10. Once the engine is tilted sufficiently, you can angle the heat stove up and out of position. This one also takes patience, but we won't replace it, so take heart.

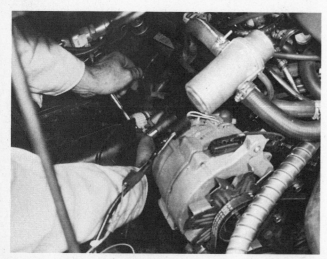

11. Now you can get that final manifold bolt that a few minutes ago, you swore was simply unreachable. Remember to remove it with care breaking this last one would be too much.

12. When all six bolts have been removed, the exhaust manifold should come off without any difficulty. Take a deep breath and a ten-minute break you deserve it.

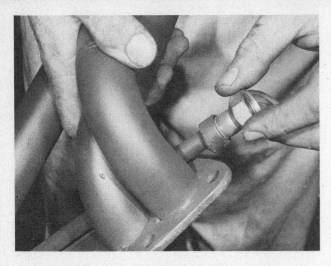

13. This fitting for the air injection manifold connection must be removed from the exhaust manifold and threaded into the header that goes on the passenger side.

14. With the engine jacked up, reach down and unscrew the oil filter. You can then angle the header unit into position from topside.

15. Kit includes a new set of shorter hex head bolts to install headers with. A 5/16-in. Allen wrench will do the trick nicely. Bolting these on is a pleasure after the others.

16. The header for the driver's side also angles into place from above. Don't forget to install the new gaskets that are provided with the kit.

17. Bolt the header in place using the hex head wrench. Again, there's no torque requirement here, but tighten them as snugly as you can.

18. Once the headers are installed and tightened, remove the jack to lower the engine back on its mount and then you can replace the mount bolt.

19. The tube leading from the EGR valve to the header is replaced and tightened snugly. Also connect the air injection manifold on this side.

20. This adapter replaces the heat stove. Metal end fits up against the front header pipe and is clamped in place securely with the device provided.

21. While Brad fastens the heat stove replacement from above, Omer makes a final cut of the inlet pipe so that it will butt against adapters on each side.

22. Adapters are installed with their gasket and bolted tightly in place. The V-6 also has its share of vibration problems, so tightly means tightly.

23. A nice, neat weld of the inlet pipe to the adapters on each side brings the installation close to completion, some four hours later. Plan on a whole day if you do it alone.

24. Spare no pains to make this final step properly. It's important. Be sure that each weld is a full 360° and then you're ready for the road.

Street Rod Headers

Even though the various header manufacturers produce free-flowing exhaust systems for virtually any year, make and model of car you care to name, as well as special header setups for the more popular engine swaps, the street rodder can still come up with enough extraordinary car/engine combinations to keep well ahead of the aftermarket header people. If you're planning on shoehorning a small-block Chevy into a Vega or Pinto, there are packaged exhaust systems tailor-made for the combination. But if you've managed to drop a Rat motor into a Crosley station wagon, then all the searching in the world for a set of ready-mades will be a total waste of time. If there's no way on earth to utilize the stock exhaust manifolds, due to chassis/body clearances, then the only way out is to whip together your own headers using assorted lengths and sizes of exhaust tubing as starters.

Naturally, when fabricating your own headers, the engine and transmission must be mounted in the chassis, and anything that might conceivably interfere with exhaust system clearance must similarly be bolted in; steering, brake master cylinder (if it's under the floor), battery (ditto), clutch linkage, and so forth. In short, you'll need to worm your header pipes down, around, and under the chassis accessories (taking into consideration clearance to allow for engine torque-

HOW-TO: Header Fabrication

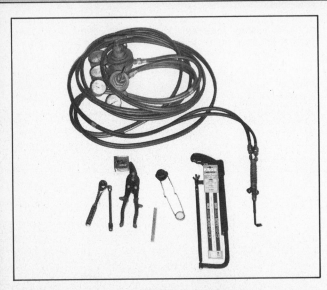

1. Welding equipment, including rod and striker, hacksaw with spare blades soapstone stick, right-hand snips, tape measure, and a 7/16-in. socket wrench are only tools needed.

2. Exhaust system pieces include header flanges for AMC V-8, gaskets and header bolts, four 90° elbow bends of both 1⅝-in. and 1¾-in. diameter, and pair of 2-port tubes.

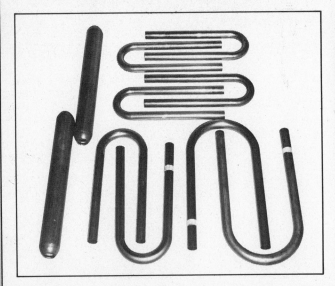

3. Other bits are 28-in. mufflers (optional), and four each of 1⅝-in. and 1¾-in. U-bends. Long "legs" of U-bends supplied enough straight tubing for project.

4. Here's why the header route was only way to go with this installation. Stock AMC right-side exhaust manifold pointed directly at '36 Ford frame crossmember.

over), so they must all be bolted in place for you to determine proper pipe routing.

However, plan your rod building procedures so that header fabrication comes *before* the body is installed. Of course, you'll have to transfer various body measurements to the chassis to make sure your header outlets aren't aimed right at the firewall or some other critical body part or mounting brackets. This can be done with the tape measure, and even cardboard templates of your firewall, cowl, and/or forward floorboard if you're so inclined. You'll learn quickly to appreciate the working room if you let body installation come at a later time, especially if that big V-8 is deeply buried back in the firewall.

The somewhat rare engine/chassis combination depicted here was typical of those for which no factory headers were available, and there was simply no way to keep the original cast iron manifolds due to frame interference. Are you ready for a big American Motors V-8 into a mid-'30's Ford? The starting point for header building was merely a handful of rather basic home-garage tools and a gas welding rig, a pile of exhaust tubing in straight lengths and U-bends, of both 1⅝-ins. and 1¾-ins. in diameter, a pair of 2-port collector tubes, and two all-important header flange plates. The latter are available from most any header manufacturer or speed shop for any American and most foreign engines you can possibly dream up. The car in question was also to be fitted with a couple of 28-in. glass-pack mufflers so these were acquired with the rest of the exhaust system pieces. But once the headers themselves are hung on your own engine, the routing of the rest of the exhaust system and the choice and placement of mufflers is strictly up to you and your particular car. Hence, we'll only go as far as the flanged header outlets in the saga that follows. ◆

5. Stock manifold was removed, header flange plate put on using special header bolts (with small diameter heads). Flange plates usually come with tube stubs welded on.

6. Tin snips are used to carefully trim tube stub away so section of elbow bend can nestle as closely as possible to block for inner fender panel clearance.

7. Piece of elbow bend is trimmed with snips, then held up for match check with stub. Good fit of adjoining tube pieces simplifies welding, keeps job looking neat.

8. First tube section is tack welded to stub, another section cut and fitted to form smoothly-flowing pipe. It, in turn, is tack welded to first section.

9. Another section of bend is trimmed and fitted to the adjoining cylinder tube. Firing order should be checked so two consecutive cylinders don't siamese together.

10. Rear two pipes will join into one later on, but now another piece of elbow tube is mated to its stub on the flange plate. First two cylinder tubes will also join.

HOW-TO: Header Fabrication

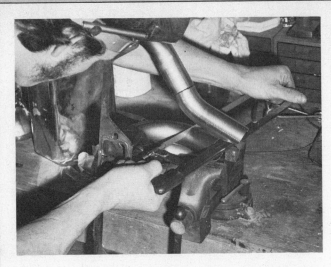

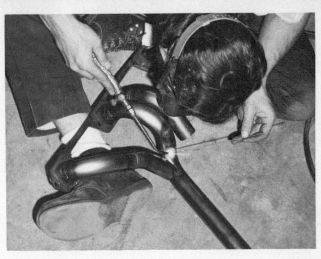

11. Flange plate is removed from engine and clamped in a vise. Blade is turned on saw to trim tubes where they will join as in a Y. Final trim will be with tin snips.

12. One pair of header tubes is joined to a straight length of tube. It won't be this long when done, though, only a few inches will be retained. Welding is just easier like this.

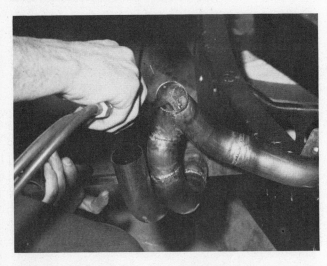

13. Where tubes joined in a Y, only one tube was trimmed before welding. Now, torch is inserted through open end and wall of second tube of Y is burned away.

14. Partially completed header is bolted back on engine for one-of-many fit checks. Clearance around accessories is a never-ending problem, requires constant checking.

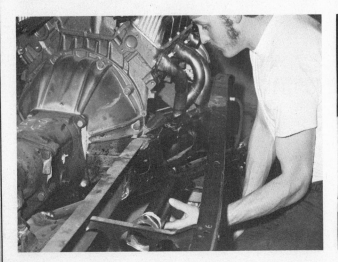

15. Tubing would have had to make a too-tight bend to be routed through oval hole in Ford frame where original pipe exited, so it's routed under the crossmember.

16. First cylinder on the right engine bank is attacked. It will join the second cylinder in another Y. This will give two oulets which will be joined by 2-port collector.

17. Note how several short sections of elbow- and U-bend tubing are fitted into system to produce smoothly flowing header contours. Again, check clearances as you proceed.

18. Final welding on right-side header brings four port tubes into a pair of Y's, then that pair into the 2-port collector at point where system passes under the frame.

19. Another angle reveals how "basket of snakes" worms its way around frame member, has been kept to block for fender clearance. Collector tube flange was prewelded.

20. Left-side header was fabricated in same way, except cylinder pairing differed because of firing order. Also, header flange plate was cut for removal over steering.

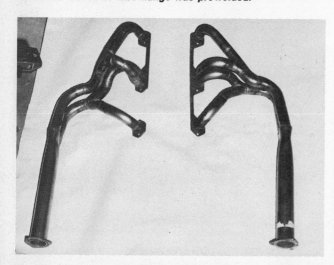

21. The headers removed from engine. Note how port pairing was achieved for alternating firing order, and how left flange plate was cut to allow remove/replace over steering.

22. Final operation was having headers sandblasted to get rid of weld scale, then having them aluminum metal-sprayed for appearance' sake. Mufflers will bolt to rear flanges.

Cosworth Vega - 4 for 1, 2 for all

Four valves per cylinder, two cams per head, the Cosworth Vega renews our faith in Detroit and proves that increased efficiency brings power, economy, and clean air too.

In recent years, import cars have made tremendous sales gains; and now, with the present fuel shortage (real or contrived), their popularity is greater than ever. The import is quite an attraction—but for how long? Since the devaluation of our dollar, foreign car prices have risen considerably causing many to buy American instead and, to Detroit's delight, shipping companies are finding it very difficult to get enough fuel. This has made it nearly impossible to transport the thousands of economy cars sitting on overseas docks. The energy crisis has definitely hurt Detroit's big-car sales but, without foreign competition, they have a chance to compensate for big-car losses with mini-car gains. Consequently, many potential import buyers are instead purchasing American mini-cars as either replacements or seconds to their gas-gulping sedans. In fact, so many, that some big car plants are switching over to small car production in an effort to meet the incredible demand; and, for once, the little guy—American Motors—has slain the giants by meeting this demand when the big three can't.

This new breed of American car was initially quite economical but each year its economy declines a little more. With the addition of heavy impact bumpers, more accessories (former luxury car owners want lux-

1

2

3

4

5

ury and economy too) and heavier "crashable" construction, car weight has greatly increased and good gas mileage and performance have taken a dive. To handle the extra weight, engines have been enlarged—but tougher emission laws have required the addition of even more smog plumbing and, apparently, Motown has just about reached the point where the engine just won't accept another solenoid and still run. Consequently, performance doesn't improve and economy drops even further—but, with an "endless" gas supply, that was once a swallowable sacrifice for cleaner air. Detroit has been reaching its goals—they've satisfied the government with safer cars and, by adding external smog devices, they've brought cleaner air and bought time to spend on researching

1. American you say? Nothing like that ever came from Detroit. Surprizingly, the Cosworth Vega is built here—handbuilt by Chevy in Tonawanda, N.Y. Its foreign appearance isn't coincidental—design originated in England from Cosworth Engineering Ltd., builders of Formula One engines.

2. Twin cam, four-valve design is the first since the '38 Dusenberg and the first time ever with e.f.i. Injection nozzles enter directly into aluminum intake runners. Large plenum chamber holds plenty of air, and going from such a large chamber to much smaller downhill runners really speeds air into cylinders.

3. Dual-throat throttle body on side of plenum connects to a log-shaped air cleaner mounted on fender panel.

4. The heart of the Cosworth's e.f.i. is this 11x8-in. computer. The computer, tucked away above the glovebox, picks up signals from engine sensors and instantaneously decides on the exact amount of fuel to the cylinders.

5. No, this isn't Motorola's "works in a drawer" but rather the business end, the brains, of the computer. Hardly repairable by your corner mechanic, guts are replaced as unit.

new types of engines. However, an apparently unforeseen monkey wrench has been thrown into the works because we've all discovered that maybe our gas supply isn't quite as endless as we thought—and now, that research time is running out. For awhile, the Wankel looked like the hot setup and it was—for low emissions—but it gets rather thirsty doing it. For that reason, the rotary Vega, expected in '75, may have been dropped for the talk has turned to silence and a new conventional (but very small) V-8 will probably take its place.

BLESSING IN DISGUISE

Out of every bad some good must come (or something like that) and the energy crisis just might turn out to be a blessing in disguise for the automobile. Here in America we have some of the greatest automotive engineers in the world, but their talents have been suppressed. They are well aware that with a minimum of smog controls, clean air, performance and economy can all be achieved by increasing engine efficiency. Furthermore, they know how to obtain that efficiency from conventional engines, but for years their "bean-counting" bosses have felt that it's cheaper to add more smog devices than it is to redesign all new engines. Financially, that's true—but if they want to continue selling cars, the approach must soon change. Mileage must be improved now, and the fastest way of doing that is by improving engine efficiency . . . so it looks like the engineers may finally get their way.

CATALYTIC CONVERTERS

The future for efficiency seems to be brightening a bit and, in some areas, changes have already begun. The catalytic converter is scheduled for its first production appearance on '75 GM cars and, according to EPA tests, its presence will bring a 15% mileage gain. The converter, located in the exhaust system, handles the

pollutants that the other smog devices miss. Its effectiveness is reported to be great enough to permit retuning for greater efficiency and economy. In fact, retuning is *necessary* to keep the converter alive. Since 1970, fuel mixtures have gotten considerably leaner as a means of reducing hydrocarbon (HC) and carbon monoxide (CO) emissions. That technique is effective but it also raises combustion temperatures closer to dangerous detonation levels and increased heat raises oxides of nitrogen (NOx).

Lean mixtures can also cause ignition misfire and when that occurs, exhaust temperature soars. Excessive exhaust temperatures can destroy a converter so, to minimize misfire, fuel mixtures will be richer and breakerless ignition will be mandatory. GM has stated that a Vega converter can survive on three spark plugs and the V-8 on six but for how long we don't know. The high overlap camshaft introduced on many '71 cars will be replaced with a reduced overlap cam producing high torque at low rpm. This will result in a flatter torque curve, improved low end performance and greater fuel economy. It is said to be a return to 1970 economy and greater driveability. The converter requires lead-free gas, and that requires a multi-million dollar conversion by the oil companies. However, at this time, GM appears to be the only converter proponent among the big three. Many fear that the converter may produce new pollutants more harmful than those it is trying to convert—primarily, sulfates and harmful sulfuric acid. Converter construction calls for .05 ounces of platinum per unit, so GM has signed a 10 year contract with a South African platinum mine to ensure a sufficient supply. The supply is large enough to prompt converter sales to AMC, International Harvester and a couple of import manufacturers. So, putting it mildly, GM is committed to catalytic

Cosworth Vega

converters—and much more than Ford or Chrysler. The EPA has given the go-ahead for converter use in '75 but, unfortunately, without thorough testing. If proven completely safe, the converter seems like a good deal; however, its possible dangers could prove it otherwise—but should we be the guinea pigs?

AFTER MARKET EFFICIENCY

We don't think so, because there is a safe, enjoyable alternative to the catalyst. Steve Martis, a local So. Calif. hot rodder, recently invested $750 in a 440 Mopar engine and after some well-planned modifications, placed it in his '70 Duster. The engine now displaces 511 cu. ins. and, in street trim (street tires and all accessories present), the car turns a 12-sec. ¼ mile, gets 14 mpg *around town* and meets '70 emission requirements without any emissions equipment—and does it all on regular low-lead gas. If Steve can do this for $750 (for details, see *Petersen's Complete Book of Engines No. 10*), then it seems that Detroit could do the same for much less per car. Proof positive that an engine built for

1. Illustration shows locations of e.f.i. components. Five sensors, some of them not shown, keep computer posted on exact fuel needs of engine.

2. Take a good look at the last picture and then identify these items. Include several feet of fuel line and you've got the complete e.f.i.

3. Looking at this cutaway, note the location of the injection nozzle on the intake manifold. Nozzle injects fuel directly into runner and downhill to intake valve. Check out the cross-flow design of head. Fuel enters on one side of chamber, gets burned and exhaust exits from exhaust port on other side. Central plug location makes for more thorough burning. Direct valve action of lobe on tappet on stem eliminates a lot of unnecessary travel associated with rocker arm and pushrod systems.

4. Cosworth cam carrier bolts to head and provides a home for two cams and 16 tappets. Those posts in the center enclose the spark plug wires. Since carrier is aluminum, cam bearings are not used. Aluminum surface of towers serves as a bearing for camshaft journal.

5. Remove the carrier and this is what you'll find. This portion of head is also aluminum and, as you can see, this is where the valves live. Double coil springs expedite valve's return to seat and portion of stem above spring is swallowed by open-ended tappet. End of stem makes contact with inside roof of tappet and this contact opens and closes the valves.

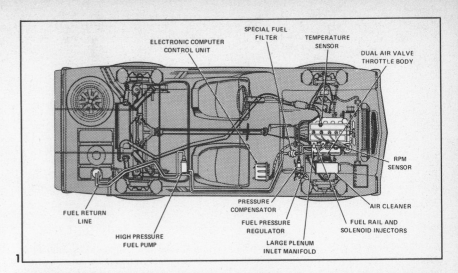

ELECTRONIC COMPUTER CONTROL UNIT — SPECIAL FUEL FILTER — TEMPERATURE SENSOR — DUAL AIR VALVE THROTTLE BODY — RPM SENSOR — AIR CLEANER — FUEL RAIL AND SOLENOID INJECTORS — LARGE PLENUM INLET MANIFOLD — FUEL PRESSURE REGULATOR — PRESSURE COMPENSATOR — HIGH PRESSURE FUEL PUMP — FUEL RETURN LINE

1

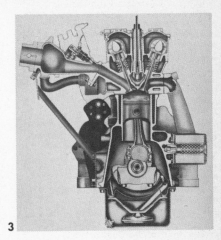

2

efficiency can combine tire-smoking performance with economy and clean air too.

The speed equipment industry has been interested in engine efficiency for a long time and, more recently, in gas mileage and low emissions. For the aftermarket, Holley produces an emissions carburetor that combines performance with lean primary jetting for economy and fewer pollutants. Detroit works closely with Holley so we may expect to see it on future production models.

For years, the hot rodder has been looked down upon by most as a greasy kid obsessed with building noisy, fast cars. Lately, there have been a few changes and a lot of unlikely people have joined the hot rod set. The speed shop has taken on a new look. It's gotten a bit crowded lately and not only with greasy kids but with conservative, card-carrying businessmen clad in Brooks Brothers suits and desperately seeking better gas mileage for their traveling offices.

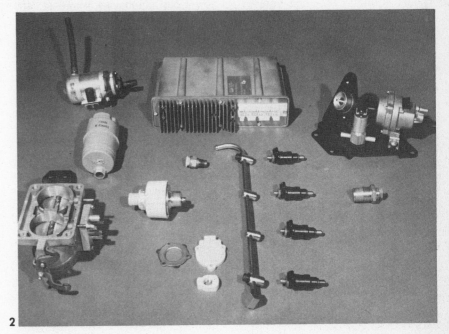

3

They've come to the right place . . . for what Detroit hasn't provided, people like Hooker, Edelbrock, Holley and Racer Brown Cams have. For example, Edelbrock has a new manifold called the Streetmaster. It's now available for Chevy only but, due to the great demand, it's being designed for others too. The manifold is easy

to install and completely legal because it's designed to be used with factory smog equipment. On a stock 327, Edelbrock reported a 5-mpg increase with nothing more than the manifold change. Headers increase engine breathing for a gain of 2-5 mpg, and Racer Brown, Crower (the Gas Stretcher) and Isky (the Mile-a-mor) are all producing mileage cams (probably similar to GM's '75 cams) claimed to improve mileage by 2-4 mpg. Crower began working on his new cam back in '72 for the purpose of reducing emissions, but as Bruce has said: "The principle is still the same, make the engine more efficient, use less gas and it's a clean engine." Detroit is limited by research time so they've been working with Edelbrock, Holley and some other aftermarket people for awhile now and that's an encouraging sign.

GOOD NEWS

There's more good news from Detroit; in fact, the most refreshing news in years and quite surprising in these days of harsh emission laws, gas shortages and low-performance cars. It's the Cosworth Vega—and as its builder, GM truly deserves the Mark of Excellence for engineering. Twin overhead camshafts in an aluminum head, four valves per cylinder located in pent roof combustion chambers, Bendix Electronic Fuel Injection (e.f.i.), long runner aluminum intake manifold, stainless steel tube headers, transistorized breakerless ignition, a forged crank and impact extruded aluminum pistons are just a partial list of engineering exotica found in every showroom Cosworth. However, as the memory of the supercar fades and factory performance drifts deeper into oblivion, it's difficult attaching the word "showroom" to an American engine bearing racing credentials. But, that's where it all began.

Back in '70, Keith Duckworth, creator of winning Grand Prix engines and the brains behind England's Cosworth Engineering Ltd., designed the 16-valve head that now sits atop the Vega block. In '69, Keith learned that GM was working on an aluminum four-banger as a possible power source for the yet-to-be-produced Vega. Duckworth had been wanting to build a strong 2-liter racing engine—and preferably aluminum—so news of the Vega block really turned him on. Chevrolet was most cooperative. Duckworth made a 1969 visit to Detroit to inspect the new engines and one year later, Vega block castings arrived at the British shop. Within a few months, Cosworth's first Vega engine was complete and running. Chevrolet's interest in the project quickly grew, bringing an offer to pay for the engine's development in exchange for three complete cylinder heads—Duckworth agreed. Ready to race, the engine produced 270 hp at—would you believe—8750 rpm and 170 lbs.-ft. of torque at 7000 rpm, making it the most powerful unsupercharged 2-liter in racing. Its first competitive experience came in '71 at South Africa's Springbok Series and its performance was so impressive that by Spring, Lola and Chevron had ordered the first 18 made.

GM'S 16-VALVE PROJECT

In the early months of '71, Chevrolet with the eager support of General Manager John DeLorean, began their own 16-valve program. Not since the last Duesenberg Model J (1938) has there been an American engine with four valves per cylinder. Excitement pervaded the program and, within a short time, a running car was delivered to DeLorean—a '71 Cosworth Vega complete with wide wheels, tires and heavy duty suspension. If all went well, this would be Chevy's answer to the 260Z, the BMW 2002 tii, Alfa's GTV and other GT cars. As a new image car it would bring fresh publicity to Chevrolet and particularly to the Vega line. However, in the months to follow, the Cosworth project appeared to be losing ground to Wankel power or optional turbocharging, but those programs were eventu-

ally shelved bringing new emphasis to the twin-cam.

Financially, the 16-valve project has been a bit unusual. From the very beginning, it has been known that the Cosworth would be an expensive car to build, particularly when limited to just 5000 first-year units. Engines are hand-built at Tonawanda and the cars constructed off-line at Lordstown and, adding to the amazement, Chevrolet has said that assembly will be done *right* regardless of time. Shot-peened rods, forged cranks and magnafluxing—included in every car—is an expensive way to go, proving that little cost has been spared by a usually frugal management. Consequently, it was a surprise to many when the go-ahead was finally given. Investing so much in creating a new image car is a little hard to accept. There's got to be another motive for its production other than mere image.

The twin-cam engine includes some components completely new to Detroit production cars—computer-controlled fuel injection, four valves per cylinder and two camshafts—all of which combine for greater efficiency and hence lower emissions, greater economy and performance. 5000 cars won't pay for all the labor and tooling necessary to produce them, but 5000 cars on the highway could save plenty of time and money on research that would otherwise have to be spent in the laboratory. Reports from owners and dealers will determine just how well the engine works and how it holds up in everyday use. If those exotic components prove to be dependable, and successful in maintaining low emissions and good mileage, then they could be applied to other engines for the same results. Bendix, supplier of the twin-cam's fuel injection, has recently moved its emissions research department to Michigan in preparation for what might be a profitable future. Tests have shown that with a modified Bendix system and a catalytic converter, a stock Vega can meet the super

Cosworth Vega

tough '76 Clean Air standards. So, if all goes well, the Cosworth may be the first of many to use this new approach, and that would be nice. The TC Vega is definitely a testbed for things to come, and perhaps that's the primary motive behind its initial production.

E.F.I.

Electronic fuel injection (e.f.i.) and the four-valve design are the key to the Cosworth's efficiency, and the combination is an automotive first. The Bendix injection system is the first electronic system used on an American car since Bendix first tried in the 50's. In '57, GM introduced mechanical fuel injection (Rochester) on a few Corvettes, Chevys and Pontiacs, but Rambler went the electronic route (Bendix) on a very few Rebels. The system had its problems and didn't survive the year. In '58, the Chrysler 300-D offered a $400 option—the Bendix "Electrojector." After too much publicity, the system flopped and less than 15 ever hit the road. Years later, the electronic system returned—but only overseas under the Bosch (a Bendix licensee) name. VW's 1600, Volvo, the Saab 99 and some models of BMW and Mercedes all share the unit and now, a similar unit distributes fuel to the TC Vega. The heart of Vega's e.f.i. is its 11x8-in. computer. The computer is wired to sensors located on the engine and these sensors determine the coolant temperature, air pressure in the intake manifold, temperature of the intake air, engine speed and throttle opening. The computer receives the various messages and immediately calculates the exact fuel needs of the engine and sends a signal to the injectors. Injector solenoids are then activated and the injectors are triggered to stay open just long enough to deliver exactly the prescribed amount. The injectors are located at the top of each intake manifold runner, and the runners extend downward in a straight line to each intake valve thereby creating a direct fuel/air flow. The Bendix system provides equal fuel distribution to the cylinders and only the minimum amount necessary for the engine at any given moment of operation. The result is very little fuel waste, lean operation for good mileage (20 mpg overall), minimum HC and CO emissions and improved response and performance.

16-VALVE HEAD

Complimenting the e.f.i. is Vega's 16-valve head. The head is almost identical to the racing version with the biggest difference being in the combustion chambers—the Vega chambers are cast and the real Cosworth ones are machined. Even the valve sizes are the same—a diameter of 1.4 ins. on the intake and 1.2 for the exhaust. However, something different has happened beneath the head. Different pistons bring high compression (11.5:1) and more power to the 270-hp racing engine. To survive the low-lead, no-lead pump gas, Chevy's Cosworth engine has deep-dish pistons for reduced (8.5:1) compression and lower (130) horsepower. Nevertheless, when comparing figures with its cousin, the Vega GT (8.0:1, 85 hp), 130 net hp and 115 lbs.-ft. of torque at 5200 rpm from 122 cu. ins. is not too bad.

Chevy's Cosworth head is all aluminum (reduces weight by 14 lbs. for 305-lb. total) and consists of two pieces, an upper and a lower. The upper half is the cam carrier—it houses the two cams and tappets and because it's aluminum, the cam towers need no bearings. The aluminum is soft and it makes a good surface for the cam journals. Camshaft

overlap on the Cosworth is 68° compared to 83° for the 85-hp engine. Lift has also been reduced from .4199-in. (75-hp engine) and .4302 (85 hp) to .350-in. for the intake and exhaust on the twin-cam. Reducing the lift makes for a smoother idle and better low end torque. The larger ports and headers of the Cosworth have improved breathing enough to allow use of the milder cam; however, without these modifications, the smaller engines must rely on higher lift for better breathing. The tappets live in bores that extend downward to the valves below. Like the conventional Vega, the tappets are solid and open at the bottom to enable direct contact with the valve stems. However, unlike the single-cam Vega, the tappet doesn't envelop the valve spring, only the upper part of the stem. This extra length of valve stem (about the length of the tappet) makes contact with the inside roof of the tappet. Therefore, when the cams rotate, their lobes take turns in pushing the tops of the tappets, and the tappets in turn push down on each valve stem. This opens the valve and when lobe contact is lost, spring pressure closes the valve and sends the tappet rising in its bore to await another lobe. This direct contact of lobe-to-tappet-to-valve makes for high speed action without the usual delay of rocker arms and pushrods.

The single-cam Vega has an adjusting screw in the side of each tappet which permits it to be raised or lowered in relation to the cam lobe (see "Camming a Chevy Vega"), but when you've got two cams, things are a bit cramped and accessibility to such a device is limited. Therefore, in the Cosworth, as is the case of the Fiat and Audi Fox, valve adjustment is made by adding or removing shims from the tappet tops. To reiterate, the Cosworth head is composed of two halves. The upper half includes the

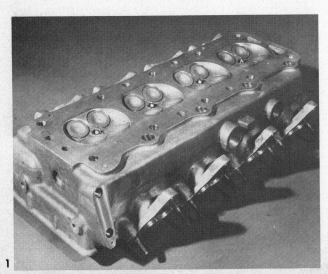

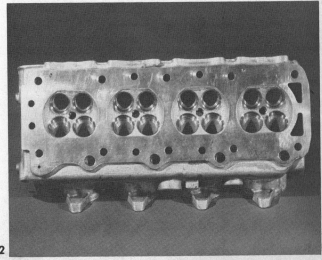

camshafts and tappets and bolted to it is the lower half containing the valves and springs, combustion chambers, spark plugs and ports.

Each combustion chamber contains four valves, intakes on one side, exhausts on the other with one camshaft per side. The intake and exhaust valves are each tilted 20° from a vertical position to coincide with the contour of the ports. The result is a smooth flow of intake and exhaust without the usual bends and sharp corners. Fuel and air is injected directly into an intake runner where it continues downward in a straight line to the intake port. Velocity of the gas is very high because of this direct path. The computer-controlled injection provides only the necessary amount of fuel, so waste is small but what there is is exhausted through a gracefully curved exhaust port into header tubes and out the pipe. Four valves canted at 20°, produce a pentroof combustion chamber with a spark plug situated in the center. The lead in gas acts as a lubricant and without it, valve seats wear faster. As a protection, inserts of sintered iron have been added to the aluminum head.

PISTONS, RODS AND CRANKS

Just below the head are the forged aluminum pistons. They are of deep dish design to lower compression, with large cutouts for sufficient valve clearance. Another interesting feature is the chamfered edge of each piston.

1. Tell that head to roll over and this is what you get. Larger intakes are on bottom, exhaust on top with the spark plug exactly in the center. Position of valves (20° from vertical) forms a "V" or more commonly, a pentroof combustion chamber.

2. Remove the valves and you've got Swiss cheese. Valve seats are sintered iron to protect soft aluminum against valve pounding produced by unleaded fuel.

3. Now here's the entire cast. Please hold your applause while we announce them. Wrinkle finish cam cover is a nice way to top off a pretty package. Directly above it is the cam carrier sans cams and above that is the lower part of the head. To the right are the springs, intakes, tappets with adjusting shim side up, exhaust valves and remaining springs. To your far left are the cams, one for intakes, one for exhaust. You may now applaud.

4. Intake side of head shows intake ports. Ports are siamesed to increase velocity of air/fuel mixture.

5. Exhaust ports are oval and they're large to ensure good scavenging to steel tube headers.

The area between the top ring and the top of most pistons is very small but large enough to collect unburned fuel and increase emissions. By chamfering the top of each piston, a tight fit is assured and unburned gases are reduced. Joining the pistons to the crank are the same connecting rods used in the standard Vega engine; however, they've been magnafluxed and then shot-peened for extra strength. The crankshaft in

3

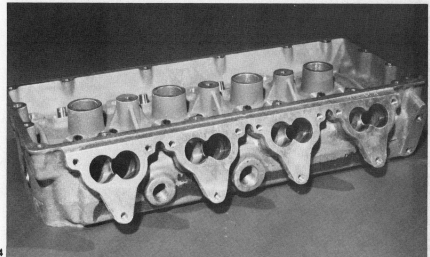

4

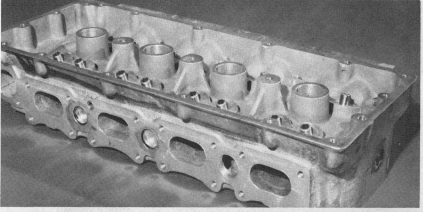

5

Cosworth Vega

the common Vega is made of cast steel, sufficient and rather inexpensive. Once again, sparing no expense, the crank on the Cosworth is forged and hardened by the Tuftriding process for greater strength. Engine displacement has been reduced from the standard 140 cu. ins. (2.3 liters) to 122 (2.0 liters) by shortening the throw on the crankshaft. This reduced the stroke from 3.62 ins. to 3.16 ins., and by maintaining the same bore (3.50 ins.), an oversquare bore-to-stroke relationship has been created. The shorter stroke means less piston travel and higher engine speeds plus less engine vibration—a big problem with most inline fours, especially the Vega. Also, by reducing displacement, the engine now

qualifies for 2-liter competition in a production class.

BREAKERLESS IGNITION

In keeping with the total engine concept, GM has included Delcotronic breakerless ignition. What else could they do? Using breaker points on such an exotic engine would be tantamount to wearing sneakers with a tux. The rubbing block, an integral part of all breaker systems, is in continuous contact with the revolving distributor shaft causing the points to open and close. Unfortunately, the block is usually nylon or phenolic (plastic) and wears with use—and as it does, point gap and ignition timing are altered, resulting in incomplete ignition and increased hydrocarbon (HC) emissions. The breakerless system has no points or rubbing block to

wear so timing remains constant for more thorough burning of each gallon and, hence, greater economy and fewer emissions.

Four valves per cylinder, two cams per head, computer-controlled electronic fuel injection and breakerless ignition—a great way to increase engine efficiency. Due to these design features, only PCV and TCS (transmission controlled spark) will be needed to meet '74 emission standards. Additional fuel and power-robbing smog equipment will not be required. Although expensive and limited in initial production, the Cosworth Vega will be a refreshing revival of the American performance machine and, if the demand is as great as expected, hopefully others will follow in the same direction toward a faster, yet cleaner and more economical, small car.

1. Phantom view eliminates all privacy. Note great length of plug wires. We hope they're durable, if not, go fish. Fishing out a broken insulator is going to involve some work. Cog-toothed belt runs both cam sprockets and grooves on the back drive the fan and water pump. Belt has proven very reliable on the standard Vega. A smaller belt drives the distributor sprocket. This turns a gear which meshes with the shaft gear to turn the shaft.

2. Breakerless distributor is located at front of engine where it is driven by a small cogged belt riding on the sprocket shown in upper right. Distributor slips into upper hole of housing while the gear shaft with sprocket on end goes in the front.

3. Pistons are forged aluminum and deep sumped to lower compression, the crank is forged steel (standard crank is cast iron), and it's been Tuftrided for greater durability. The rods are stock Vega but they've been magnafluxed and shot-peened to reduce stress. Throw on crank has been shortened from the stock spec resulting in a shorter piston stroke and fewer cubes, 122 vs. 140.

1

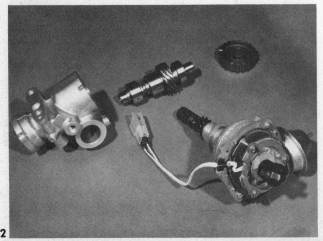

2

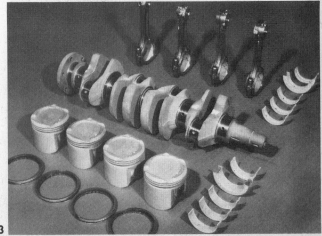

3